WATERMILLS
& WINDMILLS

The publisher would like to thank Mr. Keith Chisman, of the Draper's Mill Trust, for the loan of his copy of this rare book.

W. H. Evernden

SPRINGTIME
(By Stelling Minnis Mill)

WATERMILLS & WINDMILLS

A Historical Survey of their Rise, Decline
and Fall as Portrayed by those of Kent

WILLIAM COLES FINCH
M. Inst. C.E.

ARTHUR CASSELL
Sheerness

First published in 1933, by The C. W. Daniel Company.
New impression 1976, by Arthur J. Cassell Ltd.

© Executors for the late W. Coles Finch 1976.

ISBN 0 903253 02 X

Printed in Great Britain
Photo-litho reprint by W & J Mackay Limited, Chatham
from earlier impression

A TRIBUTE

TO

The sincere and genial Miller Folk
with whom I have had interesting associations and for
whom I shall ever have a kindly and happy remembrance

ACKNOWLEDGMENTS

In order to avoid tedious repetition, the appellation 'Mr.' or 'Esq.' has been omitted throughout this gratifying list of names.

I AM anxious first to acknowledge the generous help accorded me by the Director-General of the Ordnance Survey, Southampton, by the loan of the early maps of Kent from 1596 onwards. Also similar help by my friend, R. F. Brain, who gave me free access to his extensive library and collection of rare maps, prints and paintings.

I am likewise particularly indebted to William Holman of Canterbury, and his son "Jack," for their most valuable assistance, without which this volume would have been far less complete. "Jack," although still a lad at school, revels in windmill lore and construction, and appears to have absorbed all the accumulated knowledge of the members of that well-known firm of Canterbury millwrights of some 115 years standing, Messrs. Holman Bros. He knows not only the various exterior peculiarities of the mills' construction but also their internal economy. I might add that in many instances he and his father spared no pains in discovering for me information not at the time in their possession. They also obtained for me many old pictures of long-vanished windmills and valuable notes concerning their history.

With the foregoing assistance and with my own pictures and notes, a collection of many years, the task I set myself went merrily for a time. As the work progressed, however, it became more evident that a very large number of mills were entirely lost, far beyond the memory of the oldest survivors of the milling trades. The task became greater than I had anticipated and I had little spare-time, after fulfilling my professional duties, to scour the countryside or to indulge in much interesting correspondence with miller folk for traces of long lost windmills and their history.

Curiously, at that time, A. W. Tiffin, of 'Woodside,' Staplehurst, who had been likewise smitten by windmill charms, offered to help me in the work, and we saddled horses right away. The result is the volume which lies before you. His collection of notes, maps and pictures was placed unreservedly at my service, as well as his indefatigable energy and absorbing interest.

I am also much indebted to :

M. Rowland Packer, of Chatham, who has aided me considerably in many ways. Many of his pictures appear in this volume.

7

Dr. F. William Cock, of Appledore, an acknowledged authority on archaeological and other matters in connection with Kent.

The late Halford L. Mills, of Smarden and Tenterden, an authority on matters relating to the history of the Weald.

Edwin Bradley, of Leybourne House, Dover, who, as a retired corn merchant, gave me several notes of interest.

Edward Bennett, of Shoreham, the Editor of the Magazine of *The Men of Kent*, who has given me much help for this and previous volumes, and has readily answered questions in connection with windmills in his district.

Miss M. I. Batten, whose book on the Windmills of Kent, Surrey and Sussex (*English Windmills*, Volume I, Architectural Press), written on behalf of *The Society for the Protection of Ancient Buildings*, has proved a valuable work of reference.

Rex Wailes, an authority on the construction of windmills, for photographs and much practical information.

W. H. Evernden, of Faversham, for helpful information and many interesting photographs.

Frank Pain, for his knowledge of many mills, particularly in East and Mid Kent, and for willing assistance in many ways.

George Jarvis, of Bethersden, for information of Kentish windmills repaired and demolished by him.

E. A. Mummery, of Dover, for help given in connection with the mills of East Kent, and for kindly checking the notes on those mills.

J. Russell, of Cranbrook, for his able co-operation regarding the mills in the Weald of Kent, and for lending many photographs.

George Harmer, of Ashford, who, by reason of his connection with the late millwrights, Messrs. Hill, was able to give much practical help.

C. W. Welby, of Herne Bay, who lent many pictures and cuttings and supplied many notes.

E. T. Clark, of Maidstone, for cordial co-operation, with pictures, cuttings and various particulars.

Herbert Filmer, of Faversham, for his untiring efforts to obtain accurate information.

F. J. Blinkhorn, of East Farleigh, for helping with mills of the Maidstone area.

A. Pinyon, of Rye, for great assistance with a difficult subject—the windmills of Tenterden.

A. V. Wratten, of Hollingbourne, who has been most helpful regarding mills around Maidstone.

A. Tanton, of Woodchurch, for assistance readily given in connection with many mills and for enquiries made.

Geo. E. Ride, of Minster (Sheppey), for the benefit of his knowledge of a large number of mills and for help cordially given.

A. J. Golding, Curator and Librarian of the Maidstone Museum and Public Libary, for varied help and for facilities afforded in the study of old maps and records.

The following list is of owners of mills, millers and their descendants, and people directly connected with individual windmills, who have generously given information in interviews and correspondence. This list indicates the *source* of much of the information in the historical notes and also shows the effort made to obtain authentic information.

ACRISE—Mrs. E. J. May.
ALDINGTON—G. Prebble.
APPLEDORE—Dr. F. W. Cock.
ASH—J. Brockman.
ASHFORD—"X. Willis."

BADLESMERE—F. J. Cavalier.
BARHAM—Messrs. T. Denne & Sons Ltd.
BARMING—Mrs. E. M. C. Carr.
　　　　Rev. W. C. G. Sharp, M.A.
BETHERSDEN—J. T. Adams.
　　　　H. Jarvis.
　　　　George Jarvis.
BEXLEY HEATH—Mrs. F. E. M. Young.
　　　　H. A. Strickland.
BIDBOROUGH—D. C. Apperly.
BIDDENDEN—G. Hatcher.
　　　　Messrs. Dallaway Bros. (Heathfield).
BIRCHINGTON—Wilfred P. Hudson.
BLACKHEATH—H. Whitelocke, Central Library, Lewisham.
BLEAN—Albert Price.
　　　　J. E. Wallis.
BOUGHTON MONCHELSEA—
　　　　H. E. Wood.
　　　　T. Gates.
BOUGHTON-UNDER-BLEAN—
　　　　Mrs. Miles.

BOXLEY—Miss M. Foster.
BRABOURNE—M. Hancock.
BREDHURST—G. Naylor.
BRENCHLEY—Rev. P. S. Whelan, M.A.
　　　　T. Else.
BRENZETT—Miss Nash.
BROMLEY—Herbert Alderton, F.L.A.
BROOK—F. Hammon.
　　　　M. Hancock.

CANTERBURY (ST. MARTIN'S MILL)—
　　　　Mrs. Drew.
CHARING—Mrs. W. H. Clarke.
　　　　Rev. D. R. Fotheringham, M.A.
　　　　W. Newton Clark.
　　　　Mrs. Charles Norwood.
CHATHAM—Edwin Harris.
　　　　John J. Freeman.
　　　　E. F. Daniels.
CHILLENDEN—A. H. Laker.
CHISLEHURST—W. Brigden.
CHISLET—H. G. Lanham.
COBHAM—Mrs. Travers.
CRANBROOK—J. Russell.
　　　　F. Butt-Gow.
　　　　F. G. Crampton.
DARTFORD—S. K. Keyes.
　　　　A. Cumberland.
　　　　W. Mitchell.
DEAL—E. A. Mummery.

DEPTFORD—
    F. J. Peplow (Borough Librarian).
    Thankful Sturdee.
DETLING—G. Brown.
DODDINGTON—H. Preston.
DOWNE—Bernard Darwin.
    A. H. Nicholls.
DYMCHURCH—A. Tanton.

EASTLING—Thos. Read.
EASTRY—H. H. Clark.
EDENBRIDGE—A. T. Goodwin.
    Miss M. B. Winch.
EGERTON—Herbert Millgate, Senr.
ELHAM—W. Hayward.
ELMSTED—T. H. Gambrill.
ERITH—H. A. Strickland.
    Geo. I. L. Houghton.

FARLEIGH, EAST—F. Larking.
FAVERSHAM—Herbert Filmer.
    A. W. Austen.
FOLKESTONE—W. Martin.
    C. W. Martin.
    W. Marsh.
    Mrs. Adams.
FRINDSBURY—G. E. Ride.
    W. Manwaring.
FRITTENDEN—T. Durey.
    Mrs. A. T. Millen.

GILLINGHAM—Walter Stedman.
GOUDHURST—W. P. Haskett-Smith.
GRAVESEND—F. R. Bevan.
    I. Newton Moss.
    Alex J. Philip, M.B.E.,
      F.L.A. (Borough
      Librarian).
    F. A. Mansfield.
GUSTON—E. A. Mummery.
    S. J. Mummery.
    Geo. Sheaff.

HARBLEDOWN—M. Hancock.
HAWKINGE—E. Jarvis.
HEADCORN—Messrs. Millen Bros.
HERNE—F. R. Wootton.
HERNE BAY—C. W. Welby.
HIGHAM—A. H. Maytum.
HILDENBOROUGH—Mrs. Turnbull.
HOATH—E. Fuller.
    Miss. E. Fernie Smith.
WEST HOUGHAM—E. H. Tanton.
HYTHE—F. Pain.

IDE HILL   Miss M. Farrell.

KESTON—J. Fells.
KINGSDOWN, NEAR SEVENOAKS—
    Miss R. Hankin.
    W. Norton.
KINGSTON—F. J. Fagg.
KIPPINGS CROSS—C. W. Lambert.
KNOCKHOLT—T. Bond.

LANGDON, EAST—Mrs. Butt.
    Mr. Johnson.
LEEDS—Walter Blinkhorn.
LEIGH—A. W. Tomlinson.
LENHAM—F. Pain.
LENHAM HEATH—E. Tanton.
LYDD—E. H. Greening, M.P.S.
LYNSTED—W. R. Ward.
    G. E. Ride.
LYMINGE—D. E. Fisher.
LYMPNE—V. Laker.

MAIDSTONE—F. J. Blinkhorn.
    Wm. Day.
    E. T. Clark.
    A. V. Wratten.
    W. French.
MEOPHAM—Messrs. J. & W. Norton.
NEWCHURCH—T. F. H. Waddell, J.P.
NEWINGTON, RAMSGATE—P. Mack.
NONINGTON—E. Gasston.

NORTHBOURNE—D. A. Peters.
E. M. Fuller.
NORTHFLEET—F. A. Mansfield.
F. W. Boorman.

OARE—Herbert Filmer.

PETHAM—T. H. Gambrill.
PLUCKLEY—R. Buss.
PRESTON, FAVERSHAM—
Herbert Filmer.
PRESTON, WINGHAM—H. J. Dunn.

RINGWOULD—Capt. J. E. Monins.
ROCHESTER—Alfred E. Horsnaill.
W. J. Glover.
RODMERSHAM GREEN—E. Hopper.
ROLVENDEN—The Hon. H. J. Tennant
F. Coombe Baker.
RUCKINGE—A. W. Pearce.

SANDHURST—Miss Harwood.
C. Burt.
Mrs. Malton.
E. Collins.
SELLINGE—Mrs. Rushton.
SEVENOAKS—Geo. C. W. Bennett,
(Sevenoaks Public Library).
SEVENOAKS WEALD—Rev. R. C.
Taylor.
SHEERNESS—G. E. Ride.
W. J. Wood.
SHORNE—C. H. de Trafford.
SISSINGHURST—F. G. Crampton.
SMARDEN—H. N. Cornes.
H. I. Hicks.
SOUTHBOROUGH—J. H. Fielder.
SOUTHFLEET—E. Snelling Colyer.
J. J. Chambers, J.P.
STANFORD—G. R. Holt.
STELLING MINNIS—H. W. Davison.
STOKE—T. Mallion.

STROOD—G. E. Ride.
SUTTON VALENCE—W. R. Ward.
SWINGFIELD—T. S. Gammon.
S. G. Barwick.
F. Pain.

TENTERDEN—A. Pinyon.
A. Ridley.
The late Capt. A. A.
Black.
F. Batt.
A. H. Taylor.
TONBRIDGE—G. E. Skinner.
J. Barton.
R. Spickernell.
John C. Knocker.
TONGE—Charles Wicks.
TUNBRIDGE WELLS—
A. Fletcher (Borough Librarian).
Arthur W. Brackett.
A. R. Kelcey.
J. Weeks.

ULCOMBE—G. Wells.
UPHILL—Lewis Kettle.

WALTHAM—Mrs. Monger.
Prior Dilnot.
WHITSTABLE—Laurence Irving.
WILLESBOROUGH—W. Manwaring.
WINGHAM—H. J. Mayes.
WITTERSHAM (Old Post Mill)—T.
Hinkley.
WITTERSHAM (The Stocks Mill)—
The late N. Forbes-Robertson.
WOODCHURCH—A. Tanton.
WOOLWICH—Philip C. Bursill, F.L.A.
(Borough Librarian).

YALDING—Mrs. Tame.
John Weston.
Miss E. Turner-Smith.

To those friends who generously helped in the matter of pictures, due acknowledgment is made beneath the prints.

It is not within my power to mention individually the much larger number of people with whom I came in contact in my windmill peregrinations, for I did not even know their names ; each and all spared no pains to add their quota to my store of windmill knowledge.

I am pleased to state that in no single instance did I meet with other than a ready permit to wander where I chose, in, around, and over the old windmill and take photographs. In many an instance the owner brought out time-worn and stained pictures of the mill "as she used to be" and kindly lent them to me for possible reproduction.

The author would like to hear from readers interested in mills. Further information, corrections or pictures would be welcomed as useful for inclusion in future editions.

WATERWORKS HOUSE,
    LUTON, CHATHAM.

September, 1933.

MAP AUTHORITIES CONSULTED

1596   Phil. Symonson, of Rochester.
1610   J. Speed.
1695   Robt. Morden.
1719   (History of Kent), Dr. Harris.
1736   E. Bowen.
1769   John Andrews, Andrew Dury and William Herbert.
1829   Greenwood & Co.
1819-43   Ordnance Survey Office.
1858-72   ,,   ,,   ,,
1903-10   ,,   ,,   ,,
Sundry local maps, estate plans, etc.

CONTENTS

PART I

WATERMILLS

PART II

WINDMILLS

13

PART III

OUR DAILY BREAD

PART IV

THE WINDMILLS OF KENT

FROM EARLIEST TIMES

ILLUSTRATIONS
(Alphabetical)

MAPS OF KENT

* There are 410 Mills given in the Historical Notes. Six of these were discovered after the map was completed.

INTRODUCTION

IN recent volumes on Rural Life,[1] I frequently touched upon the fascinating subject of corn, mills and millers. The interest aroused brought many requests that I should extend and amplify what I had written, and make yet another volume. It has been pleasant to yield to the request because everything to do with old mills appeals to me, although, in the course of an active and exacting life, it has not been easy to gather the material and give to the subject that meticulous care it deserves.

*   *   *   *   *

I would inform the reader at the outset that this book is intended primarily as a pictorial and historical record of the happenings in Kentish Corn Mill Land. In the preparation of this record I have been obliged to remind myself continually of its purpose, having been frequently tempted to digress upon the hundred-and-one irrelevant though interesting incidents and anecdotes which have come my way.

A more interesting and popular volume might have resulted had I succumbed to the temptation to write a roving account of my rambles, but several facile pens have already done that with exquisite taste.

Even while engaged in this effort, two or three excellent books on the subject of windmills have appeared, and I understand that a personal friend, a specialist in the construction of windmills and the engineering secrets of their internal economy in particular, intends to write a book on this branch of the subject. Hence, the simpler and more pleasant task of describing tramps over Windmill Lands has been fairly well covered, and an engineering book is to be attempted. For me remained one very important thing not hitherto attempted. I have taken one county only and, commencing with the watermills recorded in the Domesday Survey, I have traced the abandonment of many of these mills and the introduction of the windmill; then, century by century, the growth of the windmills, their utility and prosperity ; and, lastly, their gradual abandonment until now, when we are faced by their entire disappearance.

It has been my endeavour to show what part the decline of the corn mills has played in the almost complete annihilation of that old-time rural life and prosperity, of which we were so proud and upon which the very life of

---

[1] *In Kentish Pilgrim Land ; Life in Rural England ; The Lure of the Countryside ; The Medway River and Valley.*

the nation has depended for the renewing and replenishing of the nation's manhood and maintaining the stamina, blood and sinew of our race.

Truly, in noting the gradual disappearance of our corn mills, we find an identity with the rise and fall of prosperity and contentment in the agricultural world, down to the inevitable depression and distress which is threatening the whole of our rural life and industry.

With the vanishing of our corn mills, dwindles the prosperity of the country. With the thousands of acres of corn land now laid down in grass, stand idle thousands of sturdy and willing men.

*   *   *   *   *

The many plans, the lists of corn mills of one county at various periods and the general information concerning their rise and fall, may be taken as typical of what has happened everywhere in Great Britain and as providing a true index of the many adverse changes that have come over the countryside.

To the more casual reader, should he have but a passing love for these old mills which provided our daily bread for many centuries, I would commend the map dealing with the year 1930. Here he will see at a glance the positions of the few remaining active specimens as well as the several derelicts, picturesque in their decay. This may lead him to think seriously of the difficulties of country millers, who cannot hope to compete with the mammoth steam roller-mills in our seaport towns whither grain is dumped from afar.

Changed conditions have all but exterminated the miller folk, not the old-time grasping, dishonest miller folk of fiction but the frugal, generous, honest and splendid artificers of the corn mill world. There is now but a precarious living afforded to the remaining few, who hope, yet hope in vain, that better times lie ahead when they may again win their daily bread from between the revolving stones instead of losing on their milling efforts and gaining mere subsistence by means of side-lines—such as poultry, pigs, faggots, rabbits, fruit—or in other ways of making both ends meet.

*   *   *   *   *

As to the illustrations, I may explain that for many more years than I now care to recount, I have been aided in my hobbies by my camera. Thus have I fallen particularly to the charms of Kentish corn mills.

My reward has been a collection of rare pictures of windmills the greater number of which can only be recorded as derelict or long since vanished.

At last *The Society for the Protection of Ancient Buildings* is giving its attention to the neglect of ancient mills, and I was pleased to be able to contribute pictures to the first volume of their series of *English Windmills*. I can only regret that the expense of publication prohibited reproduction of all the pictures I would have freely given, although I am happy to be able to include them in the present volume.

The photographs are placed mainly in pairs—active mill alongside the derelict it later became. I felt this to be important, for soon there will be no corn windmills or watermills left, and perhaps no other record than such pictures for purposes of history or of art.

Nothing of what has already appeared in the text of my other volumes is repeated here, save where the information is vital to the continuity of the story. The same care has been used with regard to the illustrations and, where possible, pictures of mills which may have appeared elsewhere are substituted by newer ones of the same mills. In some cases I have included pictures that I felt were superior to my own and which were willingly given by others for the enhancement of this work.

* * * * *

In Part IV of this volume there is an extensive historical record of all these windmills, gathered from every available source, regardless of time and expense. It was felt that such a record would prove of increasing value to the County of Kent in years to come. It is believed, too, that the historical and constructional details will interest those who have been connected in one way or another with our Kentish mills, especially to the large number of miller friends who, I am sure, will be delighted to possess a 'Mill Book' in the preparation of which so many of them have found it a pleasure to assist. I trust also that the historical notes will not be without pleasure and profit to the general public.

It should be specially borne in mind that no detailed written history has yet appeared of our Kentish windmills. For the most part the matter accumulated herein had to be gathered from personal contact with millers and those who have had direct association with the various mills, as well as from visits to the mills and their sites. Practically the whole of the information is, therefore, 'first hand.' The effort to gather and link up all these particulars has not been made any too soon, for the number of mills and of those who know their history is fast diminishing.

The difficulties and setbacks in the course of compiling this work, and there have been many, were but a source of encouragement, the more so on account of the valuable assistance given by my friend, Mr. A. W. Tiffin, to overcome them.

PART I
WATERMILLS

And mouldering lichens creep and mosses grey
  Cling round its arms in gradual decay,
Amid the hum of men—which doth not suit
  That shadowy circle, motionless and mute.

So by the sleep of many a human heart,
  The crowd of men may bear their busy part,
Where withered, or forgotten, or subdued,
  Its noisy passions have left solitude.

Ah ! little can they trace the hidden truth !
  What waves have moved it in the vale of youth !
And little can its broken chords avow
  How once they sounded. All is silent now.

                                        Ruskin.

CHAPTER I

THE WATERMILL IN EARLY TIMES

THE whole subject of corn mills hinges so completely upon the means whereby we once obtained our daily bread that we must look back to the early days of watermills, the forerunners of our windmills, with which they have survived and run contemporaneously for many centuries.

Earlier still there were the 'stone crushers and hollows,' followed by the first grinding mill, the 'saddle-stone,' the 'mortar,' the 'hand-stone mill' or 'quern.' It is said that when the Romans abandoned Britain in A.D. 448, "the country was studded with the discarded quern-stones with which they had ground their grain by hand." These 'querns' were followed by 'slave' and 'cattle' mills.

It was these crude mills which carried us through the earliest days of the 'milling world,' of which there is any record, about two thousand years ago, when the primitive Greek or Norse watermill became known to us.[1]

It is certain that at least two different types of watermill were in existence shortly after the Christian era, and in due course they were established in Britain, as elsewhere.

The earliest known allusion to a watermill occurs in an epigram by Antipator of Thesalonica, who flourished about 85 B.C. :

> Ye maids who toiled so faithfully at the mill,
> Now cease your work, and from those toils be still :
> Sleep now till dawn ; and let the birds with glee
> Sing to the ruddy morn on bush and tree ;
> For what your hands performed so long and true,
> Ceres has charged the water-nymphs to do.

The earliest mention of an Anglo-Saxon mill is said to occur in a charter dated 664. In the year 762 and onward, frequent reliable references occur to charters granted for mills.

For information as to who invented the watermill, and for proof of its early entry into Britain, I would send the reader to that

---

[1] The Norse mill, the first known to the Britons, was probably introduced by the Teutonic tribes who over-ran these islands in the fifth century. There is no evidence to support the theory that the Romans introduced the water mill into England. However, in due course the mill of Vitruvius certainly did reach Britain, and was extensively adopted throughout the kingdom by the Saxons, displacing its early forerunner, the Norse mill.—*The History of Corn Milling*.

excellent work, *The History of Corn Milling*, where the subject is exhaustively treated, as well as to my two volumes, *The Lure of the Countryside* and *Life in Rural England*.

To get some definite and reliable idea of the progress made in the introduction of watermills into Kent we cannot do better than consult the Domesday Survey, where we learn that there were 7,500 watermills noted in England. This reveals that prior to the Conquest the country abounded with them.

I find that the Domesday watermills in Chenth (Kent) total 351¾, a list of which is here appended. The fractional parts of a watermill, the ½ and ¼ mills, will at once attract the attention of the reader, as they did mine ! The explanation is : "places possessing several mills, the rent given is that of all the mills stated, and at places possessing only portions of mills the rent quoted is that of the portions, not of the entire mill."

Knowing the rivers and streams of Kent fairly well, I was concerned at the total figure given, wondering how and where such a large number could have been situated. I wondered, too, whether the rainfall at the period under consideration could have been more profuse than now, for with the few remaining water-mills there is, save at flood season, but a limited supply on many of the streams I have in mind.

We cannot, however, cast a shadow of doubt on the Domesday records, which were compiled between 1080 and 1086. Of this wonderful record it has been truly said : "It affords us statistics of the milling resources of the kingdom of a more comprehensive character than has at any period since been effected."

We are told that wherever a mill is specified in the Domesday Survey we generally find it still subsisting. It would be an interesting but, I fear, a difficult task to find traces of most of the mills referred to in the following list.

DOMESDAY WATERMILLS IN CHENTH (KENT)

SCHEDULED IN 1080–1086

As given in Bennett and Elton's *The History of Corn Milling*

The modern spellings of names are given side by side with the old, as traced from various sources, to make them intelligible.

Old	Modern	No. of Mills
Aldringtone	Aldington	3
Alham	Elham	2
Alnoitone	Elnothington-in-Hollingbourne	2½
Apeltres	Appledore	1
Avdintone	(?) Aldington	1
Bichelei	Beccles-in-Chalk	1
Bevgsberg Hd.	(?)	1
Bix	Bexley	3
Borchetelle	Borstal	2
Bacheham	Beckenham	1
Berchevelle	(?)	1
Berham	Barham	3
Berlinge	Birling	1
Bermehnge	(?)	1
Boglei	Boughton Malherbe	1
Boltvne	Boughton-under-Blean	2
Borham	Burham	1
Borne	Patrixbourne	6
Boslev	Boxley	3
Brebvrne	Brabourne	2
Breistede	Brasted	2
Broteham	Wrotham	3
Bronlei	Bromley	1
Brvnfelle	Bloomfield	1
Bvrnes	Bishopsbourne	3
Cantvaria	Canterbury	4
Certh	Chart Sutton	2
Certeham	Chartham	5½
Ceteham	Chatham	1
Celca	Chalk	1
Cerce	(?) Eastchurch	1
Cheringes	Charing	1
Cilleham	Chilham	6½
Ciresfel	Chelsfield	1
Codeham	Cudham	2
Coglestane	Cuxton	1
Crai	Foots Cray	1
Craie	Paul's Cray or North Cray	1
Dictvne	Ditton	1
Dovere	Dover	2
Elesford	Eynesford	4
Eddintone	Addington	2

Old				Modern				No. of Mills
Elentvn	..	..	..	.. Allington	..	..	..	.. 1½
Erhedre	..	..	..	.. Crayford	..	..	..	.. 3
Eslinges	..	..	..	.. Eastling	..	..	..	.. 2
Esledes	..	..	..	.. Leeds..	..	..	..	.. 5
Estanes	..	..	..	.. Stone	..	..	..	.. 1
Estreia	..	..	..	.. Eastry	..	..	..	.. 1½
Esnoiland	..	..	..	.. Snodland	..	..	..	.. 3
Estvrai	..	..	..	.. Sturry	..	..	..	.. 10
Estraites	..	..	..	.. Street, in Lympne	..	..	..	1
Essetesford	..	..	..	.. Ashford	..	..	..	.. 2
Estvrsete	..	..	..	.. Westgate, Canterbury	..	..	20
Etretone	..	..	..	.. (?)	..	..	..	.. 1
Etvselle	..	..	..	.. (?)	..	..	..	.. 4½
Ewelle	..	..	..	.. Ewell	..	..	..	.. 7½
Fachesham	..	..	..	.. Faversham	..	..	..	.. 2
Ferebvryne	..	..	..	.. East or West Farborn in Harrietsham	..	..	..	.. 2
Ferlagam	..	..	..	.. Farleigh	..	..	..	.. 5
Ferningeham	..	..	..	.. Farningham	..	..	..	.. 1½
Frandesberie	..	..	..	.. Frindsbury	..	..	..	1
Fvlchestan	..	..	..	.. Folkestone	..	..	..	.. 11½
Gegham	..	..	..	.. Ickham	..	..	..	.. 4
Gelingeham	..	..	..	.. Gillingham	..	..	..	2
Gomersham	..	..	..	.. Godmersham	..	..	..	1
Grenviz	..	..	..	.. Greenwich	..	..	..	.. 4
Hagelei	..	..	..	.. Hawley	..	..	..	.. 1
Hallinges	..	..	..	.. Halling	..	..	..	.. 2
Hariardesham	..	..	..	.. Harrietsham..	..	..	..	2
Haslow	..	..	..	.. Hadlow	..	..	..	.. 2
Hede ..	..	..	..	.. Hythe	..	..	..	.. 2
Heham	..	..	..	.. Higham	..	..	..	.. 1
Hoilingeborde	..	..	..	.. Hollingbourne	..	..	..	2
Hortone	..	..	..	.. Horton, in Chartham, or Monk's Norton	..	..	..	.. 4
Hortvne	..	..	..	.. Herne	..	..	..	.. 2½
Hov ..	..	..	..	.. (?) Hoo	..	..	..	.. 2
Lelebvrne	..	..	..	.. Leybourne	..	..	..	.. 1
Leminges	..	..	..	.. Lyminge	..	..	..	.. 1
Lerham	..	..	..	.. Lenham	..	..	..	.. 3
Levisham	..	..	..	.. Lewisham	..	..	..	.. 11
Litelcert	..	..	..	.. Little Chart..	..	..	..	2
Litelbroteham	..	..	..	.. Little Wrotham	..	..	..	2
Lolingeston	..	..	..	.. Lullingstone	..	..	..	1
Martin's Saint	..	..	..	.. Saint Martins, Canterbury..	..	11½
Marovrde	..	..	..	.. Mereworth	..	..	..	.. 2
Meddestane	..	..	..	.. Maidstone	..	..	..	.. 6
Merseham	..	..	..	.. Mersham	..	..	..	.. 2
Mellingetes	..	..	..	.. West Malling	..	..	..	1
Meletvne	..	..	..	.. Milton, next Gravesend	..	..	1
Metlinge	..	..	..	.. East Malling	..	..	..	2

Old				Modern				No. of Mills
Middletone	..	..	..	.. Milton	..	..	..	.. 6
Monocstune	..	..	..	.. Monkton	..	..	..	1
Mundingeham	..	..	..	.. Little Mongeham	..	..	..	1
Nedestede	..	..	..	.. Nettlestead	..	..	..	2
Neventone	..	..	..	.. Newington; or Newington nr. Hythe				4½
Nordevde	..	..	..	.. Longport, Canterbury		..	..	8
Norflvet	..	..	..	.. Northfleet	..	..	..	1
Nortvne	..	..	..	.. Norton, or Norton near Faversham				3
Ofeham	..	..	..	.. Offham	..	..	..	2
Oistreham	..	..	..	.. Westerham	..	..	..	1
Olecobe	..	..	..	.. Ulcomb	..	..	..	1
Ore	..	..	..	.. Oare	..	..	..	.. 1
Orpinton	..	..	..	.. Orpington	..	..	..	3
Ospringes	..	..	..	.. Ospringe	..	..	..	1
Otefort	..	..	..	.. Otford	..	..	..	8
Oteham	..	..	..	.. Otham	..	..	..	1
Otringeberge	..	..	..	.. Wateringbury	..	..	..	3
Pecheham	..	..	..	.. Peckham	..	..	..	1
Piventone	..	..	..	.. Pevington	..	..	..	1
Prestetone	..	..	..	.. Preston, near Wingham	..	..	1
Postinges	..	..	..	.. Postling	..	..	..	3
Rapentone	..	..	..	.. Ripon, Ashford	..	..	..	¼
Riesce	..	..	..	.. Ryarsh	..	..	..	1
Ringletone	..	..	..	.. Ringleton in Woodnesborough		..	1
Rochelei	..	..	..	.. Roxley	..	..	..	1
Rocvlf	..	..	..	.. Reculver	..	..	..	1
Romenel	..	..	..	.. Romney Marsh	..	..	..	1
Sabreshant	..	..	..	.. (?)	..	..	..	1
Salteode	..	..	..	.. Saltwood	..	..	..	9
Sedlinges	..	..	..	.. Selling	..	..	..	1
Sifletone	..	..	..	.. Sifletone	..	..	..	1
Sievetone	..	..	..	.. (?)	..	..	..	1
Sondresse	..	..	..	.. Sundridge	..	..	..	4½
Stochinberge	..	..	..	.. Stockbury	..	..	..	1
Svdtone	..	..	..	.. Sutton Valence	..	..	..	2
Tanet	..	..	..	.. Minster-in-Thanet	..	..	..	1
Tangas	..	..	..	.. Tong	..	..	..	1
Tarent	..	..	..	.. Dartford	..	..	..	5
Testan	..	..	..	.. Teston	..	..	..	1
Tvrnha	..	..	..	.. Thurnham	..	..	..	1
Westclive	..	..	..	.. Westcliffe	..	..	..	2
Westselve	..	..	..	.. West Shelvem in Lenham	..	..	1
Welle	..	..	..	.. Westwell	..	..	..	1
Wi	..	..	..	.. Wye	..	..	..	4
Wicheham	..	..	..	.. Wickhambreaux	..	..	..	3
Wingeham	..	..	..	.. Wingham	..	..	..	2
Wivarley	..	..	..	.. (?)	..	..	..	1

351¾

If the reader refers to *The History of Corn Milling* he will find a wealth of interesting facts that throw light upon the conditions of life in these early days. He will find that frequently the miller was valued together with the mill, as in the case of St. Martin's, Canterbury, where with 11½ mills, ten men were subject to the mill owners.

The low annual rentals of the mills surprised me until I found that in 1889, when *The History of Corn Milling* was published, the value of the money rents was equal to about 110 times the amounts stated in the time of the Domesday Survey. Some of the rentals are as follows :

St. Martin's, Canterbury, 11½ mills ..	£12
Meddestane (Maidstone), 1 mill ..	5/-
Norflvet (Northfleet), 1 mill ..	10/- with a fishery
Prestetone (Preston near Wingham), 1 mill	*Sine censu* (no value)
Dovere (Dover), 1 mill	48 ferlinges of wheat
Berlinge (Birling), 1 mill	10/- and 330 eels

The map facing, made for this book, shows the watermills noted on the nineteenth century maps. They are, we must presume, in the main, survivors of the Domesday mills. I have also plotted on it the earliest known windmills of Kent, the early 'post mill' type, which appear on the Symonson map of 1596. No pains have been spared to make it as complete as possible, although some of the mills are missing, owing to the havoc made by time in their ranks. Many old maps have been consulted and many long journeys made, to show the area in which it was possible, because of the presence of running water, to establish the watermills. The succeeding windmills were not so greatly restricted. As later maps disclose, they became scattered all over the county, but only occasionally in close proximity to the earlier watermills, and it will be noticed how the windmillers of the early sixteenth century placed their windmills in areas where there was no running water from which they could gather energy.

One frequently sees mention of the ruthless extortions of the ancient miller ; and we learn that, by the time of Richard II, the mill monopoly owned by the lords of the manors was becoming intolerable. No one could build a new mill without a licence from the Crown, and it was about six times as difficult to get a licence to build a mill to grind flour than it was to get a licence to sell beer and spirits. In the revolt of the peasants against this system

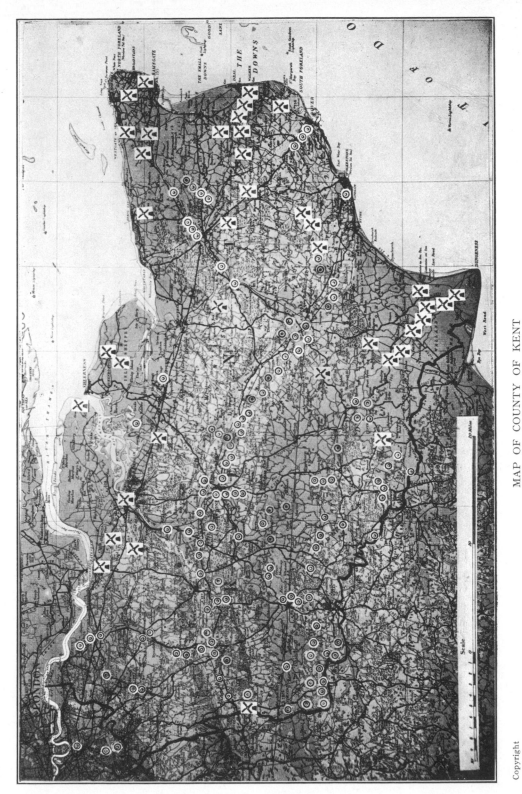

MAP OF COUNTY OF KENT

Showing the sites of 136 Watermills standing in about 1819-43, and the sites of the 39 Windmills of 1596.

See page 32

Facing page 32

W. Gurnell

Facing page 33

THE MILLER'S DAUGHTER

W. E. Prosser

STURRY MILL

they included among their demands that they should be permitted to use handmills and grind their own corn.

"Six hundred years ago," says Dr. A. Jessopp in *The Coming of the Friars*, "no tenant of the manor might take his corn to be ground anywhere except at the lord's mill ; and it is easy to see what a grievance this would be felt to be at times, and how the lord of the manor, if he were needy, unscrupulous or extortionate, might grind the faces of the poor while he ground their corn."[1]

Mr. C. J. Cornish, who has written many splendid articles on the subject of our watermills, says :

> Next to the parish church the parish mills had the largest history. They are far the oldest amongst the surviving 'antiquities of agriculture' even in our old country, and where the buildings have been renewed again and again in the course of centuries the site of the mill and of the mill-cut is often the same as that occupied by each in the days of the Saxons. This can be verified by anyone who will note the position of any mill he knows, and compare it with the record of the Domesday Book which registered and assessed every mill in England.
>
> These were nearly all Saxon mills built before the Conquest, most frequently by some far-seeing abbot or prior of a monastery, who first cut the mill stream and converted 'force' into 'energy'.

The mills attached to the abbeys and monasteries were probably the largest and best in the country. There the corn was ground for the great and growing garrison of 'clerks,' whether priests or lay brethren, who swarmed within the abbey walls. Busily occupied, whether in daily work or in daily prayer, the earlier monastic brethren earned their bread thoroughly, and the abbots and priors saw that they had it. To-day there is still, here and there, an Abbey Mill grinding corn, though not for holy 'clerks.'

We are told that at Oxford the Castle Mill, one of the most picturesque buildings of feudal as opposed to collegiate Oxford, stands across the stream at the foot of the tower, whence the Empress Maud escaped by night over the frozen river and across the snow. Winchester abounds in ancient watermills, some built by monks of the vanished Hyde Abbey, where King Alfred was buried.

Boxley Abbey Mill at Sandling Bottom, on the road to Maidstone, was a monastic mill, given to the Abbey at Boxley about 1316 by Alexander Kumba. Alas, the wheel has recently been destroyed.

The mill on Holborough Brook, which also runs into the

---

[1] For further reference to this subject, see *In Kentish Pilgrim Land*, pp. 103-106.

c

Medway, was built on the site of one erected by Hamo de Heth in 133. A mill has existed here for over a thousand years, for one on the torrent here in 836 was given by King Egbert and Ethelwulf jointly to Bornmode, Bishop of Rochester.

In the Archbishop's Palace gardens at Maidstone may still be seen the arches which, early in the thirteenth century, conducted the waters of the Len to the watermill, one of the first mentioned in the Domesday Book.

A study of the subject of these old mills in association with our ancient monasteries would show what a great benefit was conferred by the monastic brethren on rural England. They will always be held in honour by the lovers of country life as the great pioneers of agriculture, the inventors of most good things in the orchard, the garden and the farm. They were engineers, architects and builders in what was then a wilderness. The calibre of their work as land-owners may be judged from their barns, typical examples of which remain to us at Maidstone and Boxley. Temples of Ceres would have been their title had the builders lived before the Christian era.

CHAPTER II

WATERMILLS IN DECAY

THERE are still many relics of watermills on the tributaries of our rivers, but they are fast becoming fewer, and no more pleasant task can be attempted than that of searching them out, for they invariably lie in the most delectable surroundings.

In the season of floods, when the swirling torrent has choked to the full the arches of the mediæval bridge and overflowed the river banks, submerging large areas of the adjacent land, converting it into one great lagoon, through which peeps every little hill and tree-clad mound, here and there a dwelling completely surrounded by the flood—what wonderment and interest ! In summer time, when nature decks with a wealth of wild flowers and grasses the borders of our willow-fringed streams—what cause for rejoicing !

Then there is the fascination of the mill-ponds so frequently found near the old watermills, where the methodical rumbling of the mill and the roaring of the waters escaping over the weir are a fitting accompaniment to nature's adornment. Bird-life on the waters and in the tree-clad margin offer further delight, as we watch the martin and swallow skim the glittering surface of these little lakes in search of insect food.

It is in these picturesque isolated spots that are to be found our ancient watermills, the survivors of the original Domesday mills so numerous on every available stream in the country—the providers of flour through the centuries. Here and there may be found a specimen still performing the old-time task, grinding only coarse grain for cattle and poultry, working perhaps but occasionally as the limited supply demands. Here and there, too, are mills where the reliable engine has supplanted the falling water, or is working in conjunction with it, as, similarly, auxiliary power has aided the windmill.

At one of these almost deserted places recently I found the mill derelict, a picture of desolation. The few human souls living in the once busy valley seemed to hold a wistful reserve, evidently feeling keenly the fickleness of fate, mourning the neglect and decay of the old mill and miller's house, the emblems of their 'good old times.' The rushing waters and the tumbling weir—these 'out-pensioners' in the scheme of things—seemed to show their resentment in a less passive way. They appeared in spiteful mood now that man has no further use for them and their restless energy and service are allowed to run to waste. Could they not have been given a new lease of life in generating electricity for the scattered farms and homesteads?

*   *   *   *   *

Writing upon the subject of our Kentish watermills, to which he has devoted much time and study, my friend and fellow-townsman, Richard Brain, tells us that a Kent Directory of 1913 states that fifty-eight mills were then driven by water power.

There are a great number of old ones in picturesque decay, the streams now only waiting for the installation of the turbine to resume their useful work, which can be carried on night and day with practically little cost. That little stream, the Loose, which runs into the Medway at Tovil, formerly drove sixteen mills.

The small stream called the Shode, or locally spoken of as The Buster, rises near the Pilgrim Road at Wrotham, meanders past Ightham, serving the lake at the large Basted paper mills, which supplied the paper for our postage stamps, then runs on to turn the great water-wheel at Winfield flour mills. Passing Plaxtol it goes on to Roughway paper mills, receiving the stream from Ightham Mote, then through Hadlow, serving other mills, finally joining the Medway at East Peckham.

What is known as the Snodland Brook, which runs into the Medway at the large paper mills of Townsend Hook & Co., also rises near Wrotham. It is joined near Leybourne mills by the stream from Malling, and in wet seasons forms a considerable torrent. There are also mills on the River Len, which joins the Medway at Maidstone. A few mills are still in use. Another stream which lies near East Malling, turns the corn and paper mills there. It falls into the Medway close to Aylesford.

Sir Charles Igglesden, writing in 1902, tells us that on the banks of the River Loose "there were no less than six flour mills, two mill-board mills, and one paper mill."[1] The branch of the Stour that rises at Lenham "serves on its course several mills still, but in years gone by many more stood by its banks. From its source it came past a 'bone mill' outside Lenham, next past Chapel and Bowley, thence to Burnt Mill and Field Mill in Egerton, Swallow Mill—once an oil mill, and the paper mill in Little Chart, then Sweetloves near the Forstal and the brown-paper mill by Conyer Wood near Hothfield—the two latter are gone—and so on to Warten and Bucksford Mills in Great Chart, till the stream joins its sister at Ashford."[2]

I have recently visited these mills and noted the havoc time

[1] *Saunters through Kent with Pen and Pencil*, vol. ix, p. 42.   [2] Ibid., vol. iv, p. 54.

THE AMOROUS PAIR

W.C.F.

A HAPPY LITTLE FAMILY

H. Hicks

See page 40

The Times.

BOURN WINDMILL (CAMBRIDGE)
Specimen of the early Post Mill.

Facing page 37

See page 47

has played with them. At Bowley Mill there remain but the axle and spokes of the wheel, all else is gone. They are covered with a cloak of verdant green moss, upon which drips the water escaping from the pond above.

At Little Chart the watermill is no more used, its place is now served by electric current at the hand-made paper works ; but the extensive mill-ponds are as beautiful as of old.

Hothfield Mill is derelict and will never work again. I gleaned it was the oldest mill on the stream, nearly a thousand years old.

At Polhill Mill, on the Len, I found the whole structure had collapsed, the wheel alone remaining. The disappearance of the mill had exposed to view the oast-house which stood near. By reason of the difficulties besetting the culture of hops, it was being converted into a quaint but snug dwelling. Gone were the mill-pond, mill and weir.[1]

How closely these old watermills once nestled together is shown by the small stream which bursts from the escarpment of the North Downs in a delightful spring-pond at Hollingbourne. Traversing the water-meadows on its short journey it joins the River Len. There in but one mile of its course four watermills were once busily occupied in making flour. To-day the first and the last mill stand derelict, while the two intervening ones have long since disappeared. Here and there are indications of the foundations peeping through the hummocky grass mounds now claiming the site.

The stream still finds a devious course through the empty wheel-race and broken culverts in the valley. The once attractive mill-ponds and weirs are gone, the former having been filled up. But for a letter from one whose ancestors were millers here, I should never have explored them but have remained in ignorance that they ever existed.

It was easy to reconstruct in imagination what this short valley once offered to the traveller—the still upper pool, which used to feed the mill-leat, with its surface reflecting the passing clouds, the rhythmic, steady rumble of the wheel, the splash of the tumbling water, and the familiar trundling noise of the gear and running stones.

In following the courses of our Kentish streams there is a sad pleasure in noting the decaying mills that have survived the ordeal of the ages. I recently visited what was, in its prime, one of the most powerful mills on the River Len. A heavy fall of snow had crushed in a large portion of the granary roof and the

[1] For picture of this mill before its absolute destruction see *The Lure of the Countryside*, p. 61.

floors were dangerously rotten. All the windows were smashed. Sparrows, starlings and other birds had taken possession of every available nook and ledge and were busy with their domestic affairs. The miller's house was completely gone, exposing to view the large iron breast-wheel, which stood between the mill house and the mill. Even the floors of the granary had been cleared away, while the waters of the Len poured over the weir past this scene of desolation and decay, sweeping idly by the corn mill that, in its day, had provided not only a living for many dependent families, but also a rent of twenty shillings per day to the owner of Leeds Castle ! This is a typical instance of the futility of any effort in these days profitably to harness our streams to the task of providing 'our daily bread.'

Inside the mill the desolation was a more intensely pathetic sight. In one long row were six pairs of idle mill-stones, with all the paraphernalia used in the milling industry. All the three floors above were filled with lumber of every kind, and it was with difficulty that a camera could be set up. The windows, choked with trusses of ivy, admitted but a feeble light. Several more large mill-stones were reclining against the walls in various stages of preparation for a task they will never again perform—unless perchance a miller along the stream purchases one for a trifle to replace a worse one of his own, to enable him to carry on grinding for a short while longer.

This old watermill on the Len was not only actually neglected ; there was a peculiar *atmosphere* of abandonment about it, which one often experiences in visiting our old dilapidated windmills. One cannot even ask permission to wander over these old places. There is no one to ask, no one to refuse permission, and no one cares where you trespass or what you do, or what relic of the past you carry away as a memento of the visit. Sometimes there is even no door to close behind you.

I have found windmills to be more elusive than one would imagine, but the watermill is still more so. I prided myself that I had 'poked' round and about most of the mills in my own locality, yet only recently I discovered another on a stream I thought I knew thoroughly. The access to it was obscure and there was not a glimpse of the mill to be seen from any thoroughfare.

Noting the old church tower in the distance as it peered above the tree-tops, I left the busy main road and found the village inn. I passed over an old but complete mill-stone in the cobbled pathway. I knew of two derelict watermills not far away and presumed it came from one of those. Out of curiosity I made enquiries and was surprised to find that it came from an old mill only two hundred yards from where I stood, hidden in a tree-clad vale.

I found the mill, at least all that remained of it. It had been derelict for many years, but it must have provided a tough resistance to the powers of destruction, seeing the thick masonry of which it had been constructed. It was evidently a mill of Domesday times. The watercourses to mill-race and weir could be traced, the stream finding a difficult passage by reason of the fallen masonry in its bed. The wheel had long since gone and peeping up through the wreckage were two ponderous nether mill-stones and one complete but thin, well-worn upper stone, similar to the one at the entrance to the inn. One cannot easily steal a mill-stone, but I am still haunted by the covetous urge!

As I took a farewell glance at the ruins, it seemed as if a huge explosive shell had sent the whole edifice shattering to the ground. The place was deserted, save for a brace of pheasants which took flight as I passed. Not a soul challenged my trespass, but the abandoned pathways were aglow with a profusion of daffodils and primroses. The golden shafts of sunshine pierced the branches of the bare but noble beeches beneath which was a beautiful carpet of wood anemones. Nearby lay the remains of two freshly killed wood pigeons that had been the feast of sparrow-hawks.

The babbling stream, the tumbling weir, the garniture of flowers and the old-time music of the birds—these only had withstood the ravages of time and the changes wrought by man.

There is a certain similarity between these time-honoured haunts of man, but each possesses its own peculiar charm. Not long ago, on one large and shimmering mill-pond I noticed a bereaved and mateless swan. She was making the best of her lonely life, ignoring entirely the miller's ducks and the wild water-fowl, seemingly oblivious to all that should attract a lonely bird. She sailed gracefully about, but keeping as far from other birds as possible, nursing her grief with pride in solitude. My impression was that she considered herself too superior a creature to confide her troubles to the gobbling, gossiping crowd of meaner birds disporting themselves happily on the same pool.

I wondered what domestic tragedy had caused the 'Rift in the Lute' of her domestic felicity! Had some giddy philandering male bird grown tired of her, or was it a case of a domestic 'eternal triangle' affair in bird life, her mate ruthlessly decoyed by another heartless female bird? But perhaps they had mutually agreed to separate under the stress of incompatibility to which neither could become reconciled ! This musing led me to make enquiries, and I learned that she had really lost her mate and was genuinely bereaved.

Feeling somewhat interested in the domestic affairs of this poor swan, a week later I again visited the pool. I found her sublimely happy. It was a case of "Off with the old love, on with the new." She had attracted a fresh companion, maybe from the castle moat above, or had decoyed a male passing on his way down stream, who, being also in search of a mate, had thus become a willing captive. As the picture shows (facing p. 36), life was soon going merrily for this now happy pair.

They heeded not the decay and desolation of the old mill and cared not that through neglect the reeds and rushes and floating islands of water-loving plants were insidiously reducing the area of the surface of the pool. There was still ample room for them as well as for the gobbling ducks and the more timorous dab-chicks, from which they no longer held aloof. As I watched these busy little denizens of the pool I recalled the lines of Pope :

> As when the dab-chick waddles through the copse
> On feet and wings, and flies, and wades, and hops ;
> So labouring on with shoulders, hands, and head,
> Wide as a windmill all his fingers spread.

Some time later their happiness was complete, for parent birds and a family of six young cygnets were gliding about on the placid waters of the mill-pond by the old mill (facing p. 36).

There was much to learn from the watermiller, even about swans : That they are migratory (unless pinioned), that as soon as severe weather sets in they seek a warmer climate, returning again in the breeding season. To their discredit, too, was I told that in October and November they are ruthless with their young, driving them away, leaving them to forage for themselves. That old miller was a most observant and informative person, a student of nature, particularly in the matter of ornithological and piscatorial life.

One thing is certain—should you in your jaunts beside our valley streams turn aside for a while and enter an old watermill for a rest you will not regret it. If the old miller is there he will extend to you a ready welcome and you will gather wisdom and many tales of milling operations in olden times, in between the moments now and then when he slips away to attend to the feeding of the rumbling stones.

Yes, call on old millers ! Display an interest in their life and occupations, show yourself a good listener, and I promise you glimpses of an old world, yet a new one for you, pregnant with that fulfilment of the simple life which the 'Will-o'-the-Wisp' of wealth only promises but never gives. You will thus lay up for yourself a store of delightful memories of plain hospitality generously dispensed.

*   *   *   *   *

I remember how at a certain old mill the miller had all but closed down the sluice, as there was only a meagre supply of water, with none to waste, and the old water-wheel was just crawling slowly round. I commented upon this, whereupon the miller laughed. He told me my remark reminded him of a rude boy who, upon a similar occasion, had said: "Our old sow could eat the meal as fast as your old mill grinds it !" To this the miller had replied, thinking to score: "But for how long, my boy ?" "Till she starved to death," came the smart retort !

*   *   *   *   *

Some of my readers may recall that old song called "Take it Bob," in the opening lines of which the miller introduces himself :

> I'm a jolly old miller, Bob Bell is my name,
> And in my own village I'm well known to fame.

He tells he is too fond of a glass and blames the mill for this weakness in his character, for when he is inclined to refuse a drink the clattering of the interior of his mill calls to him and ends his wavering. Both words and music of the refrain tell their own story.

> Take it Bob, take it Bob, take it Bob, take it Bob,
> That's what I fancy the mill says to me.
> Take it Bob, take it Bob, take it Bob, take it Bob,
> Take it Bob, take it, it's better than tea !

This propensity of falling to the call of the muses may perhaps originate in long association with the rhythmic rumblings of a mill which all unwittingly, by their ceaseless chattering, call forth a jingle of words. I have before me a well-worn manuscript of some verses by an old watermiller on the Cray. I regret that their length forbids inclusion here.

"The Miller on the Cray" (Walter William Harrison) refers, in his verses, to a rather unusual occurrence in connection with a legendary 'left-handed' watermill at Longford, near Sevenoaks, whose stones ran backwards through being 'bewitched.' Yet 'left-hand' *windmills* actually exist, as at Limpsfield Chart (see Chapter V, p. 57).

* * * * *

Despite conflicting and changed conditions, to trace the course of our streams and to search out, with camera in hand, the old mills hidden away in odd corners, is still a delightful hobby. Even if the old wheel is over-run by briar and bramble and seen with difficulty, the mill house and surroundings invariably offer a pleasing picture. They will become more alluring as the years roll on, though silence may reign where once the laughter of happy children echoed up the valley. The old mill house, unfit for habitation, may have tumbled into the stream. But water-loving flowers still grace the margins of sparkling mill-ponds the summer through, to outbid desertion by man.

PART II
WINDMILLS

Behold ! a giant am I !
  Aloft here in my tower
  With my granite jaws I devour
The maize and the wheat and the rye,
  And grind them into flour.

I look down over the farms ;
  In the fields of grain I see
  The harvest that is to be ;
And I fling to the air my arms,
  For I know it is all for me.

I hear the sound of flails,
  Far off from the threshing floors
  In barns, with their open doors.
And the wind, the wind in my sails,
  Louder and louder roars.

On Sundays I take my rest ;
  Church-going bells begin
  Their low, melodious din ;
I cross my arms on my breast,
  And all is peace within.
                              Longfellow.

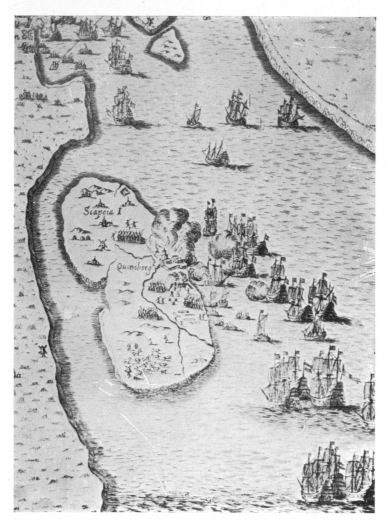

MAP REPRESENTING DUTCH ATTACK ON SHEERNESS, June 20th, 1667
Showing two Windmills on the Isle of Sheppey and two on the adjacent Coast Line.
From the Author's volume, *The Medway River and Valley*, p. 53.

See page 56   *Facing page 44*

A VIEW NEAR FRINDSBURY IN KENT
Quarry Mill, Oct. 1st, 1770

See page 206

R. HAMMOND'S
TENTERDEN, STAPLEHURST, BIDDENDEN, HEADCORN AND TOWN SUTTON,
STAGE WAGGON;
Sets out from TENTERDEN every MONDAY Morning, and arrives at the
GEORGE INN, BOROUGH, on WEDNESDAY MORNING.
Returns from thence every WEDNESDAY Evening, and arrives at Tenterden on FRIDAY Afternoon.
GOODS carefully conveyed to the following places.
Tenterden, Rolvenden, Benenden, Cranbrook, Milkhouse Street, Staplehurst, Marden, Stile Bridge, Linton, Coxheath, Town Sutton, Headcorn, Smarden, Biddenden, Wittersham, Woodchurch, Riding Street, Appledore, Brenzet, Brookland, Old & New Romney
Chambers and Exall, Printers, Tenterden.

TRANSPORT IN THE WEALD, 1750
"A teamster's advertisement."

W. R. Ward

See page 53

Facing page 45

CHAPTER III

THE ARRIVAL OF THE WINDMILL

WATERMILLS had been in use a thousand years before we find authentic mention of windmills. There is no definite evidence as to when windmills first came into use. The first actual undisputed date of their existence in England is 1191. This is in connection with the 'illegal mill' built by Dean Herbert in his glebe lands at Bury St. Edmunds and pulled down by the order of Abbot Samson.

About the beginning of the twelfth century charters granted to convents began to include permission to erect windmills. "Town mills," says C. J. Cornish, "were probably a later growth in England. Just as the Castle and the Abbey had their mill, so the free town, when it had once got its charter, built a mill, where the flour of the citizens would be made, free of tax, or only mulcted for municipal purposes."

These earliest mills were of rude and primitive construction. Later, probably in the thirteenth or fourteenth century, came the advent of the 'tripod post mill.' An illustration of this very early type of windmills is given on the next page.[1] It is taken from Green's *Short History of the English People*.

My friend Mr. Rex Wailes reminds me that a thirteenth century mill is shown in an ancient psalter in the possession of Mr. J. Pierpont Morgan ; another is to be seen on an old memorial brass dated 1349 at Lynn Church. In landscape scenes on old stained glass of early churches windmills are occasionally shown, as at Great Greenford and Fairfield.

Mr. F. H. Shelton tells us in the *Millers' Review* that "in a view of London in the time of the Tudors (1560) windmills are seen, and Great Windmill Street commemorates to this day the location of one in that part of the city." The Windmill Theatre now stands on the site.

These were all of the 'post mill' type, the body made to turn with the wind. This was followed by the 'sunk post mill,' but I find no record of a mill of this description in Kent, although probably there were specimens at one time. Then came the 'turret post mill,' or 'peg mill'—some few specimens of which are represented in this volume.

[1] Reproduced by permission of Messrs. Macmillan & Co., Ltd.

The final word in the design of windmills was spoken in the sixteenth century, when the 'tower' mill was introduced. This and the 'smock mill' need no description. Most of the gaunt derelicts to which we shall refer are mills of this type and, as we shall see, by the middle of the nineteenth century the country may be said to have been 'under sail,' so numerous were these 'land ships,' especially on the Downs of Kent and Sussex.

Jack miller asketh help to turn his mill aright. He hath grounden small, small ; the King's son of Heaven, He shall pay for all. Look thy mill go aright with the four sailes, and the post stand with stedfastness. With right and might, with skill and with will ; let might help right and skill go before will, and right before might, so goeth our mill aright.

The chief object of this book, however, is not to describe specifically the evolution of the windmill but rather to show by maps and data their gradual growth until they reached the zenith of their utility ; to indicate their gradual passing and almost entire disappearance as instruments of mechanical usefulness. All other aspects of the development of the windmill have been given in my earlier volumes and in the writings of other authors.

*   *   *   *   *

The question has often arisen as to which is the oldest windmill in England. It was believed to have been the 'tripod' post mill at Brill, in Buckinghamshire, which was built in 1668. A picture of this mill with its naked trestles appeared in the *Daily Telegraph* of March 3rd, 1930, where it is shown to possess its four sweeps and tail-pole but the flight of steps by which access was afforded are absent. Mr. S. P. B. Mais refers to this mill: "On the last spur northward (from the village) lay a magnificent 'peg' windmill, standing on what looked like the green crater of a dead volcano."

In the *Daily Telegraph* of March 18th, 1930, appeared the following from Miss M. I. Batten, the Windmill Secretary of *The Society for the Protection of Ancient Buildings*:

> Until quite recently the windmill at Brill was thought to be the oldest known dated mill in the country, but the Society has recently discovered one two years older than Brill. This is the post-mill at Outwood, in Surrey. The miller there possesses all the papers relating to its construction, which began in 1665, the mill working for the first time in September, 1666. It is said that the workmen saw the Fire of London from the top of the mill they were building. The mill is still working, though it has but two sails.

An illustration showed the mill apparently in good condition, save that it had lost two sweeps. The body of the mill and the round-house, steps and tail-pole appeared perfect.

The honour of being the oldest windmill in England, however, passes from Brill and Outwood mills to a mill at Bourn. Through the discovery of a deed dated 1643, it was found that the old post mill at Bourn, situated about twelve miles west of Cambridge, close to Caxton on the Royston-Huntingdon road, was mentioned and it is thought that the mill was in existence about 1636, an earlier date than previously claimed.

A splendid picture of Bourn Mill was published by *The Times* of June 8th, 1932, which no doubt many lovers of our windmills preserved. By the courtesy of *The Times* the picture is reproduced facing p. 37.

The record of the dedication ceremony at Bourn is unique, and the following from the *Cambridgeshire Times* of June 10th, 1932, has especial interest here.

> A novel and picturesque ceremony was observed on Friday afternoon, when Bourn Windmill, Cambridgeshire, was handed over and dedicated to the Cambridge Preservation Society. The mill, which appears almost certainly to be the oldest dated mill in the country, has been presented to the Society by Mr. and Mrs. Alfred C. Bossom and Mr. Mansfield Forbes. In the course of his remarks at Friday's ceremony, Mr. Forbes explained that it was quite possible that the mill would be made into a Youth Hostel if the Society were agreeable.
>
> An amusing miniature pageant, in which Don Quixote and his henchmen tried to attack the mill, preceded the dedication ceremony, but old English

singers and fiddlers in full costume repelled the attackers. After the singers had given several old airs, Mr. Hughes briefly explained the course of events which had led to the preservation of the mill and told something of its history.

The mill, said Mr. Hughes, was certainly the oldest in Cambridgeshire, and probably the oldest in the country. They knew it was old because they had found in the mill a deed of 1667 referring to its sale in 1636. They considered that good proof that the mill might probably have been in existence in Shakespeare's time.

The mill was officially "dedicated" with bottles of home-brewed beer broken on the four plinths.

Mrs. Bossom then presented the deeds of ownership to the Master of Magdalene, who returned sincere thanks to the donors for the great and remarkable gift.

Mr. Bossom, who was called upon by the Chairman to reply on behalf of his wife and American benefactors to England, declared that they should realise that that windmill was symbolic of that time in England when he thought that agriculture was the most important thing in industry. He thought we were not far from the time when we should realise how important agriculture really was to our country.

After the speeches the audience were introduced to Clive Carey (one of the original "English Singers"), who, with the others, sang a couple of old folk songs that provided a fitting climax to a brief glimpse of old English pageantry.

BIRD'S-EYE VIEW OF OLD ROCHESTER (1714)

Showing the ancient Stone Bridge over the Medway, and the early Pcst Mill near
Frindsbury Church, known as the Quarry Mill.

From the Author's volume, *The Medway River and Valley*, p. 52.

See page 206

E. H. Elliott

Facing page 48

ON WIND-SWEPT CREST
(Pluckley Mill)
From the Author's volume, *The Lure of the Countryside*, p. 21.

See page 257

W.C.F.

Facing page 49

CHAPTER IV

THE BUILDERS OF MILLS

WINDMILLS were by no means easy or cheap to build. It used to be a generally accepted fact that an average smock mill would cost £1,000 to build and would be worth £50 a year rent. The millwright was a clever craftsman and much skilled work was necessary and delicate adjustments required. For instance, in the setting out of the mortices of the sweeps particular care was needed, for if the necessary 'weather' on the sweeps was not obtained in the first place it could not be rectified afterwards.

It is said that Boaz Medhurst, the last millwright of the Medhurst family of Lewes, used to shut his workmen out of the shop when he was setting out the mortices of a pair of sweeps—chiefly so that he should be alone and undisturbed, to give concentrated attention to the job. It is also said, by the way, that his workmen, while busy with outside jobs in the yard, would give an occasional sly peep at their employer through the window, and the remark would be that "He never looks so wise as when he is on *that* job !"

The old millwright families are gradually becoming extinct, and for the repair of the remaining useful mills in the county of Kent it is becoming increasingly difficult to get reliable men to undertake the work. Among the millwrighting firms that have become defunct may be mentioned Hill of Ashford, Ralph of Sissinghurst, Humphrey of Cranbrook and Warren of Hawkhurst. To the credit of these firms may be placed the erection of many a fine Kentish mill.

Hill of Ashford built mills at Kennington, Bethersden (White Mill), Willesborough and Stanford, among many others. All four are standing, the first two derelict, but the last two are in splendid working order to-day.

Ralph of Sissinghurst built the fine White Mill at Headcorn, which is still working to-day (and by wind only), also two post mills at Tenterden (Goods Hill and Ashbourne) of both of which, unfortunately, no trace remains.

Humphrey of Cranbrook built mills at Goudhurst, Hythe and Sheerness which are now among the 'lost' mills of Kent, and also that splendid specimen of a smock mill at Cranbrook that still stands complete and working and will probably grace its Wealden village for at least another half a century, if successive owners take as much pride in its appearance and efficiency as does its present owner Mr. J. Russell.

Warren of Hawkhurst built that once splendid five-sweep smock mill, Sandhurst, which stands in a sorry condition to-day. He no doubt built many other windmills in Kent, as well as many in Sussex.   (See also page 314.)

Other well-known and reliable Kentish millwrights of days gone by include Sweetloves of Wingham, who built the Chequers' Mill at Petham, now, alas, no more : Killick's of Strood, who built the 'Model Mill' at Meopham Green, working to-day with two sweeps ; and Henry Payne & Sons, who built Mr. Glover's mill at Delce, Rochester, which stands to-day in an almost unique position for a windmill, holding its own and catching the winds of heaven above a sea of slate roofs and chimney pots (facing p. 261).

The pity is that the names of the millwrights were not more closely associated with the works of art for which they were responsible.   Only too often the names of the builders of our windmills have been lost sight of entirely.

Fortunately we still have one old and famous Kentish firm of millwrights with us—Messrs. Holman Bros., of Canterbury— and it is to be hoped that this firm may long continue to aid in the salvation of the few remaining working specimens of Kentish windmills. To their credit must be placed the erection of a large number of mills in our county, including Blean (two), Staple, Preston (near Wingham) and Swingfield (the last corn mill built in Kent in 1885), which all belong to the past ; Newington (Ramsgate), Drapers' Old Mill (Margate), Stelling Minnis and Sarre, standing to-day but used only with the help of oil or gas engines ; Northbourne (New Mill) and Herne, working to-day on two sweeps but otherwise in excellent order ; and that magnificent specimen on Barham Downs, the Black Mill, Barham, which stands complete and is almost as hard worked to-day as it ever was.

It is interesting to note that a year or two ago Messrs. Holman Bros. were given the privilege of showing that genuine mill-wrighting is an art not entirely lost to us, for they had the important task of building a new mill, at St. Margaret's Bay, near Dover. The picture facing p. 289 will show what a noble specimen of a mill she is. What a pity she generates electricity and does not grind corn !

It is also worth noting that Messrs. Holman Bros. constructed the first windmill erected at Jerusalem (facing p. 224).   This mill was built for Sir Moses Montefiore and was erected at the foot of Mount Zion, about a quarter of a mile from the Jaffa Gate, for the use of the poorer inhabitants of Jerusalem who had previously the laborious task of grinding their corn by hand-mills.

Great difficulty was experienced in landing the machinery at Jaffa, the landing-stage there was not strong enough to bear it. Each piece had to be dragged ashore by about forty men. Four months were occupied in conveying it to Jerusalem on the backs of camels, the road not being passable to carriages of any description.

All difficulties were, however, finally overcome and the machinery was fixed without loss or breakage of any portion. The tower of the mill is built of stone quarried on the spot, the walls are three feet thick and nearly fifty feet high. All the modern improvements were introduced into this mill. It drove two pairs of stones, the wheat-cleaning, flour-dressing, and other machinery.

During the course of its construction it was looked upon with an evil eye by the millers there, and one of their head men was sent to curse it. Before the rainy season set in it was prophesied that the heavy rains prevalent there would wash it away; and when the mill was found to have passed through the stormy season uninjured, it was pronounced to be the work of Satan.

The poor Jews, however, for whose use and benefit the mill was erected were loud in their praises of their benefactor, Sir Moses Montefiore.[1]

In the early days of the mill's working, an extraordinary difficulty presented itself, according to one of the men who went out there. It appears that the Arabs were too fond of lubricating oil, and would steal every drop they could get hold of ! A remark was even made that the mill would surely one day be burnt, so dry would she become for want of oil ! The Arabs even licked the bearings to get a taste of the oil !

At last a solution to the problem was hit upon. A leg of pork was placed in the barrel of oil, whereupon, on account of their superstition against such meat, the Arabs lost their appetite for the oil !

I am glad it is also possible, by the courtesy of the British Chaplain in Jerusalem, to give a picture of the mill as it stands to-day (facing p. 224). The Chaplain says that the mill was in perfect condition in 1891 but had ceased to be used as a mill. Since then it has been used as a studio and dwelling-house. At the present time it is derelict, standing on an eminence on the west

[1] *Illustrated London News*, December 18th, 1858.

side of the city, on one side of the Valley of Hinnom, the ancient Gehenna! The Chaplain also states that another mill stands in the modern Jewish quarter of Rehavia, about a mile due west of the city; it is exactly like the old Kentish mill and was probably copied from it.

My young friend Jack Holman tells me that his grandfather, J. R. Holman, made the machinery for a windmill erected by a German firm at Haifa, on Mount Carmel in Syria. The machinery was made in 1874 and was shipped from London on the s.s. *Catiofe*, bound for Alexandria, and addressed to J. Schumacher. Some of the packages weighed 2,200 lbs. I quote from a letter: "We landed the machinery at Jaffa, it having been brought in at Avat by a coasting vessel from Beyrout, and here she was run in close to the shore to expedite the unloading. To facilitate carriage the windshaft was made in three parts. On this occasion an important piece of machinery was lost in the sea at Alexandria when unloading." The letter does not say so, but it was probably replaced with the least possible delay by the Canterbury millwrights.

I must not leave the subject of our Kentish millwrights without mentioning Mr. Frank Pain, who for many years now has been travelling from mill to mill, particularly in East Kent, executing repairs.

Mr. Pain was born in 1864 at the Mill House at Selstead, near Swingfield, his father having been the miller at Selstead Mill for twenty-one years; so Mr. Pain is of genuine windmilling stock.

For no less than thirty-eight years in partnership with his brother, under the name of R. & F. Pain, he worked the Star Mill at Chatham. He was always very interested in the mechanical and constructional side of a windmill, and his life as a miller gave him abundant opportunity for studying it.

Since giving up the business at Chatham (nothing now remains of the mill) he has undertaken the repair of many a Kent mill. Despite the decreased number of mills, his services have been in great demand and he is kept well occupied. He is now in his sixty-ninth year, hale and hearty, as alive and interested in his work as ever. He has given much practical help with notes on the various mills in which he has worked and with which he has been connected in one way or another, in addition to lending a number of photographs for reproduction in this book.

See page 58

DRESSING THE MILL-STONE

From the Author's volume, *Life in Rural England*, p. 172.

W. H. Palmer

Fac..., page 52

ACRISE (Elham Mill)

See page 151

ADISHAM (Bekesbourne Mill)

See pages 152 and 311

Facing page 53

CHAPTER V

WORKING, REPAIRING, MOVING AND SMASHING OF WINDMILLS

ONE of Kent's old-time millers—he worked Pluckley Mill for half a century—once told the writer that he was brought up to believe that in order of village prosperity the parson came first, then the miller, and lastly the farmer !

Millers were certainly prosperous in bygone times, and the miller of the village was always looked up to with respect.

Before the advent of hard roads each village was self-confined and catered for its own needs. Every parish had its own watermill or windmill, and competition in the milling trade was almost unknown. No doubt the soft roads had many disadvantages. For instance, when they were almost impassable during bad weather, a farmer could not get his cart up to the mill and was obliged to unload his corn some distance away ; then, with a heavy sack of grain on his back, to pick his way among the deep ruts and puddles of a muddy road—a trying and disagreeable experience. But such disadvantages did not affect the *miller* very much. One aged miller assured me that his father had repeatedly drawn attention to the one great regret of his life as a miller— that he had subscribed to the making of hard roads ! They brought dissatisfaction and competition along with them—that was his grievance.

The inaccessibility of our Kentish villages, the difficulty of transport and intercommunication even between adjoining parishes, in early days, may be seen from a copy of an announcement of a carrier who made a weekly journey to London from Tenterden and back, which I am able to reproduce here, by the courtesy of Mr. W. R. Ward of Sutton Valence Mill. It is dated 1750 (facing p. 45).

In the days of soft roads, people had been content with things pretty much as they were (to wit, paying the miller's prices without a question !) but hard roads opened up the villages, linked them one with another and made access to market towns easy, and "folk began to look around and open their eyes and ears." Farmers not satisfied with the price paid for corn sold to the miller, or the charges for grinding, began to assert their independence for they could now easily take their custom elsewhere. It was a simple matter also for householders making their own bread, who were not satisfied with the price paid for flour from the local miller, to get their flour from another mill. Thus the miller found that he had to keep a closer eye on prevailing prices if he wished to retain and satisfy the customers of his own parish.

Hard roads had, of course, other and more far-reaching effects upon rural life, which it is not the purpose of this book to consider, but the country millers' trade was certainly seriously affected. Competition became very keen, particularly with the advent of the larger power mills in the towns, to which access was made easy, and still more so, later, by the coming of motor transport.

The village miller found that his customers were not prepared to wait for the vagaries of the wind for their grinding, as hitherto. Often, of course, in calm weather, lack of wind might hold up grinding for days, and then when the wind did 'get up' there was so much accumulated work to be done that customers had to wait their turn. At one Kentish windmill there was, on such an occasion, as many as a hundred sacks of wheat waiting to be ground, besides other corn. Such delay was often vexatious but it could not be helped, and folk just made the best of it. Then came the gradual change. Farmers found they could purchase ground corn, bran, middlings, and other feeding stuffs for their cattle, pigs, horses and poultry at a reasonable price direct from the larger mills. Cakes and concentrated feeding stuffs became more universally used for the feeding of animals on the farm. There began to be less incentive for a farmer to grow his own corn, and many a cornfield was thus laid down to grass.

In order to keep abreast of the times country millers installed various auxiliary plant—oil engines, suction gas plants, and some went so far as to install steam power—so that business was not suspended during calm weather.

Gradually, however, the larger mills took the greater part of the trade, and, owing to the low prices prevailing for imported grain, corn growing became still less profitable for the English farmer, and many more acres of cornfields became pasture land, with the inevitable result of decreased trade for the local windmills. The following letter to a daily paper summarises the matter:

RUSSIAN WHEAT

The following case could be repeated *ad infinitum*. A farmer near Salisbury, whose corn usually fetches an average of 23s. a sack, could not get a better offer than 13s. a sack two or three weeks ago, and has had to sell at that price wheat that cost about 20s. a sack to grow. The market is flooded with Russian corn at 10s. a sack, and home-grown corn has no chance at all. The farmer will have to put down his land to grass and dismiss several of his labourers and carters as he can employ them no more. Soviet corn is ruining our farmers.—Mr. E. S. THORNTON LAWES, Fouracres, Bishopsdown, Salisbury.—*The Times*, May 20th, 1931.

In one Kentish village (Woodchurch) there were once as many as twenty-seven teams of horses (108 horses) at work in the fields around a pair of mills. To-day most of the land is laid down to pasture, very little corn is grown, and there is hardly a team of horses in the district. What little work a horse would do on the land is now mainly accomplished by the tractor and other modern agricultural machinery, which have so largely replaced horse power in Kent as in other counties.

Thus, by a combination of circumstances, the work required of the local miller has diminished and, as the cost of repairs and replacements must always bear a correct proportion to the business done, the mills have gradually passed the stage of working efficiently.

* * * * *

We may note in passing that windmills took an active part in one of our earliest industries, that of providing salt from sea-water. Salt in the thirteenth century cost 44/6 for ten quarts, while sheep from Romney Marsh cost but 1/10 each, and ten geese could then be purchased for 2/3. Thus we see that one pint of salt cost more than one sheep! These figures, if multiplied to meet the present-day prices, would indicate the fabulous price of salt. Hence the inability to purchase a sufficient supply for curing purposes, and pork, which was the staple meat of the poor of the rural areas, usually became rancid.

Salt works were numerous in Kent, particularly around the coast, near to forest lands, where wood was granted for procuring salt by evaporating the sea water. It was an early industry, for we find that in A.D. 732 Ethelbert of Kent gave land and an annual grant of wood to Abbot Dun for the evaporating pans at Lympne. In A.D. 738 Eadbert included salt works in a grant to Rochester, and Coenulph did the same in A.D. 812 and 814 to Canterbury. As far as Kent is concerned, there were several other salinæ, including twenty-seven at Milton, one at Tunstall, two at Faversham, one at Ospringe and two at Stone near Faversham.[1]

In the Notes in Part IV of this volume will be found references to certain windmills which were utilised in connection with the salt industry, and on the early Ordnance Survey maps windmills

[1] Furley's *History of the Weald of Kent*, pp. 165–6.

are shown standing near to the salt-pans, but at what period they were thus utilised I have found no record.

That these old windmills were in close proximity to the coast is shown by the illustration, which is dated 1667. It is taken from my recent volume, *The Medway River and Valley*. It shows the Dutch attack on Sheerness on June 10th, 1667. Four mills are plainly drawn on the Sheppey Isle and the adjacent coastline (facing p. 44).

*   *   *   *   *

For the obvious reason of taking full advantage of the winds, a windmill is always found situated in an exposed position and is buffeted by the elements in a way that no ordinary structure is called upon to withstand. Constant attention to repair is necessary, therefore, particularly as the life of a mill in working trim is mainly that of friction and vibration. If some little thing is wrong and remains unattended to it can easily lead, in a gale, to more serious damage being done. A miller, unable to afford the minor repairs from time to time that might have kept the mill going, has found it impossible to bear the heavier cost of a substantial repair. Hence, one more mill on the road to becoming a derelict !

Often it is the question of one sweep breaking off in the wind. The other half of the pair of sweeps is then, of course, removed and the mill run with only two sweeps, the miller perhaps deciding that he will replace the other two "when he can afford it" ; but he never can afford it! With the little work the mill has to do he probably finds he can get enough wind power. It is a well-known fact that the power derived from one pair of sweeps is considerably more than half of that from the use of the two pairs. But, as every miller knows, there is an unbalanced vibration with the use of only two sweeps. In the words of one miller, "it pulls her to pieces—regularly takes it out of her, you know."

Thus when we see a mill running with only two sweeps it seems to foretell a shortened life for the structure. William Warren, the last of that famous firm of Hawkhurst millwrights, considered that the average useful life of a post mill was two hundred years and that of a smock mill one hundred years. Very few windmills were erected in Kent after 1850, and the life of those erected before then is now almost played out, seeing that in the last thirty years there has been a rapid decline in the milling trade and in the numbers of millwrights and millers. The consequent neglect of repair has considerably shortened the "average useful life" of our mills.

The sweeps of various windmills do not revolve at the same rate. The mill at Lympne was geared exceptionally low and the sweeps (which were only about twenty feet in length, as against seventy-two at many other mills) spun round like a peg-top.

The sweeps of Richardson's Mill at Boughton-under-Blean used to whirl round merrily at a rapid rate, in contrast to the slower, steadier stride of its neighbour, Miles' Mill.

The fine mill which stood at Cheriton, near Folkestone, known as Ashley Mill, was also of low gear, and the sweeps made a complete revolution to every six revolutions of the mill-stones. By way of comparison, it is interesting to note that at Swingate Mill, Guston, the mill-stones made ten revolutions to one of the sweeps, and that at Upper Deal Mill the ratio was twelve to one.

*　　*　　*　　*　　*

I possessed a fine negative of Whitfield Mill, near Dover, as a derelict. I tried in vain to get a companion picture showing the mill working but had to dismiss the idea. Then a friend of my youth, learning that I was collecting pictures of Kentish mills, posted me the only negative of a windmill in his collection, taken well-nigh half a century ago. It turned out to be of that very Whitfield Mill I had given up in despair. I had hardly turned round after placing it in safety when there was a gentle tap at my door and an elderly man, frail and delicate, entered. His dusty white clothes almost spoke and said, "Pardon, but I am a miller!" He had read one or two of my books and wondered whether certain pictures, which he had brought with him, of mills in which he had worked would be of use to me. I was delighted to have them, for there were several I needed and one of them, strangely enough, was of Whitfield Mill, taken at the same period as the one that had arrived a moment or two earlier by post.

To crown it all, at the same time Mr. A. W. Tiffin, for his own interest in the subject as well as for possible use here, had been seeking a picture of Whitfield Mill in its prime. He had been successful in borrowing from a miller friend a photograph that proved to be exactly similar to the two I had recently received! (facing p. 309). Thus within a few days I had received three almost identical pictures of Whitfield Mill.

Among the pictures given me by my elderly visitor was one of the post mill at Limpsfield Chart, Surrey, just beyond the borders of Kent, near Westerham. I have included it with the illustrations because it was a 'left-handed' mill; by the manner of the construction of the sweeps they revolve against the sun. I have placed it beside Smarden Mill, whose sweeps revolve in the usual way, so that the reader may see at a glance the difference in the sweeps (facing p. 224).

Limpsfield Chart Mill, by the way, was pulled down in 1877, and I was assured that the sale of the oak from this structure fetched £100. Maybe the purchaser of the timber gave it useful restoration in a 'Tudor' dwelling.

My friend Mr. Rex Wailes, who is a professional mill engineer and an authority on these matters, tells me that 'left-handed' mills, like Limpsfield Chart Mill, are not as rare as I had believed. At Woolpit and Drinkstone, Suffolk, both kinds may be seen only a quarter of a mile apart.

On questioning Mr. Wailes as to the cutting of the 'feathers' in the mill-stones in 'left-handed' mills, my anticipation was correct—they are cut in the reverse form.

In *Life in Rural England* (p. 172) is an illustration (also reproduced here, facing p. 52) of an old miller engaged in the difficult task of dressing a mill-stone.

I once asked Mr. Frank Pain[1] what are the usual sizes of mill-stones in windmills. He replied, "4 ft. 2 in. for Peak and 4 ft. for French burr." The largest he ever dressed was a pair of French burr stones, in Mount Ephraim Mill, Ash, which had a diameter of 4 ft. 10 in. The other pair of stones in this mill are of the opposite extreme, a pair of Peak stones only 3 ft. 8 in. in diameter. Mill-stones are rarely as small as 3 ft. 8 in., although occasionally a pair is found even as low as 3 ft., but too small to be really useful. "Anything from 3 ft. 6 in. to 4 ft. 6 in. is workable," added Mr. Pain.

An expert (Mr. A. Tanton, of Woodchurch Mills) says that the centre of the mill-stone is known as the 'eye,' and at this point, where both the nether and the upper stones meet, a piece of brown paper should be gripped tightly. The middle of the stone is known as the 'breast,' where a piece of newspaper should be gripped ; and the outside is known as the 'skirt,' and here the stones should grip a piece of tissue paper. I confess I was not aware that such refinement was called for in the dressing of the stones.

Mill-stones are not the simple things that I at first imagined, and many must have pictured them as I did, a pair of simple, circular stones, one revolving upon the other, each stone being crudely scored or furrowed to fulfil its purpose.

[1] See page 52.

It was this furrowing or 'feathering' of the stones that first tempted me to pay more than a passing attention to them. My notion of crude workmanship was quickly dissipated as I watched the stone-dresser at work with his mill-bill. The accurate, geometrical form of the furrows, causing the meal to traverse the surface of the stones and issue from the rim perfectly ground, was a revelation. It proved also that the stone-dresser must be an artist as well as a mason, and I am tempted to conclude that every museum worthy of the name should preserve for us at least two upper or runner-stones, one with its furrows worn too smooth to grind satisfactorily and the other as perfectly dressed and prepared for the task as I saw it done in the mill at Delce, Rochester. A simple device could be made showing how the system of furrowing the stones with such skill and ingenuity results in such perfect grinding ; showing also that the stones revolve in a definite direction. In a right-hand mill they are feathered right-handed and revolve clock-wise, while in a left-hand mill they are driven anti-clock-wise, the furrows in the stones being cut in reverse form.

The two figures on page 60 show the groovings of the upper or runner-stone of both a right- and a left-hand mill. If the top stone of either pair of stones be lifted off and placed face up, side by side with the under or bed-stone, the feathering of the two will be found identical in form, but when the top stone is replaced upon the bed-stone it results in the reversing of the direction of the furrows. At first, to the uninitiated, this must appear conflicting, hence I suggest the following interesting experiment :

Make two transparent tracings of the stone in Fig. 1, one in black ink and one in red, turn the red tracing face down upon the face of the black tracing and pass a pin through the centre hole of the pair. Now if the upper (red) tracing is revolved clock-wise on the black tracing (bed-stone) it will be seen how the 'feathers,' in passing over those of the bed-stone, would urge the meal across the face of the stone, towards the rim, where it is issued. It is hardly necessary to state that the corn is fed into the centre hole of the runner-stone.

Continuing the experiment, turn the red tracing anti-clock-wise for a moment, and note how impossible it would be for the grinding to be successfully accomplished if the stones were not turned true clock-wise, for the feathers would tend to conduct the meal to the centre of the stone and choke the process. Next repeat the experiment as with the stone shown in Fig. 2, but in this case the upper tracing should be turned anti-clock-wise. The result will be seen to be successful, whereas if the upper tracing is turned clock-wise a failure will be apparent as before.

If one were to imagine the upper or runner-stone to be of thick glass, through which the process of grinding was visible, a veritable

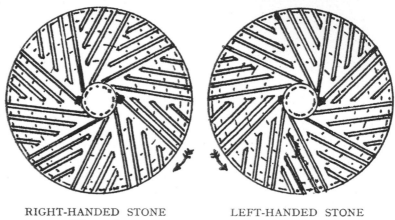

RIGHT-HANDED STONE
(Figure 1)

LEFT-HANDED STONE
(Figure 2)

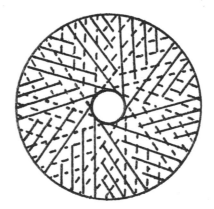

SKETCH SHOWING THE NETWORK OF MESHES FORMED BY THE FEATHERING
OF THE STONES
(Figure 3)

network of meshes formed by the feathering of the stones, as indicated in a third figure given, would be seen. And whether it were a right-hand or left-hand pair of stones, it would be noted how that no single grain of corn could escape the meshes of the net set to catch it and grind it to powder.

*   *   *   *   *

Hugh Penfold

ALDINGTON

See page 152

W.C.F.

ASH (Mount Ephraim Mill)

See page 154

W.C.F.

BIDDENDEN (Beacon Hill)
(Paul Sharpe's Mill)

See page 164

J. Russell

BIDDENDEN (Cherry Clack Mill)
Re-erected at Punnetts Town, Heathfield,
Sussex

See page 164

Facing page 60

APPLEDORE HEATH

See page 153

APPLEDORE HEATH (Great Mill)
Inscription stone in base, and copper token, "Union of Appledore, Kent, 1794."

See page 153

The old type of sweep with its canvas sails was known as 'commons.' With these old cloth sails, as one milling friend reminded me, there was no way of regulating the wind pressure on the sweeps while the mill was running. The mill had to be stopped by its powerful brake and the miller or his assistant had to climb up on each sweep and do any necessary furling of the sail cloths. "But," added my milling friend, "if the wind is too strong for your brake, or the brake is not in quite the good order it ought to be, what are you to do ?" He then told me of an incident that took place at the Black Mill at Whitstable many years ago.

The miller was working in the mill single-handed and, when he wanted to stop the mill and attend to the sails, he found the wind was too strong for the brake to hold unless he kept his weight on the brake beam. As soon as he left the brake it lifted . . . "and you can't catch a sweep while she's going!" A sailor happened to pass by at the time and the miller called for his help. While the miller sat on the brake beam the sailor went aloft on the sweeps. "But if the brake had slipped, then it would have been worse than Cape Horn for the sailor !"

The later type of 'patent' shutters were also not without their difficulties in the experience of my milling friend. As can be readily understood, constant oiling was necessary all the way up each sweep and at the quadrants in the centre, in order to ensure the delicate adjustment of the shutters. Sometimes the shutters were covered with ice in wet, cold weather, which made it an unpleasant task for the miller to go aloft with a hammer to break the ice in order to allow the shutters to operate !

The following, from the pen of Mr. Rex Wailes,[1] about two types of sweeps, is interesting :

> The spring-sail, which supplanted the common-sail type was invented by Andrew Meikle in 1772. Here the shutters were of canvas, stretched over hinged wire frames and actuated by a sail bar, similar to the laths of a Venetian blind. In early days it was common practice to run a mill with two common and two spring sails.

As confirming Mr. Wailes' statement, I have heard Mr. J. Russell, of the Cranbrook Mill, say that using a mill with two canvas sails and two spring sweeps was perhaps the best working arrangement. Many a Kent mill was thus at one time operated— old Frittenden post mill and Ashley Mill, Cheriton, are instances that immediately come to mind.

[1] *The Miller*, October 6th, 1930.

I used to be impressed by the manner in which the old 'bargee' friends of mine recognised most accurately the various sailing craft, even when far away on the horizon, by cut of jib or mainsail or other subtle indications. I have now discovered that a similar instinct was peculiar to the builders and captains of the 'land-ships,' the millwrights and the millers. It is appropriate to refer in these terms to our windmills for, in the period of which I write, England was under 'full sail.' The word 'sails' definitely applies to the time when the revolving arms of corn mills were covered with canvas and blinked from every eminence, before the introduction of 'shuttered sweeps' or 'wooden slats' as they are sometimes called.

For nearly forty years, at infrequent intervals, just as opportunity offered, I have taken photographs carefully and methodically of every mill I passed, naming the negatives for future reference. In a few instances, however, I omitted to mark the negatives with the names of the mills and as years passed it became increasingly difficult to place them with any degree of certainty. Here an old miller or millwright has been very helpful and without any apparent difficulty a mill has been recognised. In addition, he could remember every detail of its mysterious interior : the number of stones it drove, their texture, whether for grinding wheat or other grain, its power and the task it accomplished with the varying velocity of the wind—its own peculiar idiosyncrasy—for I gleaned that no two mills behaved quite alike, just as ships differ in behaviour though built to the same design by the same builder.

We may also note that the miller, as the sailor when referring to his ship, speaks of his mill as being of the feminine gender : "Ah ! she's been a fine old mill in her time." The practice of using the feminine pronoun for ships is immemorial ; it may have arisen, I am told, from the resemblance of a ship in full sail to a graceful woman.

*   *   *   *   *

I confess to a great surprise when, many years ago, I first heard of a windmill being *moved*. For such a bulky structure to be shifted from one part of the country to another seemed to me a very difficult task, and I could hardly believe that the cost of dismantling and re-erecting a mill would justify the procedure. I learnt subsequently, however, that it was no uncommon occurrence to transfer a mill, bodily or in sections, from one district to another, and in some cases mills were moved quite long distances.

A post mill, originally built at Rye, had three moves, having been transferred to Appledore, then back to Rye, and finally ended its days at Appledore again! A Biddenden mill had a long journey to Punnetts Town, near Heathfield; a large Folkestone smock mill came twenty miles by road to Bethersden; two Hythe mills found other homes at Cheriton and Ruckinge, the latter being transported by barge; a Barham mill was transferred to Margate; a fine specimen of a smock mill bade goodbye to Ashford and found new quarters at Badlesmere, near Faversham; the Ripple Mill at Ringwould came from near Folkestone. Gillingham claimed a Snodland mill, and Lympne one from Cheriton, while only a year or two ago a mill had a journey from Sidley, near Bexhill, to Leigh, near Hildenborough, where it was reassembled, is working to-day and is associated with a famous Old Barn Tea Room. It is the mill that can be seen from the railway on the main line from London to Dover.

Many other Kentish mills were moved shorter distances, from one part of a village to another or into an adjoining parish, often to take advantage of the prevailing south-westerly winds from a more exposed position. Mills at Ash, Dymchurch, Egerton, Hawkhurst, High Halden, Kingsdown, Petham and Woodchurch are some that were transferred for that reason.

Often, to remove a mill, the octagonal body was divided up into eight sections by sawing down the eight cant (corner) posts; then, in re-erection, these sections would be bolted together again. One of the original cant posts bolted together in this way can still be seen in Ripple Mill, which was brought from Drellingore, near Folkestone.

Frequently, however, the body of the mill was conveyed intact, and one can imagine that difficulties sometimes arose in the conveyance of such a huge structure. A Petham mill met with an unfortunate hindrance on its way to Stelling Minnis, hauled on a six-wheeled trolley by men and horses. The road was too narrow! The worthy miller was full of concern about the safe transfer of his old mill. A local story says that he walked backwards a little way ahead of the equippage and shouted back numerous beseeching expletives of caution, so anxiously did he guard and guide his property along the country lanes. Any unevenness of the road that caused the structure to tilt to one side the least bit gave him great alarm, and a slight loss of balance as it turned a corner in the road very nearly caused him a loss of mental balance.

These were more or less imaginary ills, but a road too narrow was a real grievance! The miller, however, found an outlet for his feelings in a bit of hard spade work, for he and his men were obliged to cut away the grassy banks verging the road and thus, after some delay, were able to make room for the unwieldy hulk to pass.

There is an amusing though simple little incident told in connection with the removal intact of a Hawkhurst mill a short distance, from Gun Green to Four Throws. The millwright, Warren, who organized the removal of the mill, used to tell the story with great glee.

It appears that a shopkeeper at Four Throws, whose premises were situated along the road the conveyance would have to pass, was greatly perturbed less perchance the structure should fall upon his shop and bring about his ruin ! He armed himself with a *clothes prop* which became very much in evidence as the huge structure came slowly by, pulled on rollers by a team of bullocks. The shopkeeper heeded not the merriment amongst the many onlookers. Fortunately for the miserable clothes prop, the shop-keeper and his shop, there was no mishap, the journey being accomplished safely for all concerned.

Such a story, of course, undergoes constant revision in the process of time and telling. I have heard several versions of it ; the latest, quite a mild one, is to the effect that it was a country 'yokel' (one of those much maligned individuals) who brandished a *hop pole* in a brave attempt to steady the mill when, as he thought, the structure slightly leant to one side.

When the old Bethersden Mill was being brought up from Folkestone it had to pass through Ashford. One can readily realise the obstruction caused in the streets of this busy market town by a traction engine and three trailing trucks conveying a huge windmill, whose sweeps alone measured seventy-two feet from tip to tip. In endeavouring to negotiate a difficult corner, part of the structure came into collision with a wall. Fortunately not much damage was done, and a few shillings were good humouredly paid there and then to make amends.

Lympne Mill was brought from Cheriton on farm wagons. In this case the mill must have been partially dismantled, or the wagons in some way linked one with another. There was no end to a miller's ingenuity.

The Hythe mill that found its second home at Ruckinge was moved almost intact by barge, and one wonders how the difficulty of passing under low canal bridges was obviated !

One mill, that of Luton, Chatham, had a long cross-country journey, being transported partly by barge and partly by road all

W.C.F.

Facing page 64

E. H. Pearson

BADLESMERE (BOUNDGATE MILL)

J. S. Howland

(As standing at Ashford before removal to Badlesmere.)

See pages 155-56

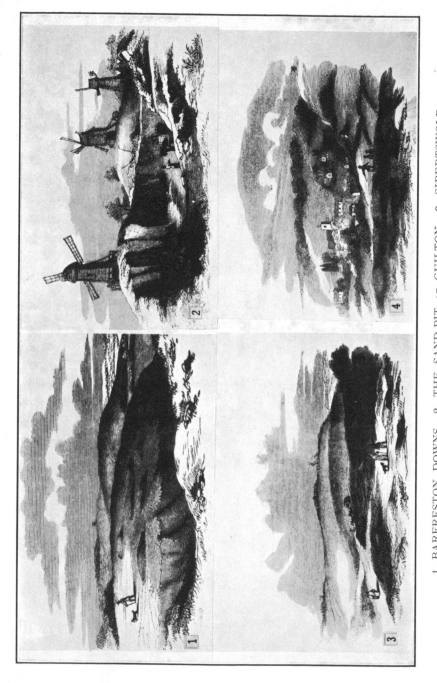

1. BARFRESTON DOWNS. 2. THE SAND-PIT AT GUILTON. 3. SIBERTSWOLD
DOWNS. 4. KINGSTON, from the site of the Tumuli, 1854-55.

Illustrations from Rev. Bryan Faussett's

Inventorium Sepulchrale (Edited by Charles Roach Smith, 1855)

See pages 156, 215, 277, 232.

Facing page 65

the way from Slough in Buckinghamshire. Doubtless this was a very costly undertaking, even in those days (1850).

This manner of removing windmills entire has been referred to in a Frenchman's adventure, on April 11th, 1765, quoted from C. G. Harper's book *The Dover Road*, pp. 75–76 :

> Between Canterbury and Rochester the coaches encountered an obstacle which savours rather of Don Quixote's adventures than of Sunday travelling in this unromantic country. This was nothing less than a windmill, which the country folk, taking advantage of that usually coachless day, were moving entire. Less fiery than the Don, the travellers outflanked the gigantic obstacle by dragging the coaches into the fields beside the road.

One wonders what were the 'whence' and 'whither' of this particular mill.

* * * * *

In these days old mills can often be bought for 'a mere song.' In fact they are sometimes given away, as it is dangerous work to pull them down and few men care to undertake it. Mr. George Jarvis, late of Bethersden and now of St. Michael's, Tenterden, has had at least three windmills given to him in payment for his work of demolition—Aldington smock mill, Newchurch tower mill, and High Halden post mill.

Mr. Jarvis, who has earned for himself a rather unenviable reputation as 'the Mill Smasher,' has also demolished a number of other Kent mills, including Headcorn Black Mill (he was paid for this work and the owner utilised the material in the building of a house on the site); Kingsnorth, the square brick base of which was heightened and made into a labourer's dwelling which stands to-day ; and two mills at Appledore Heath, a post and a smock, both of which he purchased for a small sum : the base of the smock mill still stands and is used as a shed.

The old post mills at Smarden and Frittenden would probably not be standing to-day had Mr. Jarvis been prepared to offer a little more money for them ; and he was very nearly commissioned to dismantle the old black smock mill at Smarden, but in this case it was because an American had taken a fancy to the old derelict and expressed a wish to transfer it across the Atlantic. This fancy, however, did not materialise for, although our friend from across the water could buy the mill cheaply as it stood, the cost of transfer and re-erection would have been out of all proportion ; so that lovers of these quaint old derelicts of our English countryside have been spared at least one heartache.

E

Had it not been for Mr. Jarvis's advancing years (he is now seventy-eight) and his having yielded to the persuasion of his near relatives no more to clamber about on old and tottering windmills, I am afraid the number of Kentish derelict mills would have been still further depleted. Certainly the mills at Pluckley and Benenden would not be standing to-day had he succumbed to a strong temptation to ignore the advice of his friends.

In addition to demolishing mills, however, Mr. Jarvis has often repaired them, but this side of his work has not been so well known. He is more a lover of a windmill in its entirety than of its many dismembered parts !

He has not been a corn miller. His chief connection with windmills has been in utilising them for timber sawing, to which purpose he admirably adapted them.

One of his earliest reminiscences is, however, to do with a corn mill for he remembers carrying wheat to Rolvenden Mill when he was a lad of nine years of age (in 1864). He was at work leading horses when only six and assisting with ploughing in the open fields at seven !

The first windmill he purchased was a little six-sweep mill that had a varied career. It was originally built at Pluckley, then transferred to Great Chart, where it was the predecessor of another six-sweep mill of which the base alone remains to-day. Later it was removed to Sandgate.

Mr. Jarvis, then a young man of nineteen, owning a carpenter's and wheelwright's shop at Bethersden, thought a windmill for timber sawing would be a useful adjunct to his business. He humorously tells how that one evening he rode from Bethersden to Sandgate (about twenty miles) on one of those old-fashioned 'bone-shakers,' an iron-tyred bicycle, in order to see Mr. Brissenden, the Sandgate builder, who had the mill for sale.

The mill had not been used for some years ; the authorities would not allow it ; its whirling sweeps were a danger to the public in the populated, growing Sandgate of those days (about 1875).

The purchase price was £20, and arrangements were made for the transfer of the mill. The body of the structure was conveyed whole, by road, with two or three horses, and the cap was later fetched with a one-horse van. The mill was re-erected close to Boorman's Stores at Bethersden, where it became known as the Little Mill and did useful service for many years.

Finally it was transferred to its fifth home, on the other side of Bethersden. There had been much discussion in the village regarding this proposed removal and folk were anxious to see the process. Their curiosity, however, was unappeased, for the mill was dismantled one moonlit night, and the following morning they awoke to find the little old mill had vanished !

A year or two later, the business having grown, Mr. Jarvis, then in partnership with his brother, required another and larger windmill. On his way to Dover by train one day he noticed that houses were being built near a mill in Folkestone (Dawson's Mill, Millfield, a fine white smock corn mill) and he thought it would probably soon be up for sale. A windmill is not usually left to keep company with rows of houses—the famous Delce Mill at Rochester is a notable exception.

A few weeks later Mr. Jarvis saw the mill advertised for sale and very soon took an opportunity of looking over it, found it just what he wanted and—paid £30 for it ! Only a few years previously it had been put in thorough repair at a cost of about £400 : the weather-boarding and all the main timbers were new.

The mill was duly transferred to Bethersden by road, a traction engine and three 'trailers' being hired for the purpose. The heaviest of the machinery went by rail, and when everything had arrived the mill was re-erected near the little six-sweep mill which, a little later, it replaced. The newcomer stood idle for a day or two after completion because of lack of wind, but one night the wind blew up and Mr. Jarvis left his bed to start work in the mill at two o'clock in the morning !

* * * * *

Mr. Jarvis has always had a quaint love for machinery and tackle from windmills. I cannot say how many iron windshafts he has acquired from various Kent mills, but I know that shafts from Goudhurst, Kennington and one of the Headcorn mills have all had an extended period of usefulness at the Bethersden sawmills. One of them is still in use to-day—embedded in the ground and supporting an overhead run for timber ! One shaft was in use for years converted into a crane.

His accumulation of tackle is a marvel. I verily believe that *if* windmills came again into their own, he would make quite a fortune in disposing of his treasure trove, *if* he would part with it and *if* he could spare the time to sort it over to find what was wanted (for he is a busy man); but the revival of windmills is unlikely, so that his wonderfully heterogeneous collection of tackle continues to expand !

When I heard that Mr. Jarvis lived at Knockwood, St. Michael's,

I took it for granted that Knockwood was the name of his house, doubtless specially chosen by himself as a link with his main work in life—veritably knocking wood about in one way or another, including windmill timbers—but, curiously and humorously enough, the name is just a coincidence, for Knockwood happens to be the name of the district in which Mr. Jarvis lives.

I believe it has given Mr. Jarvis real pleasure to supply any information he could regarding the many Kentish mills with which he has been associated, and his help has been very acceptable in connection with the historical notes given later in this book.

W. H. Evernden

F. Pain

BARHAM (Black Mill)

BARHAM (Breach Downs Mill)

See page 157

See page 158

W.C.F.

W.C.F.

BENENDEN (Beacon Mill)

See page 160

Facing page 68

A. W. Tiffin   A. W. Tiffin

BETHERSDEN (White Mill)

See page 160

J. Russell   H. Jarvis

BETHERSDEN (Black Mill)

See page 161

CHAPTER VI

WINDMILL LIFE AND LORE

IF, when visiting a windmill that is still in use, or one that has not been idle for many years, you meet the windmiller, you will find him a kindred soul to the watermiller, delighted to show you over his mill and let you climb with him its various stages.

You will note, perhaps, an undue vibration by reason of the mill having lost two of its four sweeps, the miller daring not to replace them on account of the impaired state and weakness of the body of the ancient structure. The years of activity and strength of the mill are drawing to a close.

The miller may call your attention to the old mill-stones, now worn so thin that often he has to pass the meal twice through the process of grinding, although it may be only of the common kind for cattle, pigs and fowls. It is probably long since he ground wheat for domestic flour. Lying around will be found many an old mill-stone converted to other uses—paving, stone steps and rockery.

Conversation with a genuine old windmiller is a delightful experience. The pity is that we have so few of them left among us. Often he has lived all his life at the mill, having been born in the mill house and succeeded his father there. He loves to chat about the old days, and frequently his memory is a vivid one. To discuss his old mill gives him much pleasure and, as he recalls its many happy associations with his own busy life, he almost seems rejuvenated. One would think, too, that the old mill itself was an animated object, as the miller tells of the work it has accomplished and what it has meant to him throughout the years. Maybe it is now derelict and it saddens him to tell of his many difficulties to keep it going and the struggle he has had of late years to make ends meet.

Speaking of his visit to Hythe with his father in 1877, Mr. Frank Pain says (in October, 1932) :

We were (my father and I) standing on the Hill above the Church, from where one can obtain such a splendid view of the Marsh. It was a bright, sunny day, with a brisk N.E. wind, and as far as the eye could reach one could see the panorama below—the villages, trees, churches and the several windmills, with their sails revolving merrily in the breeze. What prettier picture can memory conjure up than an old-time village, the dwellings clustered round the church, the windmill just aside like a sentinel on guard, at times ; at others busy and providing man and beast with the wherewithal for existence, made from the corn in the surrounding fields. As my mind travels back and I think of those days and compare them with the feverish haste and unrest of to-day, the question arises—is the world, or are the people, really any better off now than they were in those days. They are certainly less content.

This is what another miller says[1] :

There is an indefinable charm about a windmill. The very conception of employing nature's wind power to start with—then the structure and engineering ; the way it absorbs the wind power and withstands it, and all this when, in its earlier stages, it was pivoted upon one centre-post.

There is a delightful old-time word—Surge—there is more or less swing in all windmills, but oh, the charm of the surge in the old post mill.

The mill was not only a use but a necessity, while from the picturesque and artistic point of view it is beyond description.
"And the whirring sail goes round,
And the whirring sail goes round. . . ."

Sometimes in seeking information regarding the earlier history of a mill, one has to be careful not to overtax the memory of the genial elderly miller. One miller I know, however, could, in 1932, remember Milton Regis Mill working in 1859 ; and another, aged eighty-one, well remembered Boughton Monchelsea Mill being burnt down seventy-five years ago.

Usually a miller remembers events and incidents better than dates. Dates are necessary to establish historical facts but, in conversation with an old miller, it is wise to let him tell of his experiences in his own free way. Often, from the flow of general conversation, the necessary links in the chain of evidence will come to light in a natural way. *When* a thing happened is often of importance (when compiling such a record as that which forms Part IV of this volume, for instance) but *how* is far worthier in the recollections of our milling friends, in whose busy life, as the years sped by, dates had no value.

Here and there throughout Kent, nevertheless, I have noticed that a miller has kept a *written* record of dates ; not exactly a miller's log, but nearly such. A chronicle has been kept of the chief incidents in connection with the life of the mill, repairs executed, changes of workmen, noteworthy points about the weather and remarks about the kind of harvest each year brings. Swingate Mill, Guston, and Crampton's Mill, Sissinghurst, had such

[1] E. T. Clark, February, 1933.

a chronicle, and the timbers inside the White Mill at Headcorn are covered with pencilled comments dating back many years. It is a pity that no effort has been made to preserve these records.

I recently spent an interesting Saturday afternoon in the Headcorn Mill, wandering round from post to post on the second floor and jotting down many of the items of interest written up. The facts are not recorded in any sequence of date but if all the items written up (visible and now invisible) could have been copied down they might have formed a fairly complete history of the life of the mill as well as of those many items of local and national importance. Here are a few specimens :

> Gave Black Mill up Oct. 11th, 1888.
> > (This shows that the then owner, Mr. T. Burden, also held the other Headcorn mill, the Black Mill, previous to this date.)
> White Mill painted Spring, 1896.
> Mill painted, Autumn, 1901.
> 5 lambs put in field by W. Cooper 1/3 a week, Nov. 22nd, 1902.
> > (This evidently refers to the Mill Field being let at a rental to a neighbouring farmer.)
> Mill painted W. Fullagar, July, 1907.
> Aug. 5th, 1914. War with Germany.
> Aug. 12th, 1914. 12 flying machines went over Headcorn.
> May 13th, 1915. 20 hours' rain.
> June 6th, 1916. Lord Kitchener drowned.
> Aug. 30th, 1916. Very rough.
> Oct. 18th, 1916. Tom Burden gave up The Mill (sale same day).
> 1 new sweep, 1916.
> Rev. A. Gatehouse died suddenly at Staplehurst, June 27th, 1917.
> > (This gentleman was the Vicar of Headcorn.)
> July, 1917. Warren mending sweeps.
> May 30th, 1923. Big flood.
> April 26th, 1924. Storm.
> 3 new sweeps November, 1924.
> July 18th, 1926. Sweep struck.
> G. Boorman married, April 22nd, 1929.
> > (Mr. Boorman was the local butcher. The wedding, by the way, never took place, I understand, but the record was not cancelled!)

* * * * *

Frequently a mill is handed down from generation to generation, and a miller will tell you with pride the number of years the old mill has been in his family. The following are some instances I have traced of Kent windmills being held by one family for several generations :

Uphill Mill, near Folkestone, in the Kettle family from 1790 to 1931.
Hoo Common Mill, Ballard, 1799 to 1900.
Petham (Chequer's Mill), Gambrill, 1805 to 1900.
Eastry Mills, Clark, 1826 to 1932.
Lenham Heath, Tanton, 1842 to 1932.
Northbourne (New Mill), Fuller, 1848 to 1932.
Guston (Swingate Mill), Mummery, 1849 to 1922.
Tenterden (Ashbourne Mill), Pinyon, 1851 to 1912.
Woodchurch Mills, Tanton, 1860 to 1932.
Stelling Minnis, Davison, 1878 to 1932.

There are no doubt scores of other such Kentish mill-owning families, as well as families who have rented mills over long periods.

There still are, although they are rapidly diminishing, a number of large estates in the county of Kent on which stood a windmill, hired by the miller from the Squire or landowner ; Pluckley, Nonington and Chillenden are cases that come to mind. Biddenden too, where Paul Sharpe's Mill stood, that lovely old post mill, pulled down many years ago when it was believed to be our oldest Kent mill, dating back to 1555. I have heard that in the days when "Old Paul Sharpe" (by which name he was familiarly known) was the miller-tenant, Squire Schreiber once visited the mill and in the course of conversation asked Mr. Sharpe how his business was progressing. "Very poorly, I am afraid," was Mr. Sharpe's reply, followed by a subtle suggestion of a reduced rental for the mill. The Squire was much amused for, as he reminded his tenant, no rent had been paid for four years, hence a reduction could hardly benefit Mr. Sharpe much !

As I have mentioned elsewhere in this book, twenty shillings a week used to be considered a fair rental for an average windmill ; and sometimes the business proved so profitable that the miller eventually was able to purchase the mill outright. This happened, for instance, at the old black smock mill at Smarden, which Charles Buss (father of Richard Buss, who held Pluckley Mill for many years) first rented and then bought outright for £500. Similarly, at Preston Mill, near Wingham, Mr. Dunn, the father of the present owner, after renting the mill for a long time, having come to it as a young man, was eventually in a position to buy it.

Thomas Manwaring, son of George Manwaring, was born at his father's mill, Preston, near Wingham, in 1814. He assisted his father until he was about twenty-one years of age and then felt able to strike out on his own account. He hired a small mill at Strood for two years and then a larger mill, one of the pair on

Prospect Hill, Frindsbury, where he spent eleven years and worked up a good business.

Then came the fulfilment of a desire, dear to so many millers, to have a mill of his own, for he was in a position, in 1848, to purchase a mill that stood at Slough, Bucks, and remove it to Luton, Chatham. He held it for thirty-six years until his death at the age of seventy in 1884.

*   *   *   *   *

A miller will tell you to-day, regretfully, the number of other windmills that could be counted years ago from his own mill. Perhaps now it is the only mill left for miles around. If you go, say, to Barham Mill the miller will tell you that twenty years ago five other mills could be seen from there ; at Sandwich and at Ash you will learn that no less than fourteen other windmills could be counted ; and ten others were once visible from the top of Stelling Minnis Mill, where now the solitary miller well remembers their names—two at Swingfield, one at Acrise, two at Waltham, one at Stelling (Brambleton Mill), one at Bodsham Green, one at Kingston, one at Stone Street (Chequer's Mill, Petham) and one at Adisham.

I once met an old miller who said that his father, when a young man at Ripple Mill, counted no less than forty windmills with the aid of a telescope, "and they have now nearly all vanished."

As can be seen by reference to the lists of mills given in this volume, there were no less than thirty windmills in the vicinity of Rochester, viz. : Rochester, 8 ; Chatham, 9 ; Strood, 3 ; Gillingham, 5 ; Frindsbury, 5.

This locality has been a true 'Windmill Land.' I do not know of any other part of Kent having held such a cluster of mills ; it was quite a difficult procedure to find room for them all on the 1596–1930 map for this volume.

In 1878 from the stage of the old mill at Luton, Chatham (Manwaring's Mill), thirteen other mills could be seen. Mr. William Manwaring, son of Thomas Manwaring who ran the mill, very kindly gave me the following list :

Blue Bell Hill, Maidstone Road, Chatham (W. Skinner's mill).
Bredhurst Mill, near Chatham.
Star Mill, Rainham Road, Chatham.
Upberry Mill, Chatham Hill.

Frindsbury, Frindsbury Hill (Wm. Kimmins)—three mills.
Strood, Strood Hill (Killick and Field)—two mills.
Chalk Pit Mill, Chatham (Field).
Higham Mill, near Rochester (J. Rose).
Delce Mill, Rochester (Glover).
Hoo Common Mill, near Rochester (Ballard).

Mr. George E. Ride told me that in 1878, from the stage of the Great Mill at Sheerness, no less than twenty-five windmills could be counted with the aid of glasses. One of these was an Essex mill between Shoeburyness and Clacton, otherwise all of them were Kentish mills. To-day only two remain, at Rodmersham and Milton Regis, and even they are derelicts. The following is the list of twenty-four mills, with the names of their millers in 1878 :

Lynsted (W. H. Champion).
Rodmersham (T. Witham).
Sittingbourne (Mr. Harris).
Milton, Chalkwell Mill (R. Snoard).
Milton Regis (J. Barnard).
Bredgar, Dean's Hill Mill (W. Moore).
Bobbing, Key Street (Henry Goord).
Newington (George Maxted).
Hartlip (Friday Brothers).
Upchurch (Wakeley Brothers).
Gillingham Grange (J. Ride).
Gillingham, Stedman's Mills (Jas. Stedman).
Bluebell Hill (W. Skinner).
Chatham, Star Mill (J. Webb).
Lower Chatham Hill Mill (W. Skinner).
Strood, Broom Hill (W. Killick).
Frindsbury—three mills (W. Kimmins).
Higham (John Rose).
Hoo Common (R. Ballard).
Stoke (Mr. Cooper).
Minster, Sheppey (G. L. Franks).

Mr. T. H. Gambrill says that from the fan-stage of his mill at Petham (the Chequers' Mill), no less than forty mills could at one time be counted with the naked eye on a clear day. This mill stood on exceptionally high ground and often provided amusement for the miller's family on Sunday evenings in the summer months, to sit out on the fan-stage and see who could count the most mills.

Mr. Gambrill also tells of many interesting experiences connected with life at the Chequers' Mill, which was in his family the whole period of its history from its erection early in the nineteenth century to the time of the fire that consumed it in 1900. He tells of one memorable day when he was quite a youth, assisting his father in the mill, how there was a flash of lightning and a crash of thunder and his father remarking, "We'd better 'strike up'; there's a storm coming." He had begun to pull on the chain in order to open the shutters of the sweeps to stop the mill when the lightning, running down the chain to which he was holding, to use his own words, "crippled me up. I couldn't release my hold of that chain. I shouted to father and he had to tug me away by force." For some days afterwards he felt very stiff, and the sensation was as though somebody had thrashed him all over.

Some time later the local doctor had occasion to come to the mill house and happened to notice the white scars on the young man's arms (he also had, and has still, similar marks on both shoulders and under the knees). The doctor remarked on the lad's foolishness in playing about, as young men will, with an electric battery for the excitement of getting mild shocks, and would not listen to the youth's denials. "Well, you've been fooling with electricity in some way or another, then," he said. When the incident of the storm was explained, the doctor expressed great surprise that young Gambrill was "alive to tell the tale."

The doctor told the lad that he would always feel the effects of the occurrence and that the older he became the stronger would he feel it. This has proved true. All his life Mr. Gambrill has been affected whenever a storm is approaching. He is then "all of a tremble," his strength seems to go, and this is more noticeable as he grows older. He does not suffer while a storm is in full swing, only when one is gathering.

At the Chequers' Mill one pair of stones, a French burr, was kept specially for grinding the corn, brought by the farmers, into flour required for baking bread for their households. The stones were always dressed a shade coarser than the other stones used for flour-making. The farmers used not to mind so much about the 'height' or colour of their bread—it was the genuine wholemeal loaf, and that was all that mattered; "the goodness was there."

Flour sold to the general public for bread-making was from mixed wheat. The more foreign wheat used, up to a point, the 'stronger' the flour and the lighter the loaf. The French burr stones were dressed finer for this class of trade.

Mr. Gambrill was apparently quite 'a past master' at making

bread, for there was a bakery attached to his mill and he had ample practice. He relates that one day he jokingly asked the local baker (this was in the early days when bakers first began 'rounds' in villages) to go and get a half cwt. weight to keep the top of his oven on, as the bread was rising so high that it would be pushing the oven top off. The baker fell into the trap, for off he went to get the required weight, much to the delight of the miller-baker and his men.

At one time Mr. Gambrill used to supply his flour in strong bags of white duck linen. They were expensive bags and it was understood that they should be returned to the mill. From time to time a number of them were not received back and Mr. Gambrill began to think seriously that in future he would have to supply his flour, at least the smaller quantities, in paper bags. His mind on this subject was definitely made up one day when a customer came to the mill in his shirt sleeves, and "plain as a pikestaff" was one of the miller's linen bags forming a new back to the man's shirt, complete with miller's name and a picture of the mill !

In those days there was plenty of local custom at the mill. Every cottage had its bread oven and most cottagers kept a pig or two, therefore flour and pig corn were always in demand.

Mr. Gambrill remembers his grandfather, Thomas Gambrill, being very friendly with Mr. White, the miller from Mill Downs Mill, Petham, and how that, should the weather be calm and both mills at a standstill for lack of wind, Mr. White would often come up to the Chequers' Mill for company and play cards "for hours on end." The lid of one of the large flour bins was converted into a cribbage board, which is in existence to this day.

It was quite a frequent occurrence for Mr. Gambrill to be called up in the night to assist his father in the mill, the wind having increased since they went to bed. Full advantage had to be taken of the wind while it lasted and an endeavour made to 'catch up' with the work in hand. Though sound asleep he would hear his father's tap at the bedroom wall, accompanied by the usual words "Wind blows !" and they would soon be 'hard at it.' In later years he wanted no calling up in the dead of night should the wind blow, for his ears became attuned, as all millers' did, to the music of the winds.

The Chequers' Mill was very fortunate with the breezes. At her very exposed position she caught the slightest breath of wind and would often be gently at work when neighbouring mills were still.

BLACKHEATH MILLS, 1750, 1770, 1810, 1815
From Duncan's *History of the Borough of Lewisham.*

See page 167

Facing page 76

Harold H. Camburn

M. Rowland Packer

BIDBOROUGH

See page 163

W.C.F.

A. W. Tiffin

BRIDGE

See page 174

It was often of assistance to a windmiller to know what was happening at other mills. He could detect, for instance, the direction of the wind by noticing which mill in the neighbouring villages began to work first after a period of calm weather, and so judge if and when his own mill would be favoured with a breeze to set her in motion.

From Preston Mill, near Wingham, the distant Barham Mill could be seen standing up boldly on a ridge of Barham Downs and, as soon as its sweeps were seen to be revolving, the remark was passed, "Barham is off." Preparations were then made at Preston Mill for 'getting busy' and, sure enough, a quarter of an hour later the breeze would reach Preston Mill and away her sails would go.

This same Preston Mill had a nickname "Dumb and Easy." Presumably she was a quiet mill at work, hence the word 'Dumb' ; and it took very little breeze to turn her sweeps, thus she was 'Easy.'

Some mills ran very noisily, one miller admitting that his mill (Preston, next Faversham) was the noisiest in Kent ; but another Kentish miller, speaking of his mill, said : "She don't make a rattle and clatter like most mills. She runs so *whist*."

A part of Mr. Gambrill's business has been to hire out machinery to the local farms. He has known what it is to be out with one of his traction engines at a neighbouring farm, doing some threshing, and to come home from a hard day's work in the fields, snatch a bite of food and then, if the wind were favourable, start up the mill and work throughout the night with no thought of sleep. He was able in this way to get through as many as fifty quarters of corn in one night, stop grinding, close down the mill and go straight off to work again in the fields at daybreak ! One might think this sort of thing would undermine the strongest constitution but Mr. Gambrill to-day, at seventy-four, is as strong and well as many a man twenty years his junior.

It may be that in those days folk were hardier and could withstand more but perhaps there is greater truth in the statement of another old milling friend : "It doesn't matter how hard you work as long as you're happy in it and don't go worrying and fretting over it !"

Mr. Gambrill and a friend walked from Petham to London many years ago for a week's holiday—sixty miles each way. They walked to Chatham the first day, which is about half-way, and then on to London the following day.

Three different positions of the sweeps at the Chequers' Mill used to mean three different things :

At home.   Out.   Sha'n't be long.

Mr. Gambrill says that local folk well knew the signals, and it was a very convenient way of letting villagers and others know his movements.

Millers at other mills had their own signals, some of which were common to many mills. For instance, one position of the sweeps meant that the mill was having its stones dressed, was out of order, or that repairs were being carried out ; another, that the mill was for hire—waiting for work ; whilst another was known as "striking up" or "left all right" when its work was finished for the day.

A windmill custom which Sir Charles Igglesden mentions[1] is of interest. If the owner died

> All the twenty boards in the arms of the mill were taken out and the mill stood motionless for a given time, as if in grief over the loss of its owner. . . . When the wife of the miller died nineteen boards were removed ; for a child of the miller, thirteen boards ; for the miller's parents, eleven boards ; and so on down to the children of cousins, for whom one board was removed.

In commenting on the decline and fall of our windmills, Mr. Gambrill mentioned that at Waltham there is a tract of land of 365 acres, the whole of which was at one time given up to corn-growing. In one typical year no less than 1,300 quarters of corn were carried away from this land *in addition* to the large quantity used for the feeding of the animals on the farm. The whole of this acreage is to-day barren—"just let go, not even laid down to pasture."

Details of the general history of Mr. Gambrill's mill will be found in the Notes in Part IV of this volume. It was burnt to the ground in 1900 and, owing to a quibble in regard to a clause in the policy, £75 was all Mr. Gambrill received from the insurance company. The Canterbury millwrights sent an estimate for the erection of a new mill, but he could not afford it. It was a grievous blow such as would have broken many a man's spirit, but Mr. Gambrill 'came up smiling.' Although his career as a miller was abruptly termi-

[1] *Those Superstitions*, by Sir Charles Igglesden.

nated, he soon worked up the other side of his business, that of agricultural engineering, upon which he and his son are engaged to-day. They still live at the old mill house, and some of the old mill-stones are to be seen worked into the paths around the house.

* * * * *

I know of no explicit understanding between windmillers that there should be no work done on the Sabbath, but certainly on Sundays most mills have always been at a standstill. In the days when windmills held their own, of course, the Sabbath was more strictly observed universally as a day of rest but, in any case, very seldom has a windmill been seen at work on a Sunday. It was just 'not done,' and any transgressor of the unwritten law would be sure not to prosper in business or would suffer in some way directly or indirectly as a result of his sacrilegious labour !

> A Sunday well spent
> Brings a week of content,
> And health for the toils of the morrow ;
> But a Sabbath profaned,
> Whatsoe'er may be gained,
> Is a certain forerunner of sorrow.

In the deeper words of Emerson : "The Sabbath is the core of our civilisation, dedicated to thought and reverence."

There is an appealing echo of those days when the miller hallowed the Sabbath, in the familiar lines by Longfellow :

> On Sundays I take my rest ;
> Church-going bells begin
> Their low, melodious din ;
> I cross my arms on my breast,
> And all is peace within.

Many years ago the old Black Mill at Sandwich was to be seen at work on a Sunday. It was not the least bit surprising, therefore, to other windmillers in the surrounding villages when the old mill was burnt to the ground. It was a foregone conclusion that, sooner or later, calamity would befall the miller! "Ah !" said the millers in turn for miles around, as from their respective mills they saw the old mill in flames, "she will not work any more now on a Sunday. Just what I thought would happen to her some day."

It must have been a severe trial of faith and principle at times not to set the mill at work on the Sabbath, for it sometimes happened that windy Sundays followed successive weeks of calm weather and the miller was sorely tempted to make the most of the wind while it lasted.

Sometimes a miller, busily at work in his mill late on Saturday night, and the wind keeping up, would continue grinding until two or three o'clock on Sunday morning. His conscience would not suffer much from this temporary lapse of principle because most other folk were in bed, sound asleep and none the wiser! Similarly, if by reason of his acute 'wind sense,' a miller awoke late on Sunday night to find there was sufficient wind to start up the mill, he might succumb to the temptation to steal an hour or two from the Sabbath.

"The wind blows," someone remarks at a miller's supper table. He leaves the table immediately, and soon the sweeps are revolving against the darkened sky and all through that night. If the wind does not abate, all next day and the next the mill is at work, the miller perhaps getting no proper rest all through. He may just lie down on a heap of sacks in the mill and enjoy a nap when everything is in order and the grain is being fed to the mill-stones all right, but if the slightest thing goes wrong or the stones run 'dry,' he is awake again and attending to things immediately.

I once remarked to a windmiller that surely he was gifted with a sixth sense to be so attuned to the music of his mill that he was able to detect at once some little irregularity in its smooth running. He claimed no such advantage, but merely suggested that after many years of work a miller gets thoroughly accustomed to the rhythmic sound of a mill at work, that any interruption of the regular motion would arouse any true windmiller from the deepest sleep.

"Talking of regularity," I said, "doesn't the irregularity of your life, snatching your meals just when you can, at work on and off all hours of the day and night, upset your health?"

"Well, no, I cannot say it does," the miller replied. "We miller folk seem to ail nothing and we live to a pretty good old age, as you may have noticed. I have heard it said, though, that the reason why many of us are stocky and thick-set is because of our not having sufficient 'growing' sleep and because of carrying heavy sacks of corn about, but I don't think there's much truth in that. Some folk go so far as to say that they can always tell a miller by his build. Others say they can recognise him by his breathing, for some millers suffer from what is called 'the miller's throat,' brought about by breathing in so much dust in the mill. But there is a surer way of telling a miller than that."

W. H. Evernden   A. W. Tiffin

BOUGHTON-UNDER-BLEAN (MILES' MILL)

See page 170

W. Norton   A. W. Tiffin

BOUGHTON-UNDER-BLEAN (RICHARDSON'S MILL)

See page 171   *Facing page 80*

J. W. Bryan

BLUEBELL HILL

See page 169

J. Charlton

BLEAN

See page 167

W.C.F.

BREDHURST (Naylor's Mill)

See page 173

W.C.F.

BREDGAR (Dean's Hill Mill)

See page 172

Facing page 81

"By his hands you mean, I suppose?"

"That's it," he said, as he held out his left hand and showed me the bluish marks caused by many tiny fragments of steel having flown off the mill-bill, with which the stones are dressed, and embedded themselves in his flesh, in time becoming so numerous that the middle, fourth and little finger of the hand are quite discoloured, as well as the knuckles. The left hand is, of course, the one to suffer, due to its position in holding the mill-bill.

"But *all* millers do not dress their own stones, do they?" I enquired.

"No, not all," he agreed, "though most of the 'older school' do. But, like the old millwrighting, stone-dressing is becoming a lost art. Windmills are going out of date, the younger generation does not learn the art, and the stone-dressers that used to travel from mill to mill are now few and far between. There's been little enough work for them of late years, anyway."

* * * * *

I have been assured that it was quite a common retort in years gone by, if anyone boasted of having travelled a lot : "You've never been farther than ten miles from a windmill." I am not sure whether this was intended to signify a repudiation of the traveller's claim but it seems to show a generally accepted notion that windmills were plenteous, which they are certainly not to-day.

Another saying in connection with our mills the significance of which I am not quite sure about is : "A windmiller's dog would always make a watermiller's." This may have been prompted by a spirit of rivalry between the two types of miller. It certainly implies that more skill is needed for a windmill than a watermill, for if a dog is clever enough to be of practical service in the one he would of a surety be a satisfactory animal in the other.

* * * * *

Why does a miller wear a white hat?

Many a Kentish miller will smile at seeing this problem in print. It is hoary with age. For the benefit of those who were not fortunate enough to have been born into a family of the miller fraternity, another simple (*sic*) way of propounding this deep problem is as follows :

F

"For what ostensible reason can it be that a human being, whose avocation it has become to extract the farinaceous ediments from the cereal crops, discovers the absolute necessity of investing that part of his frame, supposed to contain the brain, in a covering the hue of which shall counterfeit the blanched aspect of frozen vapour falling from the clouds."

(*N.B.—I have never met a miller who could answer the problem!*)

CHAPTER VII

WINDMILLS IN DECAY

IF in search of old windmills, and you are fit, there are few days that should fail to tempt you to pursue your Quixotic occupation. One early morning winter trip of mine stands out vividly. It was along the crest of the Downs, where at all times there is a fascinating loneliness, especially in winter. Upon this occasion there had been a considerable fall of snow during the night ; it was lying very deep and the rising sun was throwing a ruddy glow.

The old black windmill (facing p. 128) became a study in black and white and the scattered villages beneath the crest, one vast transformation scene. Save that here and there the wild creatures had outwitted me, I was first to mark that spotless mantle. I can, as it were, hear now the Crunch ! Crunch ! of myriads of those ice crystals brought in by nature to make that great display.

The glittering carpet of the hoar frost spread on Downland, the sparkling bough and twig of coppice trees ; these in due course replaced by the endless succession of wayside flowers ; later the charming wild fruits and golden russet foliage of trees ; again the March winds, to gather up and sweep along the crisp brown leaves ; and each display set to music by the birds. Such is the pageant by hill and dale that always awaits the traveller who tramps in windmill land, scenes lost to those who keep to the beaten track or the great highways.

On another occasion, above a distant tree-clad knoll, you may note one or two broken skeleton mill sweeps. You bear in the direction by narrow winding road or narrower old mill lane, through fields of waving corn—its rustling music a soft symphony whispering a requiem for the passing of an old mill that has run its course and remains but a shelter for bats and owls.

Standing in the shadow of the old derelict, you forget the mill for a moment as there is opened up before you a view of transcending breadth and beauty. The old mill has lured you to the crest of the noble, rolling Downs and the gorgeous wide expanse of the Weald, meeting in the misty distance the clear blue sky.

A refreshing breeze fans the cheek and carries sweet scents from nature's distillery of the hills,

> . . . the close-bit thyme that smells
> Like dawn in Paradise,

while in continuous succession, the skylarks rise from the grassy slope unto the heavens, carolling forth their inimitable lays until all but lost from view, then returning silently to earth, to nest, to mate, to young ; one divine lyric finished ; then another ethereal minstrel soars and continues the rippling melody. . . . Your thoughts then may return to the old mill, and its great size impresses you.

Nobody is about. The mill is deserted. You peep inside and are saddened by the sight. All is neglect and ruin. Ladders, stages, floors, all are gradually falling ; a jumble of old chains hang idly, derelict shafts, bins, trays—one huge heap of desolation.

You examine the exterior of the mill, guess its age and wonder how much longer it will brave the elements. The weather-boarding is already broken in parts, admitting shafts of light in which, as you trespass in the darkened mill, the disturbed dust rises and scintillates.

You turn away, taking in one sweep the view before you— the beautiful wooded acres of the Weald of Kent, its undulating scenery and old-world villages and hamlets. You note the scattered old timber dwellings, farms and churches and the mosaic patterns of pasture-land ; the fields, woods and orchards, here and there a glimpse of river, stream and sparkling pool which mirror back the passing clouds.

Taking a few deep and long inhalations of the pure air, you retrace your steps, feeling sorry for those who never leave the beaten track, are never lured by a tottering old windmill to such joys as you have just experienced.

"It is still true that the loveliest treasures of our countryside are reserved only to him who approaches them humbly on his own pair of legs."[1] This certainly *is* true ! The pleasures and treasures unwittingly stumbled across in one's jaunts in search of wind and water mills cannot be translated into words. Even just turning aside from a trackway one has often trod, perhaps with hardly an intention save that of an inborn inquisitiveness as to what may be concealed there, is often unexpectedly rewarded.

[1] Mr. A. G. Gardiner, *Sayings of the Week.*

Although I have tramped the near hills and valleys from my boyhood, I feel I have not seen more than the fringe of the magical garment with which nature decks her fair acres, nor met half the exhilarating experiences.   Even when the equinoctial gales are here in March and September, they greet us with an invigorating hustling.   I have then often, by way of idle amusement, turned my head aside, encouraged the wind so to pass my mouth that it was possible to produce a complete chromatic scale by its aid, thus forming a veritable human mouth organ.

In this matter of the music of the winds I would quote a letter which I received about two years ago from one who had read my book, *The Lure of the Countryside* :

> We are friends although I have never seen you, nor do I pretend to know anything of Nature as you know it, but it has a lure for me which ever attracts. I find the wind in the trees sings to me, speaks to me, and I can tell blindfolded the kind of tree, fir or elm, thro' which the wind passes. Wonderful music comes to me over the wind-swept Downs, and the long grass of Autumn has melodies which bring tears all unconsciously.

How typical of the spirit which pervades those who, in the daily round of life, see and love the countryside. And so is this from a famous writer :

> There is no countryside like the English countryside for those who have learned to love it ; its firm yet gentle lines of hill and dale, its ordered confusion of features, its deer-parks and downland, its castles and stately houses, its hamlets and old churches, its farms and ricks and great barns and ancient trees, its pools and ponds and shining threads of rivers, its flower-starred hedgerows, its orchards and woodland patches, its village greens and kindly inns. Other countrysides have their pleasant aspects, but none such variety, none that shine so steadfastly throughout the year.[1]

There are always simple little happenings crossing one's path on the countryside, pregnant with lessons of tenderness, exciting sympathy for the 'lower creatures' ; trivial at the time they may be, but they leave their impression on the brain and increase the store of piquant little episodes treasured in memory.

In one of my searches for remains of our corn mills, I was anxious to get a picture of an old windmill that to-day stands at Leigh, near Hildenborough (facing p. 225), but until a year or two ago was situated on the outskirts of Bexhill. It was transferred to Kent and, after undergoing a process of rebuilding, reconditioning and refitting, put to work at its old-time task of grinding corn.

[1] H. G. Wells, *The History of Mr. Polly.*

In the shadow of the mill a fine-looking horse was sheltering. As I entered the field the creature took a long-range view of me. I thought the contrast between this sleek white horse and the drab, dull old mill would be a feature in the picture, so I hastened to make the exposure. At that very moment he left the mill and trotted smartly up to me, sniffed the camera, and was obviously most inquisitive. Finding I had brought him no tasty morsel and, not being particularly interested in photography, he wheeled round in disdain, 'swish' went two white legs up into the air, uncomfortably close to me, and off he trotted without being snapped. His white legs came close to snapping my camera instead.

*   *   *   *   *

Let us now climb the crest of the Downs with their familiar spurs upon which still stands many a rugged windmill braving the elements in their roughest mood.

Lord Conway of Allington, the noted mountaineer, who has trodden the roof of the world in many lands, pays a striking tribute to the beauty of Kentish scenery as viewed from the summit of the North Downs. He writes :

> He that cannot thrill with joy over the views of undulating woodland and plain in the home lands will have little to learn from the wide-scattered regions where glaciers crawl down into the depths of valleys and where snow-ridges cut their sharp outline against the clear blue of a cloudless sky. . . . . I have beheld vast panoramas of the Pacific seen from Andean heights, or from the top of Karakoram peaks, or from arctic mountains, when the eye could pierce over the immense ice-pack to apparently limitless distances ; yet still the view over the Weald of Kent from the platform of the North Downs yields me as glorious a thrill as any I have derived from those other revealed expanses.[1]

Most of the mills of my youth are either gone, the worse for wear or idle in the clutches of decay. With them in mind I cannot but lament the loss of that "greatness and security of which the mill was a symbol," in spite of Sir T. McAra's recent expression before the Master Printers' Association : "I dislike the phrase 'The Good Old Days' ; the good times are those that lie ahead, and not the times of the past." Let it be admitted that in many ways we have gained much, but very often the price paid for it has been too great. And so much of that price is "bereaved landscape."

[1] *The Observer*, June 4th, 1933.

This countryside of ours is at the heart of all our literature and all our history. . . . It has always been the background of our national life, and if we lose it we lose something that is vital to our English character. . . . A beautiful England need not necessarily be an unprogressive England. Changes must come, but these need not interfere with the beauties . . . and the changes may be all to the good if you replace old beauty with new beauty and not new ugliness.[1]

Not less than our ancient churches, bridges, rivers, streams and woods, our old corn mills are always enthralling. And the soul not moved by the ever-recurring miracle of the first primrose, or by a peep into the nest of a wild bird—maybe of the hedge sparrow, with its clutch of heavenly blue eggs—will be hard indeed to thrill.

> . . . dim fragments meant
> To be united in some wondrous whole.

PRIESTWOOD MILL, MEOPHAM.

The search for only the sites of our long lost windmills provides many difficulties and disappointments, but no little adventure and surprises. The problem in finding the actual site arises so often from the fact that the wreckage from the mill's destruction has absolutely disappeared. I well remember hunting for the spot where once stood Priestwood Mill at Meopham, distinctly shown on the Ordnance Survey Map of 1819, in the somewhat wild surroundings of Harvel. I lost count of how many I asked if they knew of the site. In the end I met an elderly husbandman and learned that he "had heard tell of it" but he knew nothing definite. He counselled me to go to where he believed it to be near.

"Take first to the left, then straight ahead until you come to the 'Amizonan' Tiger."

"I beg your pardon, but did you say '*Tiger*', and *what* 'Tiger' is it?"

"Am . . . an Tiger," he again mumbled.

"And what is that?" I asked, having heard of the Bengal and some other tigers, but never of this one.

"A *woman!*" he replied, and continued : "Turn down beside the Inn, bear left until you come to a thatched cottage, beside which is a narrow lane, then enquire again."

I followed the instructions and soon ran full-tilt into a sign-board. I had found the "Amazon and Tiger Inn"! In true St. George's style was portrayed a powerful woman mounted on a prancing steed, and her spear was deeply embedded in the body

---

[1] "Charms of Rural England," *Observer*, March 8th, 1931.

of an attacking tiger. I thought of the Amazons who came to the assistance of Troy under their queen, Penthesilea, who was slain by Achilles, and wondered what reason there could possibly be for such a fierce display in a place where the wildest creatures I saw were flocks of green plover and a few frightened rabbits.

I turned down by the inn as directed, gained the thatched cottage and then entered the "narrow lane"—which turned out to be the old mill lane, a long one and a blind one at that. Beneath the tall whitethorn hedge and on either side, the primrose and violet peeped out. Here it was decreed by fortune that I should meet another old man, bowed with age and with hair and beard snowy white. Had the mill been standing I should have taken him to be the miller himself.

I learned that the mill had been gone over eighty years. He pointed to an isolated copse in the centre of a freshly ploughed field of large extent : "That's where she stood and that oak tree over there marks the very spot."

The oak was tall and towered above the underwood in solitude. I forced a path to the centre of the knoll and stood beneath the tree, noting its bole was about nine inches in diameter. I probed the surface of the ground round it but there was no trace of any foundations of the old mill.

I retraced my steps, joined the main road and, after a journey of a few miles, pulled up at the first inn for refreshment. I asked both the landlord and his wife if they could give any reason for so strange a name being given as "Amazon and Tiger" to the house I had lately passed. Each muttered the name and jointly replied : "Never heard of it."

Then a silence fell, and I departed.

SHOTTENDEN.

On another occasion I went in search of Shottenden Mill, sometimes known as Perry Wood Mill, in the Selling parish, near Faversham. This mill had family associations. My son-in-law, as a Canterbury boy, often made journeys with a school fellow to this isolated spot on the top of a wooded knoll difficult of access, and would hide such treasures as boys possess, in the ground beneath the gaunt timber tripod which carried the centre post of the mill. Here marbles and tops were safe until the season came round again for them. Being a navigator by profession, he gave me the bearings which took me to the knoll, but he had been many years at sea and did not know the old mill had disappeared.

I first found the "Rose and Crown," which I learned stood in four parishes, then climbed the steep circuitous path up which the boyish treasure trove once travelled, though certainly not the way the farmer took his corn to the mill. Gaining the summit, I came on to a flat grass-covered clearing surrounded by trees. Not a vestige of the mill remained. Yet, as clearly as if the four radiating blocks of masonry which carried the feet of the timber tripod had only recently been removed, I found the four excavations in the ground, like four unfilled graves. I should have taken a picture had there not been a little picnic party occupying the ground. They would certainly have wondered what possessed me to 'take' four holes on the top of a high hill.

I had always considered it an important mill, one of the earliest ; contemporary, no doubt, with Quarry Mill, Frindsbury, and Rolvenden, which, with Perry Wood Mill, are noted on the 1596 map.

From enquiries of several elderly people living near, I learned that about 1913 the mill was only carrying two sweeps, and that it last worked about 1910 and was then allowed gradually to fall into decay. The spot was once a favourite one for picnics, Sunday school 'treats' and other 'outings.' It was thought that the mill might at some time cause disaster to visitors, especially to the younger folk who played in and around it. The old structure was, therefore, pulled down about 1920. Some of the old timbers were purchased by Mr. George Reeves, of Whitstable, where the main post and brake-wheel can still be seen in the grounds of 'Granary House,' Canterbury Road.

A special interest attaches to this picturesque old mill, made the subject of the following poem and photographed for reproduction here (facing p. 292).

SHOTTENDEN MILL[1]

On the top of a hill
Stands Shottenden Mill ;
And whenever the breeze is blowing
The sails swing round,
And the corn is ground,
And the mill is always going.
Round and round, with hearty good-will,
Sweep the sails of Shottenden Mill.

All the year round
Corn must be ground,

[1] From *Kentish Lyrics*, by Benjamin Gough. Houlston & Wright, London, 1867.

For God sends bread for the eater ;
    So there's no standing still
    At Shottenden Mill.
Round and round, fleeter and fleeter,
Merrily swing the sails of the mill
On the top of Shottenden Hill.

    Sunshine or mist,
    There's always a grist
To grind, or for man or for beast ;
    Light winds or strong,
    Short days or long,
Never from labour released.
Round and round, with a whirr of good-will,
Swing the sails of Shottenden Mill.

    This hard-working mill
    On the top of the hill
Is oak-braced with many a rivet ;
    And it braves the wild storm's
    Most terrible forms,
And long may it stand to outlive it.
Hurricanes fierce have swept over the hill,
But firm as a rock stands Shottenden Mill.

    And sailors see
    This mill out at sea,
And a welcome beacon it stands
    Their passage to guide
    Until they outride
The tempest and Goodwin Sands.
Brave hearts, steering with courage and skill
By this beacon sign on Shottenden Hill.

    In the olden day,
    The book-learnèd say,
On this hill was Cæsar's camp ;
    But now they grind corn
    Where the blast of the horn
Was heard, and the Roman's tramp.
And the country smiles in peace and good-will,
And plenty of wheat at Shottenden Mill.

    Round and round,
    With a humming sound,
Go the sails by night and by day ;
    And the grists are sent
    Till the stock is spent,
And the flour is carried away.
And round and round go the sails of the mill
Which stands on the top of Shottenden Hill.

TENTERDEN.

When rambling round about Tenterden I remembered the somewhat rare occurrence of a watermill and windmill in close proximity and became keen to search them out. It was easy to find the old Ashbourne watermill. The pond was full, slowly overflowing the weir and tumbling into the mill stream. The dripping mill wheel was partly exposed in the mill race ; only its big iron-bound wooden axle looked fit for work. The wheel itself was sadly dilapidated and to all appearances a 'derelict'. Yet "it did work when there was water enough," as I was told with pointed emphasis and the meagre flow from the pond over the weir soon confirmed. It is true of most of these scattered mills, the flow of the stream as a rule is but sufficient to provide them with a short and irregular supply of water. Thus every miller has to keep on the *qui vive* for the water coming down to his pond and be ready to start up his mill or lose even that rare opportunity of grinding his corn. This spasmodic working of the mills on the smaller streams of Kent will account for the presence of the small but very numerous watermills recorded in the Domesday Book, when the county of Kent boasted at least 350.

There was nothing to be seen of the windmill although I succeeded in finding the exact spot upon which it once stood overlooking the watermill. The mill grounds are now cut up into building plots, on one of which can be seen a small, rough, weed-covered mound. It was there the windmill stood until it was pulled down in 1912. The picture facing p. 293 shows it in process of demolition.

As I stood upon that mound where once stood the old windmill and looked down upon its very much older companion and rival, I marvelled at the persistency of the watermill. Despite its rise in a much earlier period of corn-milling history and the advent of the post mill which almost sealed its fate, it had outlived the latter, not a stick or stone of which now remains. The watermill has, to an extent, even defied modern engineering and still rumbles along at its old-world task in its old-world way. And what is true in particular of Tenterden watermill must be true in general of most watermills, for there are more of them grinding corn to-day than there are of windmills.

BIDDENDEN MILL.

The coming of the Flemish weavers in 1337 and the prosperous trade they built up which flourished until the prohibition of exportation of white cloth from England in 1616, when the cloth-makers left Kent to settle in Lancashire and Yorkshire, come to mind as one contemplates the peaceful village of Biddenden. Its corn mill (facing p. 96) probably provided in days gone by the flour used for making the bread (and cheese) for the famous 'Biddenden Maids Charity.'

The 'Biddenden Maids,' Elisa and Mary Chulkhurst, were joined together in birth at the hips and shoulders. In this state they lived to the age of thirty-four, when one sister died. Her sister refused to be separated and expired six hours afterwards. The date is said to have been either 1134 or 1534 (the old-fashioned numeral five is so frequently taken as a one).

The gift in more recent years has taken the form of a distribution, yearly, at Eastertide, of cakes (or biscuits) upon which is made an impression of the Biddenden Twins.

Many years ago I tramped to Biddenden and took my gift of a 'Biddenden Cake' to preserve as a memento. When I wanted to make a picture of the cake for this volume, alas ! it was gone ; a wily mouse had long since made a meal of it. Not to be defeated, I visited the village once more for another cake, and was told that the distribution, by two Trustees of the Charity, was on Easter Monday, at the Old Workhouse, between the hours of ten a.m. and two p.m. At a quaint little shop in the village street I left sixpence for postage as I could not return on that day to attend the function. By post two days later came the cake. It was a great disappoint-ment ! The cake of many years ago was an attractive, cream-coloured, crisp biscuit ; to-day's, made by the Biddenden baker, is less tempting. The villagers consider it to be but flour and water (unleavened bread). The effigy of Elisa and Mary Chulkhurst seems to be stamped less distinctly than of old and, like the wind-mill itself, to be the worse for wear ! As will be seen from the photograph reproduced (facing p. 96), the ladies' caps appear as crude haloes ; features they have none and, though having but two arms between them, the biscuit does not show the shoulders joined. The inscription and figures are sadly indistinct ; hence, on page 93, I give a copy of the card on sale in the village, for the information it contains.

Sir Charles Igglesden tells us that "a tombstone near the south-east corner of the church records the death of Thomas Collings, who died in 1813 at the age of ninety-eight years, and who, in his ninety-sixth year, reaped corn in company with his son aged seventy-four and a daughter aged sixty-six years."[1]

---

[1] *Saunters through Kent with Pen and Pencil,* Vol. V, p. 40.

ELISA & MARY
CHULKHURST

A IN
34
Y' 1100-

BIDDENDEN.

BETHERSDEN MILL.

When I visited Bethersden White Mill in 1930 it possessed but two sweeps. I gleaned it had ceased work about seven years earlier and for the last two years had worked with only those two sweeps. Already decay and neglect had set its seal and soon yet another imposing smock mill, another artistic specimen of engineering skill, will have vanished.

I was invited to ramble over the dusty interior and, accompanied by an intelligent auburn-headed boy from the Mill House, I enjoyed the experience. My guide took me across the old marl-pond to the most convenient point of vantage from which to take a picture. Approaching this pond I noticed on its margin a wire enclosure over which an unhappy gander was craning his neck, begging to be released that he might disport on the pool. The lad called to the bird, and it knew its name. It seemed a queer name for a bird, so I asked : "Why do you call the bird 'Moses' ?" He replied : "When he came astray we found him in the 'bull-rushes,' and that is where he still loves to dabble, knowing that there we have a trouble to capture him and return him to his pen."

Mr. J. B. Paddon, in his booklet on the Windmills of Kent, mentions that the miller, Mr. Wood, had worked in twelve mills—six wind and six water—for sixty years without a break. Of the windmills Bethersden was the only one remaining (the derelict shown facing p. 69) and, of the watermills there are none working to-day.

WITTERSHAM.

One meets with many pleasant surprises in the course of rural rambles. Here at Wittersham, in the garden of the home of

Mr. Norman Forbes-Robertson,[1] stands Stocks Mill (facing p. 317). It is fortunate for this fine old post mill that it is in his keeping, for it is well preserved.

The willing and courteous manner in which Mr. Forbes-Robertson conducted me over the delightful garden, and to the top of the mill, from which I revelled in a glorious view, gave an added pleasure to that particular 'windmill jaunt.' I was not surprised to find that mine host was a lover of birds, for if one can love a garden and an old windmill, one must of necessity love birds too. He had allowed owls to retain undisputed possession of the upper portion of the mill, which had been partitioned off for their use, where in safety they rear their young. A large door is left open to give access and, in the interior, tempting provision is made for nesting purposes. He found that they purloined apples from the store in the mill, a liberty they were allowed to continue ! The nocturnal visits of these birds to the fruit department were frequent, as evidenced by the accumulation of their mutings and the peculiar large pellets of feathers, hair and bones ejected by them, after swallowing their prey of birds and mice.

LYNSTED.

At Lynsted scarcely anyone seemed to have heard of the old derelict mill, but I was fortunate eventually in finding a local Solomon who was able to direct me to it. Pointing to a fine large house surrounded by trees and orchards, my informer said, "That is called Mill House." I entered the drive, knocked several times and got no answer. I was about to leave when a fine smooth-coated retriever in a most friendly mood came from a sheltered side-walk. From the welcome he gave me we might have been old friends. I was rather taken aback by it. His tail wagged, his body oscillated from side to side and his intelligent face smiled his welcome. Rubbing against my legs and showing every form of friendship as only a dog can show, he turned round, set the pace and led the way to the side-walk, looking back at every few yards to see if I were following. He seemed to say, "Come along, I know what you want."

Arriving in the garden at the rear of the house, my guide led me to a lady seated at needlework. This was the daughter of the house, and she also gave me a friendly welcome. I learned that by reason of sickness in the house the knocking was unheard and unanswered. But the dog's quick ear had detected my presence.

[1] See note on page 305 *re* death of Mr. Norman Forbes-Robertson.

I was asked to feel free to take any picture I chose of the old mill which stood in the garden and presently was shown a picture of the mill as it had stood, without fan and sweeps, forty years ago. That was before my hostess's father removed the cap, erected on the tower a summer-house, and converted the base into a store.

It was a pathetic moment when I was offered access to the summer-house poised on the old mill, from which no doubt a glorious view was possible. I would have availed myself of the opportunity but, when I was told that since the death of her father none of the family had entered, I felt I could not trespass there. Giving me the photograph of the old mill, which I have reproduced (facing p. 236), my hostess left me to my own devices.

Taking a picture of the mill as it stands to-day was a difficult task. It forms a picturesque ruin, draped in a purple pall of wistaria, an appropriate colour for so sad a reminder of the dead. Of the mill itself I hardly saw anything, as it was so covered in. I moved about in order to make the attempt and eventually found one direction the view from which was not blocked with trees. Here I was obliged to elbow my way through a dense fig-tree loaded with large and luscious fruit for gathering and the miniature perfect figs to provide the next year's crop (facing p. 236).

The amiable and deeply interested dog stayed with me the whole time of my visit and, as at my entry of the premises, so when I left he escorted to the gates and watched me out of sight. A 'doggie' welcome he had given me, almost human in its sincerity.

HARBLEDOWN

During my search for information about Kentish windmills of the past, I wrote to Mr. Marcus Hancock, of Mersham, by whose family an old mill at Harbledown (now, alas, vanished) was held for thirty-three years (facing p. 192). When replying to my letter he enclosed manuscript of the following :

In the old days when the Cathedral City of Canterbury had its City Mill and Westgate Mill, utilizing the water power of the Stour, on its two-branched course through the town by King's Bridge and Westgate Tower Bridge, the higher ground in the vicinity was dotted with windmills.

To the north-west stood Blean Mills, two in number, afterwards only one ; on the eastern side the strongly built and elegant St. Martin's Hill Mill on the high ground overlooking the city.

Then down on the south-east side, in a spot near what is now Ethelbert Road stood a very old grist windmill. Farther east was a windmill beyond

Bekesbourne, then to the right of it along the Dover Road was Bridge Mill, in the hollow ; while up on Barham Downs was the well-built Barham Mill, where the wind seldom failed to swing its sweeps around. There it was so cold in winter that the miller of those days was forced to duplicate his clothes. Thus, double-shirted, he mocked the freezing blast in this wind tower.

But nearest and homeliest, only just outside the city boundary, stood the mill of Harbledown, always at work when the wind would blow, but quietly waiting when the air was still. From its stage could be seen, when the westering sun was low, the finest view of the Cathedral, grandly central in the varying of the evening light, that showed the roofs that crowded round. From the western side was a view across the hop-gardens to the London Road, vanishing between the trees toward Dunkirk.

There at the mill lived Charles Hancock, who became the owner in 1859, only retiring in 1892 when seventy years were his. Then the mill seemed to lose heart at the departure of its owner. Perhaps it missed the thoughtful care that kept everything in order, and the cheerful hearty smile of the miller, who loved the mill. One tenant after another, but none prospered, till at last the property passed into the hands of a Canterbury firm. Then the mill was doomed as unsafe, and a traction engine was sent up to pull it down.

The old friend was gone, and the artistic charm of rising bank disappeared. Many mourned the loss, but the mill will be seen no more looking over the Stour Valley, with the Cathedral full in view.

The following was the postcript to Mr. Hancock's letter :

In this part of Kent we have only two working windmills left—Willesborough and Stanford.

Since 1880, when I first knew this part, the following mills have gone : Waltham (two mills), Elmsted (Bodsham Green), Lyminge (two mills), Lympne, Aldington, Brabourne (Mill House still there), Stone Hill Mill at Sellinge, Brenzett, Ruckinge, Woodchurch (two mills standing but idle), Bethersden (nearly done), Smarden (two mills, post and smock, standing, but idle), Pluckley (derelict), Kingsnorth, Kennington (ruin), Wye, Charing (body of mill only left) and, further afield, Molash, Challock and Shottenden Mills. These are but a few of the host of the past.

*   *   *   *   *

It is not surprising that a number of windmills in Kent have been destroyed by fire. Essentially wooden structures, often tarred externally, they made ready fuel for the flames ; and once a fire was started there seemed to be no checking it. The firemen's efforts were usually concentrated on preventing the flames from spreading to neighbouring buildings, sheds and haystacks.

A large number of such fires can be attributed to accidental causes but doubtless many a mill has been purposely set alight. Burning up a useless derelict mill solved many a problem for its owner. Worth little or nothing, dangerous in its dilapidated

Ridley's Studios, Tenterden   W.C.F.

BIDDENDEN (Town Mill)

[See page 165

W.C.F.

SIGNPOST OF THE TWINS

See page 92

W.C.F.

A BIDDENDEN CAKE

See page 92   Facing page 96

W.C.F. Ridley's Studios, Tenterden

BRENZETT

See page 174

E. A. Botting E. A. Botting

EGERTON (STONE HILL)
Before and after the gale of December 2nd, 1919.

See page 199

state, "encumbering the ground," "occupying useful land," unsafe for demolition in any other way, difficulty of getting the Government's sanction for the removal of a landmark perhaps, and the ignoble and fraudulent realisation of insurance money—these are no doubt some of the true explanations of many a mill fire.

The following Kentish mills are known to have been destroyed by fire in one way or another. The details, where ascertainable, have been included under their respective headings in the Historical Notes :

KENTISH MILLS BURNT DOWN

Adisham (Bekesbourne Mill)
Boughton Monchelsea
Brabourne
Canterbury (St. Lawrence Mill)
Challock Lees
Chatham (Luton Mill)
Cliffe (Dance's Mill)
Cobham (Darnley's Mill)
Deal (North End Mill)
Eastry (one of the four)
Faversham, Forbes Road
Frindsbury (Quarry Mill)
Gillingham (one of Stedman's Mills)
Gillingham (Huggin's Mill)
Hartlip (Friday's Mill)
Keston (Olive's Mill)
Kingsdown, Sevenoaks (post mill)
Lenham (Town Mill)
Lenham (Downs Court Mill)
Lydd (two mills)
Lyminge (Black Mill)
Minster, Sheppey
Minster, Thanet (one of the pair)
Petham (Chequer's Mill)
Queenborough, Sheppey
Ramsgate (Hereson Mill)
Rochester (Friday's Mill)
Sandwich (Black Mill)
Sheerness, Mile Town (The Little Mill)
Staple
Staplehurst
Strood (Field's Mill)
Swingfield (New Mill)
Tenterden (Leigh Green Mill)
Upchurch (Wakeley's Mill)
Westerham, Hosey Common
Westwell (Tutt Hill Mill)

G

Sometimes a mill, in its lofty, unsheltered position, was struck by lightning and thus set alight—Challock Lees and Cobham mills are instances. Fires did not always result, however, but the damage often proved serious, such as the shattering of a sweep (as at Headcorn and Bidborough), necessitating a costly repair or replacement, which in some cases could not be afforded.

Heavy gales have also taken their toll of our mills, directly or indirectly. It is seldom that a mill is blown over entirely. There have been instances—such as a post mill at Acrise and a smock at Waltham—but a mill has to be very old or derelict to collapse completely in a high wind. Often, as with lightning, it is the costly damage done by gales that has sounded the death knell of a mill.

Occasionally, owing to the faulty working of the fantail gearing, and the cap and its sweeps not being turned into the wind, a mill has become 'tail winded.' At such times a strong wind, driving with full force behind a mill, has often lifted cap and sweeps clean off (as at Reed Mill, Kingston) and sometimes the body of the structure, too (as at Egerton).

Even if the damage is not so serious as this, the sweeps, being back to the wind, may be forced to revolve in the reverse direction, thereby causing damage internally as well as to the sweeps (as at Preston, near Wingham). The picture of a Hawkhurst mill, facing p. 176, will show the kind of thing that can happen when a mill is 'tail winded.'

*   *   *   *   *

In their enforced idleness and decay the ragged, dismembered, derelict old windmills, scattered about on hill and mound, stand as it were in reproach that their work should be done and their graceful completeness but a memory.

It was about thirty years ago when I first fully realised that our windmills were vanishing fast and in a few years might be as extinct as the dodo. This realisation came primarily as the result of conversations with old millers, particularly Mr. Frank Pain at Star Mill, Chatham, which mill became dangerous and has since been pulled down. As being typical of what has happened throughout Kent, Mr. Pain told me that whereas at Rochester and Chatham, from different points of vantage, within, say, sixty years, forty active mills could have been counted, in 1883 only twenty-nine were still at work. From then onwards the greatest number were thrown out of use, and in 1905 only two remained active.   To-day there remains a solitary one, Glover's Mill (at Delce, Rochester), whose sweeps may be seen revolving against a sea of slate roofs of cottages, over an area which once comprised a manor farm, huge granary and broad acres of cornfields.

This sole survivor of forty corn mills, named after its owner, stands active only by his tenacity and energy.   It battles on, despite overwhelming difficulties, and places the citizens of Rochester under a debt of gratitude, which they could in some measure acknowledge with an occasional coat of paint for the mill's preservation.   A picture appears facing p. 261.

Other English counties are suffering similarly.   Quite recently an old Norfolk, Suffolk and Essex millwright, who, in the days gone by, often made as much as £5 per week at repairing mills ("some twenty years ago, when it was a full-time job and one had to be up with the lark and work till dusk") to-day pulls down more mills than he repairs.

> It is only the last half-century or so that windmills, as part of our economic equipment, began to fall into decay. In the seventies of the last century, at any rate, the whole countryside was dotted with them ; and children travelling by railway to the seaside were kept amused by seeing who could count the most windmills from the carriage window. Now one may travel a day's journey and never spy a windmill all the way, or when one is seen it shows but a sheer hulk, its frame gaping, and its wings falling away, like a ragged beggar sunning.[1]

The increasing quantity of wheat coming from abroad direct to the large roller mills along our coast is the main cause of the abandonment of our scattered windmills ;   the broad acres of corn by which they were once surrounded are now all but a memory.

A poem by Lord Darling in the *Sunday Times*, of which the following is an extract, suggested that the very landscape is bereaved by the disappearance of this symbol of security and greatness.

> Is it more cheap, upon the whole,
>   To buy abroad our grain,
> Let Labour languish on the dole,
>   Or windmills work again ?

The old derelict capless tower mill that inspired Lord Darling's poem is Halnaker Mill.   It stands, deserted, on the top of the Downs, to the north-west of Chichester.   It was built in 1750, and a picture of it is given in *English Windmills* (Miss M. I. Batten), Vol. 1, p. 95.

Our windmills, the 'land-ships' of past days, veritable wind-jammers certainly, are doomed.   They are fallen victims to steam and electricity.   We shall see no more corn windmills built.   There

[1] A daily paper.

are quicker and cheaper methods of grinding grain into flour. Is it too much to hope that the few mills that remain to humanise the landscape may be preserved to us?

One readily recalls many pictures of mills by our great painters, or of rural scenes in which a windmill is the prominent feature—for windmills always had a special attraction for the artist and lovers of the beautiful, and their beauty is enhanced by their utility.

Where would our artists be without their beloved mills, Constable and Cotman, Old Crome, Stark, Gainsborough and the others? I mean the real artists, not those who paint three dying mushrooms or kippers on a plate, the expiring Jezebel, or a dynamo in a fit.[1]

*   *   *   *   *

It is but a short step from the sublime to the ridiculous in art as in other matters, hence we find the windmill does not escape the attention of the cartoonist who relies upon the silent eloquence of a picture to convey that concentrated wisdom which could only be imparted less impressively in words. Here are three cartoons:

DON QUOTA AND THE MILLERS

Don Mac Quota : "Sancho! What was it that happened to the other Don Quixote and the windmills?"

[1] John English,.

"Yes, Sonny, I can remember when those sails were spinning round **and round** all day long."

DON QUIXOTE ARRIVES
Lord Birkenhead joins Mr. Lloyd George's party at Algeciras.

We often hear of the strange uses to which our old windmills are converted,—a church (as at Reigate Heath), a petrol station, a local museum and a summer retreat[1] but seldom of a windmill home. It is occasion therefore for more than ordinary remark when one reads in a daily paper an article by a woman who is fascinated by the idea of a home in one of those monuments to a "local industry that is dead."

> . . . To dwell in an abandoned windmill is to have at least an imposing residence, a place haunted with the white figure of the industrious miller. We become historian of the days when the grain was brought to the door on the backs of pack-horses, or the shoulders of peasants or, later, when the great farm wagons came and went with sacks of wheat and flour.
> . . . We show the devices of the place, reveal how the whole mill or, perhaps the turret only, was turned to set the sails to the wind, and how the grinding of the grain was done.

Some years ago I narrowly missed the opportunity of possessing a windmill snuggery (Star Mill, Chatham, facing p. 128), but during conversion it threatened to collapse. It was too far decayed to be saved but I marked its site with one of its old millstones which is still to be seen to-day. Chance once made E. V. Lucas the tenant of a windmill for a while—

> Not to live in, and unhappily not to grind corn in, but to visit as the mood arose, and see the ships in the harbour from the top window, and look down on the sheep and the green world all around. For this mill stands high and white, indeed, that when there is a thunder cloud behind it, it seems a thing of polished aluminium.
> . . . There is no decay—merely inanition. . . . A week's overhauling would put everything right. But it will never come, and the cheerful winds that once were to drive a thousand English mills so happily now bustle over the channel in vain.

There is a certain distinction and attraction in finding a tag attached to an old and abandoned 'grinder' when the premises are converted to a new use, such as providing refreshments for those who now travel by car and motor-bus along our once quiet rural roads. Often we find an enticing request to take tea at 'The Old Watermill Gardens,' or 'The Old Windmill Refreshment Rooms.' The traveller enjoys his refreshment the more because it is accompanied by the sound of falling water from the idle mill-wheel, the splashing of the waters over the weir of the mill-pond, or the hust-

[1] There is the classical instance of Alphonse Daudet who spent a summer in a mill. In my book *Life in Rural England* will be found a free translation of extracts from his book *Lettres de mon Moulin*.

R. F. Brain

BROMLEY (METCALF'S MILL)

See page 175

W.C.F.

A. W. Tiffin

CHISLET MILL

See page 187

CHISLEHURST COMMON AND MILL   W. Brigden

See page 186

CANTERBURY (From Whitehall)   Facing page 103

See page 95

BRENCHLEY   T. Else

See page 173

CANTERBURY (From Harbledown)

See page 95

ling of the breeze through the dilapidated sweeps of an old wind-mill.   There are, of course, many other similar evidences of the change that is taking place in rural England.   Hop oast-houses, for instance, are converted into attractive dwellings, and old barns have taken a new lease as dance halls.

*   *   *   *   *

Windmills are elusive things and it is not often one runs up against a local octogenarian who just remembers it or has heard of it from someone older than himself. It is none the less joyfully amazing, the interest shown unsuspectingly by so many different types of persons, the hospitality found in most unexpected places.

And yet I am reminded of an incident that befell my friend Donald Maxwell, the well-known artist and author.

Having bought a sack of wheat, he made tracks for the nearest windmill to get it ground into the 'old-time' flour ; but, to use his own words, "It was difficult to find, for I seemed to be driving all over Essex, following, to the best of my ability, the various and contradictory directions as to route that I gleaned from well-meaning pedestrians."

Whether he at last found his mill and later got his stone-ground flour and finally his whole-meal loaf I never heard ; but knowing him to be a man undeterred by difficulties, I have little doubt he attained the object of his search.

*   *   *   *   *

When arranging rambles in windmill land I suggest that you should take at least one journey when the fields are ripe with golden corn.

I have stood in a veritable sea of waving wheat, waist high, over which in the near distance towered the picturesque old mill (facing p. 245), and have conjured up pictures of the days gone by when, in that self-same spot, I have listened to the music of the voices of the harvesters busy with scythe and sickle, of the women and children helping to garner the grain and later of the gleaners echoing around. But this was in the days when the miller, husbandman, farmer and field-workers saw in the bounteous yield their assured sustenance and were safe in the comforting knowledge that their occupation between this harvest and the next was a certainty. Then, indeed, was the harvest a time of rejoicing.

After such a reverie, as I made my way back home, the words of Ruskin provided the true canon :

> To watch the corn grow, and the blossoms set : to draw hard breath over plough-share or spade ; to think, to love, to hope, to pray,—these are the things that make men happy.

PART III

OUR DAILY BREAD

. . . earth repays with golden sheaves
The labours of the plough.

Wordsworth.

W.C.F.

Facing page 106

W.C.F.

CANTERBURY (St. Martin's Mill)

W. Manwaring

See page 177

J. M. W. Turner, R.A.

CHATHAM, FROM SPUR BATTERY

Showing the Feather Mill, the Star Hill Mill (Rochester), and the distant Frindsbury Mill on the horizon.

See pages 183, 206, 262.

W. Tombleson

VIEW NEAR GREENWICH

See page 214

Facing page 107

CHAPTER VIII

FROM THE WHEAT PLANT TO THE LOAF

WE are told that even as late as the landing of Lord Allenby's expeditionary force in Palestine during the Great War, a "true wild wheat" was found, but this is not a reliable statement, for nowhere is wheat found in a wild condition.

Wheat belongs to the commonest of all plants, the restful-green grasses. Of these there are over 300 general and over 3,000 separate species scattered throughout the world. The daily food of millions of people is derived from cultivated species, such as rye, barley, oats, maize, wheat and rice.

Botanically the study of all the various grasses, with their separate interesting peculiarities, provides a wide and fascinating subject. The wheat grain or seed is really a fruit, erroneously described by some writers as a 'berry,' but we may continue to call it by the familiar name 'seed.'

The progenitor of our wheat plant, compared with the ear of to-day, was bearded, small and misshapen. Hence it is clear that, without continued careful cultivation and experimentation, no wheat would have grown to such perfect grain as we have now. Any form of damp kills the wheat grain within a year or two in England ; and it is reckoned, according to the results of an experiment made at Roehampstead, that, if not purposely grown, wheat would totally vanish as a British plant within four years.

Most of the features of the wheat plant are well known. One important point, however, should not be overlooked. This is its tendency to produce offshoots at the roots, termed 'tillers.' As early as 1768 an experiment was tried, when one plant produced eighteen tillers ; these were again divided, the result being that sixty-seven tillers were produced in one season. In March and April of the following year 500 plants were produced from the same stock, which yielded 21,109 ears. The cultivation of wheat by these means, nevertheless, is not a paying proposition ; the cost of labour incurred is excessive, hence the farmer prefers to follow the old-time method of sowing the seed.

Wheat and other corn crops are liable to certain defined diseases, which makes it important to select varieties strong enough to resist fungoid attacks. To this careful selection of the grain is due our disease-free crops.   We owe much to the now prevalent sowing of what is termed the 'red-chaffed wheat.'   One cannot fail to have been attracted by the waving fields of this particular variety by reason of its rich, golden-brown (or red-brown) colour, in contrast with the lighter colour of other varieties.

One can derive special pleasure in gathering all the wild grasses in the flowering season and examining them under a powerful lens ; their beauty is a revelation, even to those not aspiring to botanical knowledge.   Particularly wonderful is the flower of the wheat plant, the delicate silver-feathered stigma surrounded by the three stamens with their pivoted anthers, all encased in three glumes, which together form the floret.   This is inconspicuous and needs no colour to attract the insects, for the wheat-plant is wind-fertilised.

The wheat plant is a grass of the genus *Triticum*. All the wheats are cultivated from three species :

1. *Triticum mono-coccum :* cultivated in Spain and formerly grown by the Swiss lake dwellers.

2. *Triticum sativum :* the ordinary cultivated wheat, one form of which was grown by the original aboriginal Swiss, the ancient Egyptians, and throughout the Roman Empire.

3. *Triticum polonicum :* or Polish wheat, the source of which is unknown.

The original home of the wheat plant is thought to be Mesopotamia, and from there it was introduced westwards.   Its introduction into America did not take place till the sixteenth century. Humboldt states that it was accidentally introduced into Mexico by a slave, who brought it with some rice.   From the same source we learn that a Flemish monk had taken over from Ghent the first wheat grown in South America, and at Quito is preserved the earthen vase in which it was stored.   I have discussed in greater detail the origin of the wheat plant in my earlier books.[1]

In spite of the knowledge that when the wheat grain is harvested it does not keep its fertility for many years (germination dwindling rapidly and vanishing in fifteen years), we are frequently told that grains of wheat recovered from the mummy cases of Egyptian interments, when planted after a lapse of four thousand years, have yielded a rich crop of corn.   This is an improbable story, contrary to all experimental results.

[1] *Life in Rural England* and *The Lure of the Countryside.*

A grain of wheat keeps its recognisable form for an inordinate number of years but it is the husk and the starch only that are long-enduring. The tiny germ, in which life alone resides, is very short-lived. Even when kept in the driest state a large majority of the grains lose fertility within five years. In no single case, though many experiments have been made, has 'mummy-wheat' germinated.[1] The oldest seed known to have germinated—and that an oily and case-hardened kernel—has just celebrated its centenary.

Many plant seeds, however, have an infinite capacity for living in suspended animation, notably the charlock and the poppy. Theoretically, if air were totally excluded the period of fertility of wheat might be extended somewhat ; thus far and no farther will our scientists go in the matter. Bread-making is another matter, and I have particulars of wheat thirty-four years old being threshed out and made into excellent bread.

That England can no longer be considered a wheat-growing country is unfortunately only too apparent. It is to the great regions in North America, the United States and Canada, that we now look to meet the world's great demand, the magnitude of which cannot be conveyed to the mind by mere mention of acres or miles.

The methods adopted on these huge farms, both of culture and in the handling of the grain, can hardly be grasped by those whose associations, like my own, are limited to the comparatively diminutive cornfields in England. Some of the big farms in Canada vary from two thousand to ten thousand acres in extent, or from two to fifteen square miles. The ploughing is done by eight or ten ploughs working abreast of each other, while the huge machines which cut, bind, thresh and store the grain at the rate of one thousand six hundred sacks per day, are a miracle of ingenuity. Often the visitor will see great conflagrations in wheat-growing

[1] Professor B. A. Wallis Budge in a letter to *The Times*, April 23rd, 1931, makes an important pronouncement which should for ever dispose of the story that wheat obtained from the tomb of Tutānkhāmen has been made to grow. He explains how he was fortunate in being able to bring home from Western Thebes some grain of either wheat or barley found in an ancient Egyptian tomb. He succeeded in enlisting the help of the staff at Kew Gardens for an exhaustive experiment there under the personal supervision of the Curator, Dr. Thistleton Dyer. It was found, as reported by Dr. Thistleton Dyer, "that ancient Egyptian wheat or barley would not grow. . . . Many others tried the same experiment with the same result." Professor Bridge goes on to show why the belief that it will grow is so widespread : "For hundreds of years the natives have used the halls of tombs as granaries for the wheat and barley which they obtain from Syria. I have known ancient coffins to be packed in this Syrian grain and sent to England, and such grain will, of course, grow. And during the last thirty years the native dragomans annd guides have found that tourists will buy 'mummy wheat,' and they keep supplies in the tombs, carefully hidden, which they dig up under the eyes of the astonished visitor and offer him as *hunta mumiya*, 'mummy wheat,' or *sh'eir mumiya*, 'mummy barley.' "

districts—the burning of the enormous masses of straw, for which there is no further use.

We must not be tempted into details of the work in these distant cornlands. One is led to wonder, however, if this universal mechanization and mass-production is not already defeating itself by increasing unemployment as fast as it increases wealth.

The history of our cornfields tells us that man has laboured with unremitting toil for at least ten thousand years to provide his daily bread. In the old-time harvest field both husband and wife laboured together, their children perhaps lending a hand, he swinging the scythe, she gathering up the corn and binding it into sheaves.

> How soon the golden field abounds with sheaves,
> How soon the oats and bearded barley fall,
> In frequent lines before the keen-edged scythe.[1]

Towards close of day all joined in the work of 'shocking up,' that is, of gathering up the sheaves and forming them into long pyramids called 'shocks,' in which form the final ripening of the grain is accomplished. This was a familiar picture half a century ago.

In like manner wife and children laboured in the hop and fruit harvest to support the home, and the gleaning in the cornfields supplemented the earnings. This little 'stocking' was the sheet anchor of the family in sickness and adversity and alone pulled them through.

The 'Harvest Home' is little more than a memory. But the Harvest Festival services in our churches survive and, year by year, they are decorated with the fruits of the earth. In our work-a-day, as in our social, life much of this kind of grateful acknowledgment is perfunctory or else absent altogether. Among the many changes evidenced in modern life there is a falling away from old-time customs of faith and sincerity, of comradeship and sympathy. Despite the marvellous strides made in the arts and sciences, the world does not seem the happier but less contented, less grateful.

Students of rural life and its problems to-day miss many a once familiar and picturesque scene, for the customs peculiar to the several branches of agricultural work, like our wind and watermills, have disappeared. Particularly is this true of harvest time, the reaping by scythe, the making of the straw bonds with which to tie the sheaves—work for many willing hands.

[1] Hurdis.

The introduction of efficient horse-rakes and tractor-ploughs has not only banished the teams of horses from the fields but, in the haste to plough the stubble, the gleaner is likewise banished from her familiar and historic task. Ruth no longer gleans in the Kentish fields of Boaz. All is now accomplished mechanically with such unseemly haste that the most appealing annual scene in England, 'the harvest-field,' is a shadow of the past. It is something that the straight-set rows of shocks of corn sunning and ripening in the fields remain.

"The tasselled lightness of the oats, the soft-bearded barley, show a dusty whiteness in the ripe ears. Wheat-sheaves are rough and bristly with their stiff and upright heads, and carry that rich red-brown colour which is one of the pleasantest hues of the late summer when it has been painted by kindly suns."

Save for this, and the presence of the horses and the figures of the busy workers occupied in carrying the corn, the droning tractor and other mechanized devices have made sad work with the æsthetics of harvest time.

Even in the building of the stacks the sheaves are raised by machinery. The thatcher, it is true, remains to us, but that artist of the flail, the rhythmic beating of which once resounded as music from the threshing floor has, alas, passed with the bond-boy and the gleaner.

I have frequently met elderly country folk who remember their wives and families going in the cornfields near their homes to glean. They could take the corn thus gathered to the local wind-mill where, for a small charge, it would be ground into flour, sufficient to make bread for weeks and months ahead.

There is at least one Kentish windmill (at Chislehurst) that was built especially for the benefit of the gleaners. To this mill, in the early days of its history, every Monday and Tuesday, the gleanings could be brought, and fourpence per bushel was the fixed charge for grinding.

*   *   *   *   *

The vexed question of the most desirable wheats to be used in the preparation of the flour for 'our daily bread,' whether native or imported, or an admixture of both, is a difficult one and not within my province to answer. The following extract from a letter from a Kentish miller and baker of many years' standing is not without significance :

Of course with all English flour a nice showy baker's loaf cannot satisfactorily be produced. But I used to run upon the old English wheat, and bought what is known as the Top Patents (for mixing) from the large flour mills. This class of flour is from hard foreign wheat, and is very glutenous.

If country millers added a bakery to their mills, they would have an outlet for their flour. This is what I did forty-five or more years ago. When the War took place I had to shut down the bakehouse for want of help.

If the Ministry of Agriculture would impress upon the country folk to keep pigs and more poultry, and use all English flour, there might be a better chance of business for the windmills.

Country millers have fallen on evil times, as no cottagers and farmers bake their own bread from wheat grown in their respective localities and milled in their neighbourhoods. Neither do the cottagers fatten pigs as used to be the case in bygone days. Then again, the farmers for the most part have their own corn crushers to-day, run by the modern oil engine. So you see how the new order has displaced the old order of things. . . .[1]

That other controversial matter—the question of the superiority of the old-time stone-ground flour over the present-day highly refined product of the roller-mill, with its bleaching and chemical doctoring—seems to have been settled for us, whether we like it or not. Steel-ground wheat has come to stay, the days of stone-ground flour are almost over, and we may as well bow to the inevitable with good grace.

Here and there one finds an ardent advocate for stone-ground flour. I know of a doctor in Ashford who repeatedly urges his clients to insist that their bread should be made from stone-ground flour ; and an Ashford baker receives regularly each week a small quantity of flour made at a windmill (Cranbrook) in order to supply wholemeal bread to those who have taken the doctor's advice.

The wholemeal loaf is indeed becoming relegated to the past. The brown loaf appears occasionally on our table and is welcomed as 'a change,' but the attractive, doctored white bread and the numerous 'fancy' breads have come to stay, despite the food specialists who tell us that the vitamins necessary to our well-being are found principally in the wholemeal bread.

I will grant that the present system of cleaning and preparing wheat for the modern roller-mill is far in advance of the old-time methods, but then the wheat was cleaner, its journey from the English wheatfields to the windmill was a short one, and it gathered up none of the impurities said to be found in imported wheat. Besides, what matters a grain or two of 'clean dirt'?

The hygienic business in connection with food is surely being carried too far. The nation's digestion is being ruined by over-

[1] Mr. J. Brockman (Mount Ephraim Mill, Ash).

A. W. Tiffin

DODDINGTON
(Elvey's or Jarvis's Mill)

See page 195

Jack Holman

GREAT CHART

See page 180

A. W. Tiffin

CHILLENDEN

See page 186

A. Tanton

DYMCHURCH

See page 197   *Facing page 112*

W.C.F.

CHATHAM (Upberry Mill)

See page 181

J. Russell

CRANBROOK (Cranbrook Common)

See page 189

G. Hine

COBHAM (Darnley's Mill)

See page 188

Facing page 113

prepared and artificially preserved foods, including 'tinned' abominations of all kinds. Everything must be soft and tender ; anything hard or tough is banned, and the development of the jaws keeps pace with the deterioration of the teeth. Quite early in life we become toothless, dyspeptic specimens of humanity. I attribute my own freedom from these failings, and general good health, to my good fortune in having throughout my earlier years lived principally upon bread made from stone-ground flour and wholesome farm-house food of all descriptions.

The bleaching and so-called improving of the natural flour exists to a far greater extent than the general public are aware. The perusal of *The Report of the Departmental Committee on the Treatment of Flour with Chemical Substances*, as issued by the Ministry of Health, would give the reader a mild shock.

Referring to the 'bleachers' and 'improvers' used, it states that chlorine is capable of altering the gluten in such a way as to affect injuriously its nutritive value, and that its use is undesirable. This observation also applies to nitrogen trichloride.

Not being a chemist, I floundered through the results of the use of nitrogen peroxide, benzoic acid, benzoyle peroxide, persulphates, ammonium or potassium sulphate, acid calcium phosphate, and acid ammonium phosphate. I learned that "some of these probably affect the composition of the flour but little, but it were better that flour should not contain other substances," and that "the possibility of improving flour by physical rather than chemical methods" is where the committee would like to see progress made.

How many of us, when we break bread in thankfulness, are aware that the great gift of wheaten flour has been so ruthlessly and unnecessarily degraded ?

In the present day we are surfeited with knowledge, are martyrs to too much scientific theory, and suffer the deprivation of unbleached, unadulterated flour for bread.

The hale and hearty octogenarians, children of a darkly ignorant age, smile commiseratingly at us as they amble recklessly along the paths that are supposed to cut life short. We cannot wring from them their pathetic faith in hot roast pork, strong tea, beer, unadulterated butter, large families, and a happy escort of the kind angels at the close.

They thrived on these very things, and so did their forefathers ; they made a vital Empire without a shred of knowledge of vitamins ; they laughed they ate plum pudding without a thought of proteid ; they enjoyed roast beef without a dissertation on calories. . . .

H

We need a hold on the old simple truths and the old and simple foods ; what the highly civilised man and woman of to-day need are the calm mind, the working will, and the happy heart.[1]

*   *   *   *   *

Reflecting upon the subject of the old-time loaf, my mind naturally went out to an old friend, the miller at the only remaining active corn mill on the River Len, a Wealden stream once famous for its numerous mills. He is now my only surviving watermiller friend and is a man I hold in high esteem. I have mentioned him in my previous volumes.

I had not seen him for over a year and, as he is an octogenarian, I was pleased to find him well and busily occupied. It was Good Friday, and the mill-pond was full to the brim. As I approached the mill I heard the familiar Thud ! Thud ! of the revolving wheel and the deep rumble of the mill-stones.

I wondered if I could get some genuine stone-ground, wholemeal flour from English wheat, that I might once more taste the old-time bread, a dream of half a century ago. My request surprised him. He said he had no English wheat to grind and told me the reason why. He recalled how that seventy years ago, when as a lad he first came to the mill, teams of horses were continually there, chafing, stamping and neighing impatiently, while the music of their jingling latten bells was sweet to hear, for they were bringing the English wheat from the adjacent farms to be stored in the capacious granary at the mill, to be ground into flour as required.

He pointed to the heaps of corn lying near the revolving stones ; one pair was grinding golden maize, the other mixed corn— barley, wheat and oats. He said, "Not a grain of home-grown produce there !" Then followed an interesting résumé of the subject of foreign corn, away back to the time of the Crimean War (1854-56), the difficulties of that period and its influence on corn. Everything in connection with milling was fresh in his mind, not only the history of corn-milling but the ramifications of the grain trade near and far, and the influence it exercised in this country. He remarked, with a sigh, that once the country around the mill was a vast corn-producing area, but was now hop, fruit and pasture land.

I returned again to the subject of the wholemeal loaf. He could not supply me and did not really know where to get it,

[1] Maude Crossley in the *Daily Express*, September 7th, 1927.

but he said he would try.   He then explained how we came to lose the sweet flavour of the bread ; it was due, to the extraction of the 'semolina' from the grain.   This sweet germ in the grain escapes at the first contact with the steel rollers of the modern mill, which are so set as to release it in a granulated form before the grain passes on to other rollers which are to grind it into flour.   This semolina is sold for thickening soups, making puddings, etc. and is lost to our daily bread, depriving us of the sweetness and the brown crispness of the old-time loaf.

Around the spacious floors of the old mill were stacked the various 'bolting machines,' now out of use.   Some held the 'bolting cloth' of seventy years ago, one the 'wire' substitute of sixty years ago, and another the later 'silk fabric' bolter, through which the flour passed to prepare it for the table.   This, too, he said had been substituted later by an improved 'plansifter' (which he did not possess), for 'hog corn' and 'chicken food' required no such refinements.   Hence I learned that the warm meal that trickled through my fingers as it issued from the wooden spout was coarse mixed meal from common corn for feeding pigs and poultry.

Before bidding him goodbye I asked just one question more— as to the cleansing of the grain before it was made into flour.   I knew the English wheat was not washed, whereas the foreign wheat was so treated.   I learned that the home wheat, although it needed no washing, was passed through a 'smut machine' in its dry state to remove any indication of 'smut.'   If the crop were badly affected, the corn would not be used for flour.

I may add that 'smut' is a disease produced by a small fungus, incidental to cultivated corn, and is familiar to country folk when occasional ears of corn are converted into a black soot-like powder.

Imported wheat, however, had to be thoroughly washed, said my miller friend for, when washing foreign wheat, he had often seen the effluent absolutely black with Asiatic filth.

It is little wonder that I am enamoured of the sweet, old-time loaf, for as a lad I saw the sowing, reaping, garnering, threshing by flail and hand winnowing, and frequently rode with the grain to the mill ;   then returned with the flour, saw the making and baking of the bread in the old wood-heated oven and, later, when it was bespread with farmhouse butter, helped to devour it.

*   *   *   *   *

Pursuing my search for information as to the 'old' and the 'new' loaf, I paid a visit to an old but hardy windmiller.   His mill was working merrily, not making the domestic flour but coarse-ground chicken food and the like. I found him, though nearly eighty years of age, busy and fit, and as usual he gave me a ready welcome.

I asked what bread he ate. He replied, "Wholemeal, of course, otherwise I should not be in the perfect state of health in which you find me."

He then, in a manner similar to that of the old watermiller, but more exhaustively, described the old processes of making both the old stone-ground flour and the modern substitute, as well as the loss we sustained by eating the latter.

He explained how the requests for whiter and still whiter flour, and the perpetual expense in providing the additions to the machinery of his mill, finally necessitated the discontinuance of flour making.

He took from a cupboard a brown, wholesome, wholemeal loaf and said, "Here's the bread of life. I eat it every day and no other. Do the same, and you will be astounded, as it contains all the body craves for—bone, teeth and muscle."

He described the process by which such bread was made, and although it was not the product of his own mill it was readily obtainable if ordered from a reputable firm who had a sufficiently large clientele to warrant the baking of a full batch of loaves from genuine stone-ground flour. Otherwise, he told me, if ordered casually of a small baker, you would get a 'brown' loaf, not the loaf you desire but a mixture of sundry meal added to the modern flour. Disappointment would result ; the bread would still be but a poor, inefficient substitute.

He handled that brown loaf as if it were a work of art and he a connoisseur.

As I was leaving I passed his daughter carrying a huge box of eggs, from fowls fed on mixed corn from the old mill, which means that his business of miller was helped by 'side lines.'

Passing down the crazy mill-stone path to the sound of the sharp swish and whirr of the revolving sails, and the rumbling clatter emanating from the interior of the mill, I was full of musings as to the value of that genuine brown loaf.

*   *   *   *   *

Having interviewed the windmiller and the watermiller, there was but to obtain the verdict of the old-time baker, so I decided to call upon an aged baker and confectioner I have known for some thirty-five years, whose cakes were considered a luxury by a very large clientele. Somehow, by the exigences of a very busy life, both he and his cakes drifted out of our family fare. By a coincidence, table conversation one day brought forth the remark : "Nothing is as good as it used to be, including bread and cakes," which again reminded me of my old baker friend. It was decided unanimously that we would have one of his cakes. Thus, ere many days had passed, I visited his premises.

I found no display of cakes in the window, not even a loaf of bread. I noticed also that time had left its mark upon him since we last met. He recognised me more by my voice than by the dimmed vision of my form, and expressed his delight at seeing me. Though usually as reticent as an owl, he was with me, even as in the olden days, in a genial mood.

I told him the purport of my visit, and he replied : "I am sorry to disappoint you but I have made neither cakes nor bread for many years." I learned that when the modern flour, made chiefly from foreign wheat and by the steam roller-mills, was supplied to him, the result was disappointing. So that, when he realised that he could not make bread or cakes up to his usual standard, to use his own words, "I would not let the customers I had served for many years have an inferior article."

He must have remembered that in the distant past he always gave me some trifling token of his friendship—cake, buns or biscuits—for, turning round, he produced from behind the counter a tray of delicious pears and apples, grown in his own garden, of which he was very proud. Selecting the best, he grasped my hand, gave me the fruit and bade me adieu, requesting me to call again for old times' sake.

Thinking I had noticed a quantity of bread on the shelves, he explained that though he did not now make bread, for the reasons given, he obtained the best now available to keep in touch with a few old customers. But he sighed for the old-time flour which for so long he had delighted in preparing, and for the bread which he had been so proficient in making. He was now an agent for the goods of another baker who was less conscientious, less sensitive than himself, one who had never handled the old-time product of our English cornfields.

*   *   *   *   *

The following statements in *The Miller* during 1930 are worth making permanent here :

Occasional scares create an enormous demand for brown bread in the place of white—this not in the poorer neighbourhoods—but it only lasts a few weeks, when there is a gradual return to the white loaf.

*   *   *   *   *   *

American flour requires about twice as much water to make it into bread as is used for English flour. A stone of American flour which weighs 14 lbs. will make 21½ lbs. of bread, but the best sort of English flour produces only 18½ lbs. of bread ; hence the former is the more profitable.

*   *   *   *   *   *

What high hopes were raised when the chemist first started to appear in our mills, and yet, except in the study of such things as improvers and bleachers (things really added to the flour), what has chemistry done for us ? Men have come as prophets and leaders, each one giving advice and criticism in the Press and in conferences, and each one having a mysterious secret that would revolutionise milling ; but history shows there have not been any real secrets or epoch-making changes since rollers ousted the old stones.

*   *   *   *   *   *

In spite of the more perfect machines and more perfect systems now installed, many an old miller did better work than is done to-day because the 'Old Timer' had got the idea of wheat cleaning into his head, and spared no effort to ensure correct cleaning and temper.

*   *   *   *   *   *

The beauty and delicacy of modern flour-milling machinery command the admiration of engineers, but is it not remarkable that such skill is expended in removing all the most valuable constituents of the staple food of the inhabitants of the country ? That which is thus removed we call 'offal,' and we give it to the animals on our farms; they have the best of it. Modern research brings to light the fact that the health of the nation is being seriously affected by the habitual use of this ultra-refined vitaminless flour.

*   *   *   *   *   *

The good miller still uses his teeth to see if the wheat is in good condition for milling. The buyer still chews the wheat to see if it is strong. Wheat standards are still based on weight per bushel, and flour by sight, touch and smell, and the 'test baking' still stays, although the chemist has repeatedly attempted to show how unreliable it is ; and so on through other systems and practices of old times.

*   *   *   *   *

I wonder how many of my readers have had the pleasure of peeping into a huge, old, wood-heated oven, such as our forefathers used in the preparation of a loaf of bread.

It was away back into well over half a century ago that I recall being lifted up in arms while the baker swung open the big oven door for my pleasure. He kindled the light, swung the long bracket into the oven so that I might see the hundreds of loaves baking crisp and brown. I see them now, row upon row in geometrical regularity as deposited by the 'peel'—the long wooden shovel with which they were placed like soldiers on parade, and by a sharp and dexterous snatch of which the soft doughy loaf was left in any desired spot on the hot tiled floor of the oven.

I see, too, the shimmering, transparent heat enveloping the bread ; then the light withdrawn and the huge door again closed to complete the baking of the 'batch'—the name applied to the contents of the oven. The process of baking finished, the same large wooden peel rapidly withdraws the loaves and, smoking hot, the old-time windmill-bread is deposited on every accessible table or shelf to cool.

In a smaller way the same interesting business could be seen in the ovens of the old bakeries attached to our windmills, and at the farm and manor houses, where one day each week was set apart for preparing sufficient bread for the ensuing week.

In days of yore, bread making was a long job. First there was a ferment then a sponge, then a dough and at long last, a batch of bread. Time 20 hours.[1]

I recall the long process of years ago in its every detail, even to seeing the dough in large, red, earthenware crocks placed before the long fires, first covered by a spotless white linen cloth and then left in the genial warmth all night, preparatory to baking in the morning.

All this is of the past ; even the mixing of the flour and the kneading of the dough is now mechanically accomplished, while steam and other artificially heated ovens have supplanted wood-heating, and modern machinery of all kinds handles the precious loaves. Now, from the fields of golden grain until the loaf appears upon our table, it is untouched by hand—even to the point of wrapping up each loaf in transparent paper before it leaves the bakery.

That the bread is not contaminated by careless handling is all to the good. But even 'safeguarding' care can be overdone. I remember hearing of a scientific father (a doctor) who was so keen on the safeguarding that he sterilised every possible article of food before it came to the table. This effort, however, over-reached itself, for his family lost their usual robust health, which concerned him greatly. A physician of repute was called in and the doctor explained the great care that had been used. The physician pondered for a moment, then replied : ''Yes, that sounds all very well, but if you don't stop this 'safeguarding' business you

[1] "Utopia," *The Miller*, July 7th, 1930.

will have no children left to take care of ; they will all have been sterilised into the cemetery !''

Surely the lesson is obvious—that we should take these God-given gifts of food on trust, prepare them with cleanliness and care and consume them with pleasure, unmarred by the bogey of microbes. The nation has passed through thousands of years successfully without a knowledge of any of our clever, present-day discoveries about food; and it is evident that often in turning out microbes which we think are evil we may destroy the very bacteria which are necessary to life itself.

CHAPTER IX

THE DECLINE OF AGRICULTURE IN ENGLAND

This chapter is not a cheerful one because it tells of the last phase in the decline and fall of our once familiar corn mills, nestling by our bickering streams or crowning almost every eminence throughout the county.

It would have been a simpler, happier and more appealing task to have written the whole book away back in the busy windmill days, when side by side they threw the flickering shadow of their revolving arms across the broad rolling sea of ripening corn, and when all the other varied fruits of the earth were in rich profusion. At these times the natural wealth of England was reflected in the prosperity, health and happiness of those who laboured on the land. This is of the past, for almost every aspect of rural life and the countryside itself is altering with rapidity, and alas! not for the better.

Some thirty years ago the farmer cared personally for his men. He relied upon their sincerity, and they respected him and served him faithfully. To-day we find this old mutuality between master and man has vanished.

The standard of living of the agricultural worker has greatly improved of late years. The stride in the matter of education, the opportunities afforded for self-improvement outside his agricultural interests, and the ready access to numerous forms of amusement, have given him a broader outlook on life, but he is on the whole less contented than his forebears. Many have questioned whether he is any happier for the advantages modern life has brought him, and some aver that he is not such a good worker.

The following words from an authority on the subject are, however, stimulating in these difficult days :

We have as good material in our agricultural population as exists in the world—the marvel is that after all it has come through it should be so sturdy and blithe—but it has not had a fair chance. The rough time through which our farming is going is getting rid of the less valuable elements : let us be careful that it does not take out of farming some of its more valuable elements. Every year the minds of farmers and farm-workers are widened by better education, motors and wireless—the large attendance at the tractor trials was a noteworthy thing. If only we had an enlightened and continuing national agricultural policy, the best men would come to the front, and we should be able to boast—as some of us indeed, in our optimistic moments, are inclined to boast already—that we have the best farmers and farm-workers in the world.[1]

Nature still provides bountifully by blessing the labour bestowed upon the fruitful soil but in spite of this—

the tragedy of English farming stands out starkly. It is man's side of the business that has gone awry—thriftless national and personal expenditure, the nation living on its capital, the long-drawn-out methods of finance, that could, in multitudinous ways, but have resulted in the present deplorable state of the country, for thousands of farmers are actually bankrupt, though the banks do not foreclose, because they would lose everything and nothing to gain.[2]

One notes vast areas of wheat-growing land once fat, now unfed and hungry, for the farmer in despair has turned from corn to milk. Yet even here a varied range of tinned imports already threatens to create difficulties for him.

Industrialists and the working classes generally would reap the widest benefits if home agriculturalists were freed from strangulation by imports of so-called cheap food. We have the best equipped lands, the most experienced farmers and land workers ; give them a fair chance, which is the only sane way out. Greater production from our healthy soils, by producers who are controlled by strict hygienic measures, means abundant and regular supplies of the most pure, fresh, and nutritious foodstuffs, the first essentials of the word cheap. Seventy years ago we fed from the produce of this island 26,000,000 people ; to-day we only produce enough to feed the odd 6,000,000, and our plough-lands are tumbling to so-called grass-lands, with workers forced to the ranks of the unemployed and the money not obtainable to continue such uneconomic policy.[3]

I am no economist, but it is certain, if we are not to say 'good-bye' to British agriculture, the farmer must be given an immediate opportunity of helping himself, that a new state of things must make life possible for him, for at present his efforts are absolutely nullified, swamped by foreign supplies. His bank is already broken. Let us not by further delay break his heart also !

In our rural travels we see derelict watermills and tattered sweeps of windmills—typical indications of the passing of better times—and the same distressing fact is reflected in the ever-decreas-

---

[1] J. W. Robertson Scott, Editor of *The Countryman*, in *The Observer*, Sunday, September 28th, 1930.

[2] Sir Philip Gibbs, *Daily Express*, September 4th, 1931.

[3] W. Hill Forster, Secretary, Central and Associated Chambers of Agriculture, in *The Times*, September 14th, 1931.

ing area of our cornfields and arable land. At first only those versed in the subject noticed the change, but now, alas! it is obvious to the most casual observer.

The word 'change' is used advisedly as it indicates a slow adjustment in the wake of a peaceful trend of things, not a cataclysm which deluges. The old-time life, the watermill, the windmill, mode of transport, our delightful winding roads and tree-embowered lanes, all succumb before the march of so-called progress, sacrifice to 'speed,' for which, as one old countryman pithily remarked, "We ain't much the for'arder as I can see."

It is evident that much of the beautiful has already been swept away and, now that our mediæval bridges have provoked the disapproval of the road surveyors, it will be their turn soon to fall before the fetish of modernisation or be altered out of recognition, robbed of their delightful approaches and surroundings.

Scattered with a generous hand, the grand, grey old churches of our forefathers, with all they hold so dear, remain. What changes they have witnessed! The latest is the electrification of the countryside, for so often do we have to peep at churches in the distance between the steel pylons which stride across hill and dale. These, with their suspended cables, are supposed to make country life more tolerable in our scattered villages and hamlets. May that fully compensate for the trespass on our beauty spots. But, unless conditions which now threaten the rural population are speedily improved, there may be few to whom the gift of this wonderful light can minister, for our farms and cornfields will soon be as derelict as our corn mills.

*　　*　　*　　*　　*

Through a certain introspection, I am perhaps unable to offer an unbiassed opinion on these matters. I am a lover of the countryside and somewhat old-fashioned in my ideas. Quite recently a friend who had surfeited himself with leisure and the so-called luxuries of life, and who had just returned from 'taking the waters,' told me he'd had a fine time, bidding me do likewise.

I reminded him that many years ago another friend similarly admonished me, but that he had now been dead sufficiently long for the beautiful lichen and verdant mosses to cover his headstone! I doubt if what I intended to convey was appreciated.

Case-hardened philosophers of our community, who regret the passing of nothing, offer us the gilded pill of "it can't be helped—things must move with the times." For my part I prefer to recall and regret the passing of many things beautiful, of greater intrinsic worth than the facile modern 'improvements' that have replaced them.

It is good to know that in at least one county an effort is being made to form a collection of old-time farm implements and machinery. The Community Council of Kent, working through its Committee for the Preservation of Rural Kent, has set up an Agricultural Museum Sub-Committee, with Lady Northbourne as Chairman, and Mr. G. H. Garrad and Mr. N. B. Bagenal as joint Hon. Secretaries (their address is 38 Earl Street, Maidstone). This Committee is now actively engaged in getting together a thoroughly representative collection of relics of the past, and appeal to all true lovers of our English countryside to send them any implements and tools of bygone times. The Maidstone Town Council has generously lent part of the beautiful "Old Tithe Barn"[1] (or Guest House as it should more properly be called) which, it is felt, will prove a suitable home for the Museum. Needless to say, machinery from old windmills and watermills is included in a list of items that would be welcomed. Copies of this list can be obtained from the address stated. It is indeed a laudable effort.

One is often accused of living too much in the past, and of unduly praising it. Yet are we not counselled to respect our elders, so why not the age in which they lived ? It is said that the business methods of our grandfathers, if applied now, would result in bankruptcy but, I would remind the reader, many of those farmers who 'moved with the times' and adopted mechanised methods of cultivation, are already bankrupt. Why not then continue to recall the old times with pride and pleasure? Much that then made for peace and happiness is absent in these shallow days of make-haste and make-believe.

Let us also not be sparing in our praise of those of the good old days who, despite their many failings, had learned the art of living within their means, going without what they could not afford. We, who are so wonderfully wise and clever, just have what we want, whether we can afford it or not.

One thing is certain, if the olden times were slow, the world is no happier for the accelerated speed at which it now travels. As Lord Buckmaster recently stated:

[1] See illustration in author's volume : *Life in Rural England*, p. 101.

I have never thought that the chariot of progress was a triumphant car that scattered blessings along its track.

It is generally believed that the farmer always *grumbles* and *thrives.* Maybe he does the former ; at least he did so in my early days. But it is no 'wolf-cry' to-day, for the farmer is 'up against it' without a shadow of doubt.

In reference to the price of wheat, for instance, my friend Halford L. Mills writes :

When the nineteenth century dawned upon our fruitful Weald, then a land of profitable culture, wheat was selling at 86s. per quarter for the years 1799 to 1803.[1]

My daily paper of August 8th, 1931, lies before me and in a column with the bold heading, "Farmers' Ruin," the following comparative prices are given :

	s.	d.	
English old wheat	28	0	per quarter
,, new wheat	37	0	,, ,,
Production costs . . 45s. to	50	0	,, ,,
Russian wheat	18	6	,, ,,

This shows the intensity of the economic war declared by Soviet Russia on the British farmer in the matter of wheat alone, but the struggle is equally intense in a hundred ways with other necessaries of life. Arable land in England is no longer an asset but a liability.

The Soviet is obviously in desperate need of money, and that is why she is withholding grain from the hungry population of Russia to sell in the English market, with the result that the British farmer will have to sell his wheat at a loss of no less than 25s. a quarter. Every cargo of foreign wheat that comes to this country makes the position worse for the British grower, but it is adding insult to injury for the Government to allow it to come into this country tax-free—wheat which, for all we know, may have been virtually stolen. When the Government tolerate this it means that they are allowing British farmers to be ruined and their labourers turned out of employment.[2]

I also noted in 1932 that the new crop of Russian wheat had been sent over in vast quantities, arriving fully three weeks ahead of the English crop.

At the present moment fate seems determined ruthlessly to conspire against the economic stability of the nations generally,

[1] *South Eastern Gazette,* July 21st, 1931.
[2] Captain E. T. Morris, President of the National Farmers' Union.

for in addition to the Russian Soviet menace, by over-production and bounteous crops in various parts of the world, there is a surfeit of the principal necessaries of life.   Should no single ear of wheat be harvested this year, or next (1931–32), there is sufficient surplus wheat to assure the bread of the world for two years. Hence, to cut his losses, an American farmer set fire to his corn, for he found that he could only get 11 cents for what cost him 40 cents to raise.

As I write, a letter from a master miller of East Kent, dated August 14th, 1931, is handed to me.

It is sad to note what is happening to our old farm houses and our corn mills. My grandfather's fine old timber farm house, still showing the remains of the once surrounding moat, is razed to the ground because of the neglect of the roof and the expense of repair ; but worse than all is the plight of the farmer just now. Danubian wheat was sold the other day to London at 15s. 6d. for 480 lbs. How can the farmer live ?

Let me also quote from the neighbouring county :

Essex farmers who were depending on a good harvest this year are alarmed at the prospect. With Canadian wheat (Manitoba No. 1) being sold in the London market at 21s. a quarter, which is 14s. cheaper than it can be produced in Essex, many farmers are contemplating grinding the corn crop for cattle fodder. In this way they will save money, for at the present time they have to pay as much for bran as they can get for their wheat, while middlings cost more than they can sell their wheat for.

Is it not clear why, throughout the whole of Kent to-day, the county which once grew wheat for the population of Rome, there now stands less than a score of working windmills out of the four-hundred-and-four known to have existed during the last three centuries ?

By centuries of effort the English people had fitted themselves into the English countryside ; their windmills and waterwheels harnessed to their service the only inanimate forces that they understood ; their agricultural operations and implements were growths which represented such adaptations as experience suggested to successive generations. Thus behind their cultivation of the soil stretched a vista of years at least as long as that which history and legend associate with barrow, camp, or battlefield. It was in harmony with its old-world setting. My own recollections date back to 1855—a Golden Age of agriculture for squires and farmers, when the land not only supplied bread to 17,000,000, and meat to the whole, of the existing population, but employed nearly 1,100,000 rural workers. Men ploughed, sowed, reaped, and threshed almost as they had done in Biblical days, and Boaz himself would have seen little to surprise him either in the harvesting or the winnowing of his barley. Preparations for the coming annihilation of time and distance had hardly begun. Few railways had been built ; the mercantile fleet mainly consisted of sailing ships, small in number and carrying capacity ; except for short distances no submarine cables had been laid ; roads were still barred by turnpike gates, and, off the railways, horses or 'hiking' were the only means of land locomotion or conveyance. But the elders of my childhood, who went to church and prayed into their top-hats, seem even more remote than the Elizabethans from their descendants of to-day. The year 1880 makes a better starting-point than 1855. Conditions were less primitive ; preparations for the great change were advanced ; the flood of foreign produce was already trickling to these shores.[1]

My sympathy goes out to the farmer of the present day, for he is absolutely at the end of his tether. That he always grumbled we know, yet that could not well be otherwise, for as long as I can remember, English farming has been an anxious business. For one thing its success depends so much on the elements in their ever varying moods. By patience and long experience, however, he surmounted general difficulties and obstructions. Smiling and grumbling all the time, he turned up the mother earth, ploughed in, maybe, a crop that had failed, giving it a hasty burial that no time be lost, and sowed some later crop in the hope of retrieving the situation. With work and determination he prospered and, as season followed season, what he lost on the 'swings' he gained on the 'roundabouts,' balanced his accounts and came through. Nature and farmer got on very well together. The latter worked assiduously as the former gave bountifully.

Obviously agricultural life to-day is in a deplorable state, and the greatest minds are floundering in a morass of wonderment and indecision as to why and how it came to be thus ; hopeless about mending the matter, knowing full well that beneficent nature has not failed us.

Think of the irony of it all—that when the produce of field, garden and orchard is sent to the market, the salesman of the goods is often obliged to demand a cheque from the farmer to balance the account, the sale of the goods not covering the expenses !

Meanwhile, with more pointed irony, the farmer perhaps calls at a near restaurant for lunch, eats dumped meat and pays fourpence for a portion of cabbage, while he remembers that the last consignment of that vegetable he sent to the market fetched only two shillings per hundred. He mentally calculates that he is paying at the rate of about a shilling per cabbage—no less than fifty times as much as he himself received.

[1] Lord Ernle in *The Times*, Feb. 2nd, 1932.

To give a more definite instance—a farmer sent thirty-four half-sieves of good Bramley Seedling apples to Covent Garden market. A week passed and, receiving no sale note, he wrote to the salesman for an account which, when it came, read as follows :

34 h/s Bramleys	..	..	for 17/-
Tolls and market expenses	..	..	17/-
Balance	..	..	Nil.

In this particular case the grower had himself paid rail carriage, in addition to which he had all the expense of picking, packing and cartage to the nearest station.

These apples, or some very similar, were later on sold in shops and on stalls at 3d. per pound.

"Why do farmers always grumble?" Why, indeed !

And yet—

These men are the stuff which made us a great nation in many fields here and overseas. If we lose their class we lose everything, because we city folk, we 'little intellectuals' do not breathe the same air, nor keep in touch with the earth, which makes the natural man. All our spirit and history are deep-rooted in the soil which these men till, now without profit because of something that has gone wrong in the balance of life.[1]

It is obviously useless to plead the cause of the old watermiller and windmiller. Their absolute and complete disappearance is inevitably very near. With the farmer, however, despite all, one still feels there is reason for hope, that the present chaotic disastrous state is but transitory.

There is cold comfort, however, to be found in the official figures (September, 1931) which tell us that :

...in some forms of grain, the imports are 90 per cent. higher than a year ago. British fields lie barren, British farmers are insolvent, and 58,000 stout farming men have walked off the countryside to add to the army of the unemployed.[2]

This means that thousands of happy homes have been wrecked and hearts of brave souls bruised, of men who had to bid farewell to hearth and home and the once glorious fields of their cultivation.

To those who would delve deeper into the vexed problem of our economic position I would send them to that new and excellent volume, *Land and Life*.[3] There the subject is exhaus-

---

[1] *Daily Express*, Sept. 4th, 1931.   [2] Sir Philip Gibbs.
[3] By Viscount Astor and Keith A. H. Murray (Gollancz, 1932).

W. Manwaring

CHATHAM (Manwaring's Mill, Luton)

See page 185

W.C.F.

SUMMER

W.C.F.

WINTER

CHATHAM (Star Mill)

See page 181

See page 83

Facing page 128

CRANBROOK (Union Mill)

See page 190

Facing page 129

tively treated, and the reader can learn much that will throw light upon the present regrettable plight in which the nation now finds itself—how it came to be, by what changes the deplorable state may be remedied and the bankruptcy of the agricultural world and the very nation itself be prevented.

It is surely not too late for the nation to awaken, rise to the occasion, rescue the farmer from the slough of despond into which he has fallen, and prevent the canker of absolute ruin from eating into our most vital industry.

It is indeed cheering to note that the long-promised comprehensive agricultural policy is maturing. It will not save our fast vanishing corn mills but the harvest fields may again sing with their wealth of waving corn ; our orchards, hop-fields, arable lands, cattle and flocks may again bring prosperity to the farmer, to the agricultural workers and all who are engaged in the arts and crafts associated with rural life.

PART IV
THE WINDMILLS OF KENT

Ye happy homesteads, and broad orchards, hail!
The cheerful windmill, and the fields of corn,
And fragrant hop with aromatic scent!
Here would I live, and die where I was born,
On some sequestered hill in lovely Kent.

Benjamin Gough.

CHAPTER X

MAPS AND SURVEYS, 1596-1930

In building up this record of our Kentish windmills my first task was to find the most reliable early record of the number standing at a given date, to use that as a foundation, and then to make methodical researches for authoritative records of the existence of windmills at later dates.

I found the basic help in Phil. Symonson's map of 1596, which he described as "A New Description of Kent." Here is shown particularly the churches and the windmills—the spiritual and bodily needs of the inhabitants of Kent (map facing p. 134).

It is of interest to note that Phil. Symonson, as the map states, was "of Rochester, gent." In 1597, a year after the publication of the map, it is recorded that he was mayor of that ancient city.

We find from this fine old map that in 1596 thirty-nine post mills (see list on page 134) had joined the ranks of the watermills. The combined efforts of these mills provided the flour, bran, middlings, etc., required by the dwellers in the scattered villages. Evidently at this period there was but a local distribution of flour, and it will be well to bear in mind that the actual isolation of these villages from the nearest township was more complete than we can now imagine.

Without a doubt all the windmills of 1596 were of the earliest type—'open trestle' or 'tripod' post mill. It was probably this type of mill that Mark Twain discovered while on a visit to the Azores, and to which he refers in his *The Innocents Abroad*, as follows :

> Small windmills grind the corn, ten bushels a day, and there is one assistant superintendent to feed the mill, and a general superintendent to stand by and keep him from going to sleep. When the wind changes they hitch on some donkeys and actually turn the whole upper half of the mill around until the sails are in a proper position, instead of fixing the concern so that the sails could be moved instead of the mill.

In this connection I should mention that an old post mill that stood at Tonbridge until recent times was operated in exactly the manner Mark Twain humorously describes, only that a horse instead of a donkey was hitched on.

133

None of the old post mills of 1596 remains with us in Kent to-day. We have eight post mills at the present time, only two of which are working (Ash and Chillenden) ; one is in good repair but stands idle (Wittersham) ; the other five are derelicts (Frittenden, Keston, Shorne, Smarden and Rolvenden). These are all of much more recent date than those of 1596, and some are probably replacements on the same sites.

The picture of Bourn Mill in Cambridgeshire, reproduced facing page 37, will give the reader a good idea of the form of the early post mills with their open trestles.

We can imagine the mild excitement that prevailed when these mills, small and of simple construction, were being erected on the little hills and prominences, away from the brooks and streams which had their ancient watermills. We can also imagine the pleasure of the near dwellers, who thus were saved the labour of journeying to the nearest watermill, maybe at some miles distant, to get their corn ground.

I do not give a detailed record of the gradual disappearance of the watermills mentioned in the Domesday Survey. That would be a tremendous task needing a volume to itself. A detailed account, however, is given of the various windmills dotted over our Kentish countryside since 1596, and this forms part of this book.

THE 39 WINDMILLS OF KENT IN 1596
From the Map prepared by Phil. Symonson, of Rochester

Acrise	Eastchurch	Nonington
Appledore	Eastry	Northbourne
,,	Frindsbury	Postling
Barham	Gravesend	Ramsgate
Bethersden	Grain, Isle of	Rolvenden
Bettshanger	Hartlip	Romney, Old
Birchington	Herne	,,
Brenzett	Lydd	Romney, New
Bridge	,,	St. Margaret's, Dover
Broadstairs	Mongeham	Selling
Chatham	Monkton	Shorne
Cobham	Minster, Sheppey	Warehorne
Deal	Minster, Thanet	Westerham

I have not reproduced J. Speed's map of 1610. It is found to record only twenty windmills as standing in the County of Kent, and one is led thereby to conclude that between the years 1596 and 1610 many of the earlier thirty-nine mills had disappeared. It seems hardly possible, however, that nineteen mills had dis-

WINDMILLS OF KENT, 1596

Reproduced from the map of Phil. Symonson, of Rochester, showing the 39 windmills.

See pages 32, 133, 134

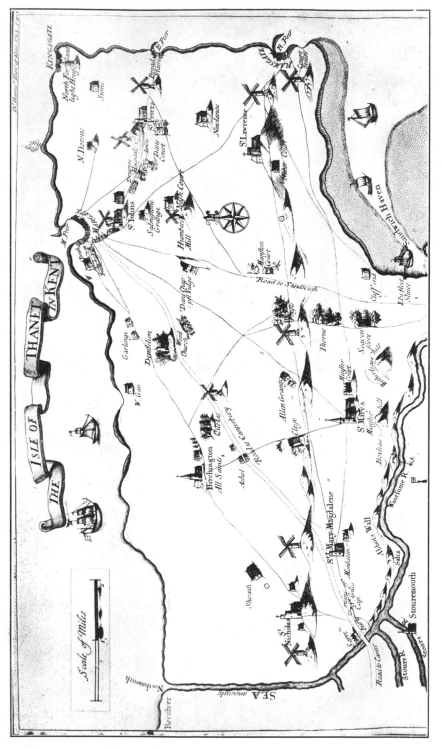

ISLE OF THANET IN KENT

Showing position of the 10 Post Mills standing in 1719.
(From Dr. Harris' *History of Kent*, MDCCXIX.)

See page 135

appeared in so short a period, and I incline to the opinion that in Speed's time a number were in such a state of decay and inefficiency that he decided to omit them. The list of the twenty mills noted in 1610 is here given.

THE 20 WINDMILLS OF KENT
From J. Speed's Map of 1610

Acrise	Frindsbury	Monkton
Bethersden	Grain, Isle of	Rolvenden
Birchington	Herne	Romney, Old
Brenzett	Lydd	Shorne
Broadstairs	,,	Snargate
Cobham	Minster, Sheppey	Westerham
Eastchurch	Minster, Thanet	

Robt. Morden's map of 1695 also is not reproduced here, but the following is a list of the twenty-three windmills noted thereon.

THE 23 WINDMILLS OF KENT
From Robt. Morden's Map of 1695

Badlesmere Lees	Denton	Mongeham, Great
Barham	Eastry	Monkton
Birchington	Elmley, Sheppey	Nonington
,,	Herne	Ringwould
Broadstairs, Reading St.	Margate	St. Margaret's, Dover
Chatham	,, Lydden	Sandwich
Chillenden	Minster, Sheppey	Woodnesborough
Deal	Minster, Thanet	

Dr. Harris's map of the Isle of Thanet, dated 1719, is of sufficient importance to merit reproduction here, for it appears to have been especially designed to show the ten post mills and their close proximity to the churches (facing p. 135).

THE 10 POST MILLS
From Dr. Harris's Map of the Isle of Thanet, 1719

Birchington	Margate, Lydden	Ramsgate
Broadstairs	Minster	,,
Margate	Monkton	St. Nicholas-at-Wade
,,		

Windmills in Kent were on the increase between 1695 and 1736, for E. Bowen's map of 1736 shows fifty-one as standing in the County. This map is not given here, but the list of mills will be considered important by the student.

THE 51 WINDMILLS OF KENT
From E. Bowen's Map of 1736

Acrise	Ash	Barham
Appledore	Badlesmere Lees	Bethersden

Biddenden
Birchington
Broadstairs
    ,,   Reading Street
Chatham
Chillenden
Cranbrook
Deal
Denton
Eastry
    ,,
Elmsted
Frindsbury
Frinsted
Goodnestone

Hartlip
Hastingleigh
Hawkhurst
    ,,
Herne
High Halden
Keston
Lyminge
Lynsted
Margate, Lydden
Mongeham, Great
Monkton
Nonington
Northbourne
St. Margaret's, Dover

Sandwich }a pair
    ,,
Selling
Shorne
Stansted
Stelling Minnis
    ,,
Stockbury
Tenterden
Throwley
Walmer
Whitstable
Wittersham
Woodnesborough
    ,,

Survey of 1769

The map facing p. 138 is the Ordnance Sheet (1903) on which have been marked, by black dots, the sites of the ninety-five windmills noted on the Survey Map of 1769—the earliest large-scale map of Kent, compiled by John Andrews, Andrew Dury and William Herbert, for King George III.

Here we find that over a period of thirty-three years since the publication of E. Bowen's map, the number of windmills had risen from fifty-one to ninety-five. It is not safe to assume that during the period forty-four fresh sites for forty-four new mills had been found but that, as in all preceding and succeeding times, there must have been replacement of those decayed or destroyed by accident. However, we are on sure ground here, both as to name and position of the existing mills. It is a wonderful map, drawn with great care, to a scale of two inches to the mile. It shows there was still a tendency to leave matters much as heretofore, that is, with the watermills to serve the watered areas, while the windmiller concentrates his activities near the coast, such as in Thanet,[1] and in other exposed positions.

THE 95 WINDMILLS OF KENT IN 1769

From the Earliest Large-Scale Map compiled by John Andrews, Andrew Dury and William Herbert, for King George III

Acrise
    ,,
Barfreston }a pair
    ,,
Bethersden
Bexley Heath
Bicknor

Bidborough
Biddenden
Birchington
    ,,
Blackheath
Boughton-under-Blean
Bredgar

Brenchley
Broadstairs
Bromley
Challock Lees
Chatham
Chelsfield
Chillenden

[1] Cobbett, in his *Rural Rides* refers to Thanet as "that spot so famous for corn."

Cliffe
Cranbrook
   ,,
Deal
   ,,
Denton
Eastry   } a pair
   ,,
Elham
   ,,   Bladbean
Elmsted, Stone Street
   ,,   Itinge
Eythorne, Upper
Folkestone
   ,,
Frindsbury
   ,,
Grain, Isle of
   ,,
Gravesend   } a pair
   ,,
Guilton, near Ash
Hartlip
Hawkhurst
Headcorn
Herne

High Halden
Hoo Common
Kennington Lees
Keston
Langdon, East
Lenham Heath
Lydd
   ,,
Lyminge
Meopham
Minster, Sheppey
Minster, Thanet
Monkton
Northbourne
Ramsgate
Richborough ⎤ "Salt
           ⎟ Pans"
   ,,   ⎨ at Stonar
           ⎦ (a pair)
Rochester,   ⎤
  St. Margaret's ⎬ a trio
   ,,   ⎟
   ,,   ⎦
Rolvenden
Romney, Old
   ,,

Romney, New
   ,,
Sandhurst
Sandwich
   ,,   } a pair
   ,,
Selling
Sheldwich
Shorne
Smarden
Stansted
Staplehurst
Stelling Minnis } a pair
   ,,
Stockbury
Tenterden
Tunbridge Wells
Warehorne
Wingham
Wittersham
Woodchurch
Woodnesborough
Woolwich
Worth

Survey of 1819-43

Between 1769 and the period covered by the Survey of 1819–43, the millwrights seem to have had a very busy time, for the number of windmills appears to have risen from ninety-five to two hundred and thirty-nine.

By comparing the map of 1819-43 (facing p. 139) with that of 1769 (facing p. 138) many changes are to be seen—old mills gone, new ones put up in fresh places. A considerable number are now present in Thanet and on the East Coast, also at Rochester and the adjacent towns, while in the Romney Marsh district many are absent. Generally in the Weald, and other parts watered by generous streams, the surviving watermills still hold sway. One notes the special attraction offered by the old Roman Road (Watling Street) and that the road stretching from the Metropolis to the coast is one long 'Windmill Way.'

It is an important map, for it shows that between 1819 and 1843, a short period of a quarter of a century, the milling industry of Kent was at the peak of its utility.

*   *   *   *   *

In connection with the Ordnance Survey maps of Kent, which have been of such great assistance in tracing the windmills of the county since early in the nineteenth century, it may interest readers studying the subject to know, from information supplied by the Ordnance Survey Office, that the original one-inch scale map of Kent was published in 1801 in four sheets. Series sheets numbered one to six were published between 1819 and 1843, but the details on these do not differ materially from the 1801 map. Subsequent editions of the one-inch map were based on the large scale survey of 1858-72, and revision surveys of 1893-97 and 1903-10, with minor corrections at subsequent dates.

"Most copies of the old one-inch scale maps extant have railways and dependent details inserted upon them to a date considerably later than that of the original survey, but these partial revisions were not concerned with such features as windmills."

*　　*　　*　　*　　*

THE 226 WINDMILLS OF KENT
From the Ordnance Survey Map of 1819–43

Acrise (Elham Mill)
Adisham (Bekesbourne Mill)
Appledore Heath
　　,,　　}a pair
Ash (Mount Ephraim Mill)
Bapchild
Barfreston
　　,,　　}a pair
Barham
　　,,　　(Black Mill)
Bearsted
Benenden
　　,,　　}(Beacon Mills—a pair)
Bethersden (White Mill)
Bexley Heath
Bidborough
Biddenden (Paul Sharpe's Mill)
　　,,　　(Town Mill)
Birchington
　　,,
　　,,
Blackheath
　　,,
Blean (Old Mill)
Bobbing, Key Street
Boughton Monchelsea, Haste Hill

Boughton-under-Blean
　　,,　　　}four, in a
　　,,　　　}　row
　　,,
Boxley, Pilgrim's Way
Brabourne
Bredgar (Dean's Hill Mill)
Brenchley
Brenzett
Bridge
　　,,
Broadstairs, Reading Street
　　,,　　}Clairmont House (a pair)
　　,,
Bromley, Bromley Hill
Canterbury (St. Martin's Mill)
　　,,　　(Black Mill)
　　,,　　(St. Lawrence Mill)
Challock Lees
Charing (Field Mill)
Chartham, Hatch Green
Chatham (Upberry Mill)
　　,,　　(Star Mill)
　　,,　　(Cherry Tree Hall Mill)
　　,,　　(Chalk-pit Hill)
　　,,　　　,,

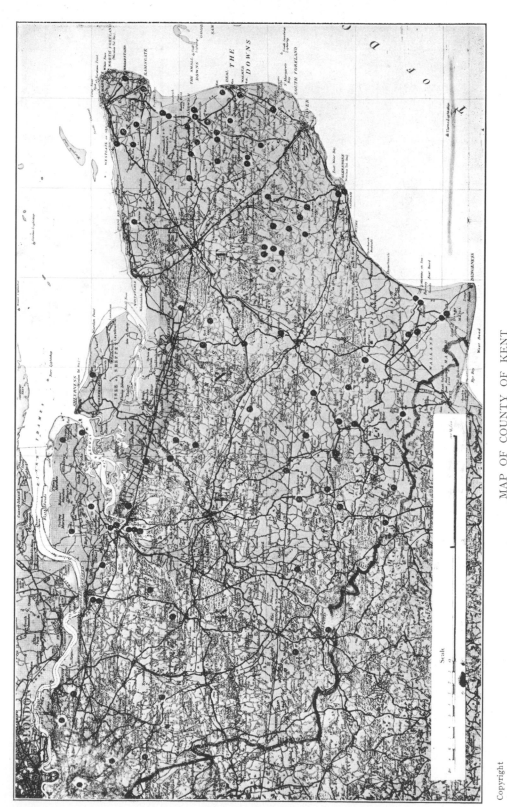

See page 136

MAP OF COUNTY OF KENT

Showing positions of 95 Windmills standing in 1769.

Facing page 138

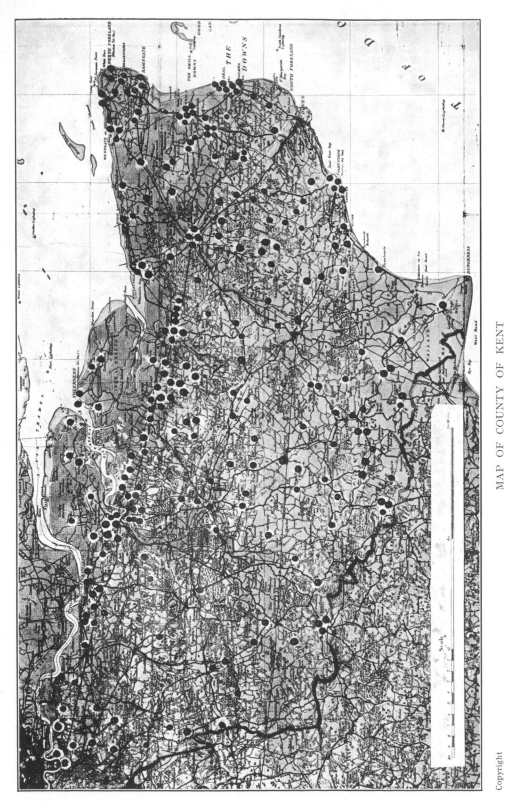

MAP OF COUNTY OF KENT

Showing positions of 239 Windmills standing in 1819-43.

Facing page 139

See pages 137-40

Chillenden
Chislehurst
Chislet
Cliffe (Dance's Mill)
Cranbrook (Union Mill)
Dartford (The Brent Mill)
Deal (Upper Deal Mill)
   ,,   (Wellington Mill)
   ,,   (North End Mill or Great
   Mill)
   ,,   (Lower Deal Mill)
   ,,   (Sandown Mill)
   ,,   (Walmer Road Mill)
Denton
Deptford, Black Horse Fields
   ,,   Windmill Lane
Downe, Gorringer's Farm
Eastry ⎫
   ,, ⎬ group of four
   ,, ⎭
   ,,
Elmsted (Itinge Mill)
   ,, ⎫ (Stone Street Mills)
   ,, ⎬
   ,, (Bodsham Green Mill)
Eltham, Mottingham
Erith, Northumberland Heath
Farleigh, East
Faversham, Forbes Road (Gravel
   Pit Mill)
   ,, (Hangman's Lane Mill)
Folkestone, Cheriton
   ,, (Folkestone Mill)
   ,, Millfield (Dawson's Mill)
Frindsbury ⎫ (Kimmins' Mills
   ,, ⎬ a pair)
   ,, ⎫ (Prospect Hill Mills
   ,, ⎬ a pair)
Gillingham ⎫ (Stedman's Mills)
   ,, ⎬
   ,, Mulberry Tree Place
Goudhurst (Town Mill)
Grain, Isle of
Gravesend, Windmill Hill
   ,, Denton ,,
Guilton, near Ash ⎫ a pair
   ,,   ,, ⎬
Harbledown
Hartlip

Hawkhurst, Tudor Hall
   ,, High Street
   ,, Gun Green
Hawkinge (The Old Mill)
Headcorn (Crow's Foot Mill or
   Black Mill)
Herne
Herne Bay (The Bay Mill)
Higham (Rose's Mill)
High Halden
Hildenborough (Watts Cross Mill)
Hoath (Fuller's Mill)
Hoo Common (Ballard's Mill)
Hythe
Ide Hill
Kennington
Keston
Kingsdown, near Sevenoaks
   ,,   ,,
Kippings Cross (Keys Green Mill)
Langdon, East (Martin Mill)
Lee, near London
Leeds (Brogden Mill)
Lenham (Town Mill)
   ,, Downs Court (Hill Mill)
Lenham Heath
Lydd
Lyminge
   ,,
Lynsted
   ,, (Union Mill)
   ,, (Champion's Mill)
Maidstone
Margate (Drapers' Mill)
   ,, Cliftonville ⎫ (Margate
   ,,   ,, ⎬ Mills—a
           ⎭ pair)
Meopham (Priestwood Mill)
Milton-next-Sittingbourne
   (Chalkwell Mill)
Milton Regis (Meade Mill)
Minster, Sheppey, Pigtail Corner
   ,,   ,,   ,,
Minster, Thanet ⎫ (Minster Mills—
   ,, ⎬ a pair)
Molash
Murston
Newington, Ramsgate
Newington, near Sittingbourne
Newnham
Nonington

Northbourne (Old Mill)
Northfleet
    ,,   } a pair
    ,,
    ,,   Perry Street (Fiveash Mill)
    ,,   Rosherville
Northwood (Thanet Mill)
Oare
Ospringe } Union House (a pair)
    ,,
Penenden Heath
Plumstead Common (The Old Mill)
Preston, next Faversham
Preston, near Wingham (Old Mill
    or Dunn's Mill)
    ,,   (New Mill or Solly's Mill)
Queenborough, Sheppey
Ramsgate } a pair
    ,,
Ringwould (Ripple Mill)
Rochester, St. Margaret's } a pair
    ,,   ,,
    ,,   (Friday's Mill)
Rodmersham Green
Rolvenden
Sandhurst, Boxhurst Farm
Sandwich
    ,,   } group of four
    ,,
    ,,
    ,,   } a pair
    ,,
Sarre
Selling (Shottenden Mill or Perry
    Wood Mill)
Sellinge (Stone Hill Mill)
Sevenoaks, Tubs Hill
    ,,   Hubbard Hill
Sheerness (The Little Mill)
Shorne
Sissinghurst (Crampton's Mill)

Sittingbourne
Smarden (West Mill, Town Mill or
    Cornes' Mill)
Southborough
Staplehurst
Stodmarsh
Stoke, Lower Stoke } a pair
    ,,   ,,
Strood, Broom Hill (Field's Mill)
    ,,   ,,   (Killick's Mill)
    ,,   (Strood Hill Mill)
Sutton Valence
Sydenham
Tenterden (Tenterden Mill)
    ,,   (Goods Hill Mill)
    ,,   (Ashbourne Mill)
    ,,   (Leigh Green Mill)
Tonbridge (Uridge's Mill)
Tonge
Tunbridge Wells (Calverley Mill)
    ,,   (Culverden Mill)
Ulcombe, Ulcombe Hill
Upchurch (Wakeley's Mill)
Warehorne
Westerham
Whitfield
Whitstable, Borstal Hill (Black
    Mill)
    ,,
    ,,   (Feakins' Mill)
Willesborough
Wittersham (Old Post Mill)
    ,,   (The Stocks Mill)
Woodchurch (Upper Mill)
Woolwich (The Co-operative Mill)
Wormshill } a pair
    ,,
Worth
Wrotham
Wye
Yalding, Rugmore Hill

SUPPLEMENTARY 13 MILLS FOR THE 1819–43 PERIOD

These mills have been traced on the 1829 Greenwood Map, but are not shown on the 1819–43
Ordnance Map. Added to the 226 mills listed for that map, a total is reached of 239 mills for
this period

Barming, Barming Heath
Cudham, Biggin Hill
Deal (½ mile S.W. of Sandown Castle, making a trio instead of a pair
    shown on the 1819-43 Ordnance Map.)

Dymchurch
Frittenden, Sinkhurst Green
Hythe, Stade Street (group of three mills)
Luddesdown
Lympne
Petham (Mill Downs Mill)
Sheerness (Ride's Mill)
Southfleet

In view of the fact that the middle of the nineteenth century saw the commencement of the 'Great Decline,' an effort was made to prepare a map showing the falling off in the number of windmills then standing in Kent, but I regret it has not been possible in the present book to give a full list of the mills existent between 1858 and 1872—the period covered by the second Ordnance Survey of the County. The maps for this period are now rare and the Director-General of Ordnance Survey regrets he could not lend his record sheets for inspection. The following list, therefore, is unavoidably incomplete.

SOME OF THE WINDMILLS OF KENT STANDING IN 1858-72

Acrise
Barfreston
Barham (Black Mill)
   ,,   (Breach Downs Mill)
Birchington (Hudson's Mill)
Bobbing, Key Street (Goord's Mill)
Bredgar (Dean's Hill Mill)
Brook, Spelder's Hill
Challock Lees
Charing Heath
Chatham, Luton (Manwaring's Mill)
Chilham, Lower Ensinge
Cranbrook (Cranbrook Common
    Mill)
   ,,   (Union Mill)
Eastling
Edenbridge
Faversham (Pumping Mill)
Gillingham (Friday's Mill)
Harbledown (The Old Black Mill)
Hartlip (Friday's Mill)
Kennington (Wind, Steam and
    Water Mill)
Kingston (Reed Mill)
Kippings Cross (Keys Green Mill)
Lenham (Town Mill)

Lydd (The Old Mill)
   ,,   (The New Mill)
Margate ⎱ (Drapers' Mills—three
  ,, ⎰   mills)
  ,,
  ,,   (Town Mill)
Petham (Chequers' Mill)
Ramsgate, Grange Road
   ,,   (Hereson Mill)
Rochester (Borstal Mill)
Sandhurst, Ringle Crouch Green
Sevenoaks, Tubs Hill
   ,,   Hubbard Hill
Swingfield (Old Mill)
Tenterden, near Church
   ,,   (Goods Hill Mill)
   ,,   (Ashbourne Mill)
   ,,   (Leigh Green Mill)
Throwley (Parsonage Mill)
   ,,   Clare's Forstal
Upchurch (Wakeley's Mill)
Waltham (Cloke's Mill)
   ,,   (Dilnot's Old Mill)
Wittersham (Old Post Mill)
Wye

THE WINDMILLS WORKING ABOUT 1900

From the records of his father's business, my friend Jack Holman has very kindly traced for me that the following 77 windmills of Kent were in use about the year 1900 :

Acrise
Adisham (Bekesbourne Mill)
Aldington
Ash (Mount Ephraim Mill)
Badlesmere (Boundgate Mill)
Barham (Black Mill)
Benenden (Beacon Mill)
Bethersden (White Mill)
Biddenden (Town Mill)
Blean (New Mill)
Boughton-under-Blean (Miles' Mill)
　　,,　　(Richardson's Mill)
Brenzett
Bridge
Charing Hill
Chatham (Star Mill)
Chillenden
Chislet
Cranbrook (Union Mill)
Deal (Upper Deal Mill)
Doddington
Eastry
　　,,
Egerton
Elham, Cullen's Hill
Faversham (Pumping Mill)
Folkestone, Cheriton (Ashley Mill)
Frittenden
Guilton
Guston (Swingate Mill)
Harbledown
Headcorn (White Mill)
Herne
Higham
High Halden
Hoath
Hougham, West
Kingsdown, near Sevenoaks
Kingston (Reed Mill)

Langdon, East (Martin Mill)
Lenham Heath
Lydd
Lyminge
Margate (Drapers')
Meopham Green
Newington, Ramsgate
Nonington
Northbourne (Old Mill)
　　,,　　(New Mill)
Petham (Chequers' Mill)
Pluckley
Preston, near Wingham
　　,,
Preston, next Faversham
Ringwould (Ripple Mill)
Rochester (Delce Mill)
Sandhurst
Sandwich (White Mill)
Sarre
Shepherdswell
Sissinghurst
Smarden
　　,,
Stelling Minnis (Davison's Mill)
Stanford
Staple
Sutton Valence
Swingfield (New Mill)
Throwley, Clare's Forstal
Upchurch
Uphill, near Folkestone
Willesborough
Wingham
Wittersham
　　,,
Worth
Woodchurch (Lower Mill)

KENT'S LATEST CORN MILLS

It will be of special interest to readers to know which was the very latest mill to be erected in Kent for corn grinding.

Swingfield claims the honour, for a splendid smock mill was

erected here in 1885 by Mr. William Holman, of Canterbury (see photograph reproduced facing p. 289).

It was built for Mr. William Prebble, to replace an older mill on the same site that had been demolished in a terrific gale during the previous year.

The New Mill (it soon became known by this title) was fitted with all the latest improvements, and was in every way a fine and well-equipped mill. Details of its history will be found on page 288, but it is sad to relate that the mill fell to the flames in August, 1911, due, it is thought, to an explosion in the engine-house adjoining the mill. The structure was burnt to the ground and thus, after a short life of twenty-six years, disappeared our latest Kentish corn mill.

The following mills are also among Kent's last mills to be erected. Particulars of all of these mills will be found in the Historical Notes :

Acrise (smock mill)	1878
Willesborough ,, ,, ...	1869
Blean ,, ,, ...	1868
Chillenden (the last post mill to be erected in the County)	1868
Rochester (Delce Mill) (smock mill)	1865
Lyminge (White Mill) ,, ,, ...	1860
Stanford (tower mill)	1857

In many instances our old windmills occupied the ancient sites of the long since vanished warning beacons of Elizabethan days, as at Gravesend, Frindsbury, Cranbrook, Hawkhurst, Mongeham, St. Margaret's (Dover), Postling, Appledore, Cox Heath, Hoo, Grain, Minster (Sheppey) and St. Peter's (Thanet).

Benenden Mill also was evidently built on the site of one of these ancient beacons, for the pair of mills that stood here in 1819 were noted on the Ordnance Map as Beacon Mills, and the hill on which the present derelict stands to-day is known as Beacon Hill.

There was a beacon, in days gone by, at Biddenden. Old maps show it as very close to the old post mill that once stood there, known as Paul Sharpe's Mill. The 1769 map shows the spot marked as "Mill-end Beacon."

The following list of windmills around the Kentish coast is taken from *The Pilots' Guide for the River Thames*, 1905. They are noted as being landmarks to guide mariners approaching the north, east, and south Kent coast from Gravesend to Dymchurch.

THE 31 WINDMILLS

Noted as being Guides to Mariners

Gravesend (Windmill Hill).
Minster, Sheppey (Pigtail Corner).
Hoo Common.
Faversham (Oare Mill).
Whitstable (Mill near coast line).
  ,, (Borstal Hill Mill).
Herne Mill.
Chislet Mill.
Birchington   } (a pair N. and S. of each other).
  ,,
  ,, (1 Naut. M., S.E. of Church).
Margate   } (a pair at Kingsgate, side by side E. and W., near coast).
  ,,
  ,, (a mill at New Town).
Minster, Thanet   } (a pair, "Thanet Mills," side by side, N.E. direction).
  ,,
Broadstairs   } (a pair, side by side, E. and W., near coast line).
  ,,
Sandwich (S. of Church).
  ,, (White Mill).
  ,, (Black Mill). (Direction N.E. of White Mill).
Northwood Mill.
Deal (Castle Mill).
Walmer Mill (doubtless Upper Deal Mill).
Ripple Mill.
Guston Mill.
Hythe (Lyntone Mill).
Dymchurch Mill.
New Romney Mill.
Lydd Mill.
  ,,   ,,

In some cases these prominent landmarks were of such value that the authorities made a grant to repair the mills in order that they should not be swept away. This is what happened in connection with Ripple Mill, Trinity House paying a substantial sum in 1895 to assist the owner to re-condition it.

Government sanction had to be obtained before an owner could remove or demolish any of these mills. Special permission had to be granted in connection with Dymchurch Mill, for instance, which had become so dilapidated and unsafe that the owner found it necessary to pull it down. At Lydd, similarly, the owner was anxious to obtain permission to clear away a derelict and

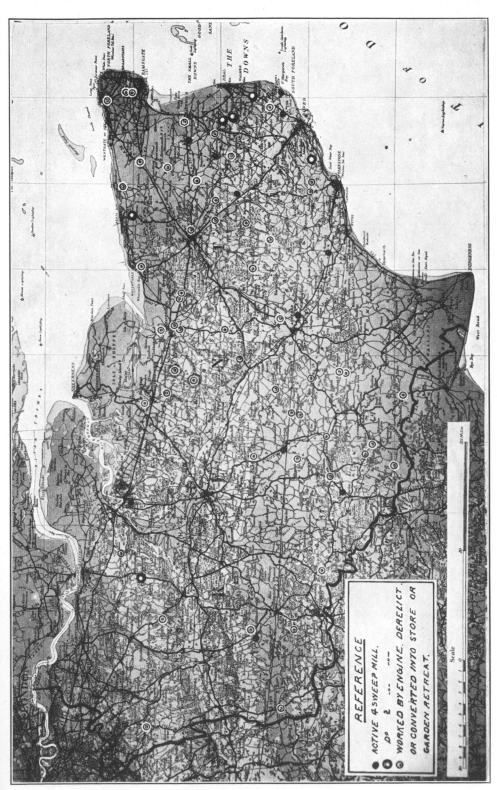

Copyright

MAP OF COUNTY OF KENT
The Windmills of 1930.

Showing positions of remaining 10 active Corn Mills with four sweeps ; 6 working with two sweeps only ; 1 New Mill for generating electricity ; and 53 others, worked by engine, derelict, or converted into dwelling, store, garden retreat, etc.

See page 147

Facing page 144

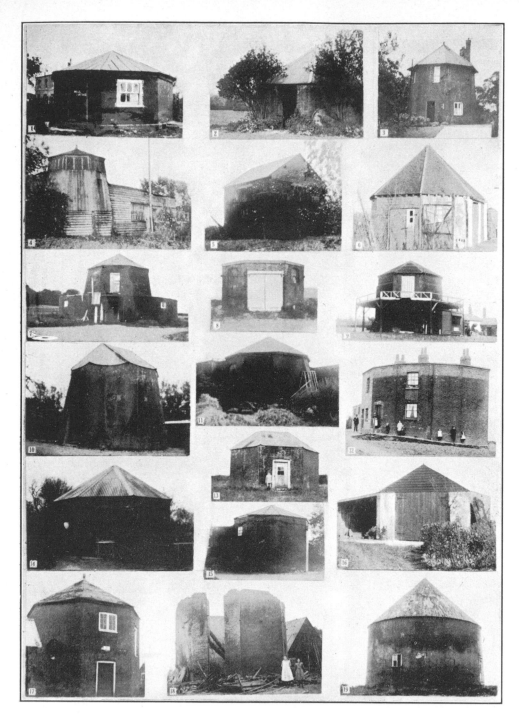

WINDMILL BASES ONLY

1. Blean. 2. Bluebell Hill. 3. Cobham. 4. Great Chart. 5. Egerton. 6. Staplehurst.
7. Higham. 8. Margate (Little Drapers'). 9. Lenham Heath. 10. Newchurch. 11. Wye.
12. Frindsbury (Great Mill). 13. Aldington. 14. Elmsted (Bodsham Green Mill). 15. Guilton.
16. Waltham (Cloke's Mill). 17. Appledore Heath. 18. Upchurch. 19. High Halden.

See page 150

useless mill, but in this case the mill caught fire and the matter was settled in quick time.

*   *   *   *   *

No map has been prepared showing the list of windmills standing during the period covered by the Ordnance Survey of 1903 to 1910, but the list I give provides a total of one hundred and thirty-four. A large number of these mills were then already derelict, of course, as can be seen by many of the pictures reproduced in this book, taken at that period.

By 1903 many of our windmills had ceased to make flour, and the old wood-heated ovens in the bakeries attached to many of them had already been destroyed. Already, did the baker's van from the near town call from house to house with 'Cottage,' 'Tin' and 'Coburg' loaves and fancy breads.

With the disappearance of the millers' ovens vanished also the old-time ovens in the dwellings of the farmer and agricultural worker. There was no stone-ground flour direct from the village mill with which to make and bake the wholesome wholemeal loaf.

THE 134 WINDMILLS OF KENT

From the Ordnance Survey Map of 1903–10

Acrise (Elham Mill)
Adisham (Bekesbourne Mill)
Aldington
Appledore Heath
  ,,
Ash (Mount Ephraim Mill)
Badlesmere (Boundgate Mill)
Barham (Black Mill)
Benenden (Beacon Mill)
Bethersden (White Mill)
  ,, (Black Mill)
Bidborough
Biddenden (Paul Sharpe's Mill)
  ,, (Town Mill)
Blean (Old Mill)
  ,, (New Mill)
Boughton-under-Blean (Miles' Mill)
  ,, (Richardson's Mill)
Bredgar (Dean's Hill Mill)
Bredhurst (Naylor's Mill)
Brenzett
Bridge

Broadstairs
Brook, Spelder's Hill
Canterbury (St. Martin's Mill)
Challock Lees
Charing (Field Mill)
Great Chart, near Ashford
Chatham (Star Mill)
Chillenden
Chislet
Cobham (Darnley's Mill)
Cranbrook (Union Mill)
Deal (Upper Deal Mill)
Doddington (Elvey's Mill or **Jarvis's** Mill)
Dymchurch
Eastling
Eastry } a pair
  ,,
Edenbridge
Egerton, Stone Hill
Elham, Cullen's Hill
Faversham (Pumping Mill)

K

Folkestone, Cheriton (Ashley Mill)
Frindsbury (Kimmins' Mill)
Frittenden, Sinkhurst Green
Guilton, near Ash
  ,,   ,,
Guston (Swingate Mill)
Harbledown (The Old Black Mill)
Hawkhurst, Four Throws (Nightin-
   gale's Mill)
Hawkinge (The Old Mill)
Headcorn (Crow's Foot Mill or Black
   Mill)
   ,,   (White Mill)
Herne
Higham (Rose's Mill)
High Halden
Hildenborough (Watts Cross Mill)
Hoath (Fuller's Mill)
Hoo Common (Ballard's Mill)
Hougham, West
Kennington (Wind, Steam and Water
   Mill)
Keston (Old Post Mill)
Kingsdown, near Sevenoaks
Kingsnorth
Kingston (Reed Mill)
Kippings Cross (Keys Green Mill)
Langdon, East (Martin Mill)
Lenham (Town Mill)
Lenham Heath
Lydd (The New Mill)
Lyminge (White Mill)
Lynsted (Champion's Mill)
Margate } Drapers' Mills—a pair
  ,,
Meopham, Meopham Green
Milton Regis (Meade Mill)
Newchurch
Newington, Ramsgate
Nonington
   ,,   (Seed Mill)
Northbourne (Old Mill)
   ,,   (New Mill)
Northwood (Thanet Mill)
Oare
Ospringe (Water Lane Mill)
Pluckley
Preston, next Faversham

Preston, near Wingham (Old Mill or
   Dunn's Mill)
   ,,   (New Mill or Solly's Mill)
Ramsgate, Grange Road
Ringwould (Ripple Mill)
Rochester (Delce Mill or Glover's Mill)
Rodmersham Green
Rolvenden
Romney, New
Ruckinge
Sandhurst, Ringle Crouch Green
Sandwich, N.W. of Town
   ,,   S.E. of Town
Sarre
Selling (Shottenden Mill or Perry
   Wood Mill)
Sellinge (Stone Hill Mill)
Shepherdswell, or Sibertswold
Shorne (Shorne Hill Mill)
Sissinghurst (Crampton's Mill)
Smarden (Town Mill, West Mill or
   Cornes' Mill)
   ,,   (East Mill or Black Mill)
Stanford
Staple, Barnsole
Staplehurst
Stelling Minnis (Brambleton Mill)
   ,,   (Davison's Mill)
Stoke, Lower Stoke
Sutton Valence
Swingfield (New Mill)
Tenterden (Ashbourne Mill)
   ,,   (Leigh Green Mill)
Throwley, Clare's Forstal
Ulcombe, Windmill Hill
Upchurch (Wakeley's Mill)
Uphill, near Folkestone
Waltham (Cloke's Mill)
   ,,   (Dilnot's Old Mill)
Whitfield
Whitstable, Borstal Hill (Black Mill)
Willesborough
Wingham, Wingham Well
Wittersham (Old Post Mill)
   ,,   (The Stocks Mill)
Woodchurch (Upper Mill)
   ,,   (Lower Mill or Great Mill)
Worth
Wye

We now come to the map and list of windmills standing in 1930. It shows that of the four hundred and four windmills known to have stood in Kent there now remain only seventy. This is a sorry enough spectacle but sorrier still the discovery, when we search them out, that there are but :

10 active corn mills with 4 sweeps,
6 active corn mills with 2 sweeps,
1 new mill for generating electricity (St. Margaret's Bay), and
53 mills not worked by wind. About a dozen of these are driven by oil or gas engine ; at least two (Hildenborough and Wittersham) are well preserved and stand in private gardens; two have been added to and converted into dwellings (Canterbury and Whitstable) ; a few are used for storage purposes or as garden retreats ; twenty-five have lost their sweeps entirely ; five have been completely decapitated ; all except half a dozen are sadly in need of repairs that will, alas! never be carried out ; and many, with tattered sweeps and decaying timbers, are absolutely abandoned, merely waiting for time and weather to effect their quietus.

One of the mills working with four sweeps—Stocks Green Mill, Leigh, near Hildenborough—is a recently re-erected specimen brought from Bexhill, and does not really belong to our Kentish veterans of the milling trade.

Thus we find that in 1930 there were only fifteen corn windmills working by the wind. Even some of these are in the first stages of decay and occupied almost wholly in grinding common grain for farm stock. They are hardly able to provide a living for the millers and their families, and certainly unable, in most cases, to afford repairs to the mills.

It is anticipated that the list on pp. 148-49 and the map facing p. 144 will prove of considerable value to those who wish to search out and have the satisfaction of seeing the remaining mills ere it be too late. I can assure them that, by relying on the list and map for guidance, much trouble will be saved and possibly many a fruitless journey avoided.

A list is also given of twenty-seven windmill bases that have remained after demolition of the main structures. In two or three cases these have been converted into dwellings but for the most part they are used as sheds and store rooms.

As will be seen from the list of active mills in 1930, the post mill at Mount Ephraim, Ash, built in 1735, is our oldest Kentish mill working to-day. It is complete with its four sweeps and is in splendid condition.

The next oldest is the early type of stageless smock mill,

Northbourne Old Mill, built about 1760, working to-day with two sweeps only.

The third oldest is Herne smock mill, working with two sweeps, built in 1781 on the site of an earlier mill that can be traced as far back as 1596.

For the oldest Kentish windmill of which anything remains to-day we must look among the derelicts, and the honour lies between Rolvenden and Shorne. Both these are of post type, doubtless very old, and might be the original mills that stood in in 1596 as noted on the Symonson map. Shorne is a mere fragment, sweepless and hardly recognisable as a windmill, the base having been built up with brickwork when the mill was converted into an observatory many years ago. Rolvenden, gaunt and quaint, is a fine old derelict, quite a favourite of mine. It looks as if it might have been an open-trestle mill, but it had a round-house at one time, which was unfortunately pulled to pieces for firewood during the Great War by soldiers stationed near.

Quite a number of our Kentish mills were used during the Great War as observation posts, men being stationed at them for signalling and other purposes. Acrise, Woodchurch, Kennington, Blean and Chislet mills are instances that come to mind.

The old post mill at Keston, built in 1716, is another quaint structure and must be counted among our oldest survivors; as also Smarden post mill, which to-day is in a very dilapidated condition. Its age is not known. It does not appear on earlier maps than 1769, although I understand there is a record extant regarding a dispute as to who should repair the round-house of a mill at Smarden in 1680. But it is not certain whether this referred to the present mill or an earlier one.

THE REMAINING ACTIVE WINDMILLS OF KENT, 1930
P.—Post Mill. S.—Smock Mill. T.—Tower Mill.

	Eleven mills working by wind with four sweeps.	Dates of Erection	Names of Millers
P.	Ash (Mount Ephraim Mill)	1735	J. Brockman
S.	Barham (Black Mill)..	1834	T. Denne & Sons
P.	Chillenden	1868	A. H. Laker
S.	Cranbrook (Union Mill)	1814	J. Russell
T.	Guston (Swingate Mill)	1849	Geo. Sheaff
S.	Headcorn (White Mill)	1819	Millen Bros.
S.	Leigh (Stocks Green Mill) (from Bexhill) ..	1928	A. W. Tomlinson
S.	Rochester (Delce Mill)	1865	W. J. Glover
S.	St. Margaret's Bay (generates electricity)..	1929	
T.	Stanford	1857	G. R. Holt
S.	Willesborough	1869	W. Manwaring

Six mills working by wind with two sweeps only.

S.	Herne	.. 1781	..	F. R. Wootton
S.	Hougham, West	.. 1802	..	E. H. Tanton
S.	Meopham Green	.. 1801	..	J. & W. Norton
S.	Northbourne (Old Mill)	.. c.1760	..	J. Court (for Lord Northbourne)
S.	,, (New Mill)	.. 1848	..	E.M. Fuller
S.	Ringwould (Ripple Mill) (from nr. Hawkinge) c.1820		..	Capt J. E. Monins

53 STANDING DERELICT OR CONVERTED
TO PURPOSES OTHER THAN THAT OF A WINDMILL

S. Adisham (Bekesbourne Mill)[1]
S. Badlesmere (Boundgate Mill)
S. Benenden (Beacon Mill)
S. Bethersden (White Mill)
T. Bidborough
S. Biddenden (Town Mill)
S. Boughton-under-Blean (Miles' Mill)

S. ,, (Richardson's Mill)
S. Bridge
T. Canterbury (St. Martin's Mill)
S. Charing (Field Mill)
S. Chislet
S. Doddington (Elvey's Mill or Jarvis's Mill)

S. Eastry
T. Edenbridge
T. Faversham (Pumping Mill)
P. Frittenden, Sinkhurst Green
S. Hawkinge (The Old Mill)
S. Hildenborough (Watts Cross Mill)
S. Kennington (Wind, Steam and Water Mill)

P. Keston (Old Post Mill)
S. Kingsdown, near Sevenoaks
T. Kingston (Reed Mill)
T. Kippings Cross (Keys Green Mill)
S. Langdon, East (Martin Mill)

S. Lynsted (Champion's Mill)
S. Margate (Drapers' Mill)
S. Milton Regis (Meade Mill)
S. Newington, Ramsgate
S. Nonington
T. Northwood (Thanet Mill)
T. Oare
S. Pluckley
S. Preston, next Faversham
S. Preston, near Wingham (Old Mill or Dunn's Mill)
T. Rodmersham Green
P. Rolvenden
S. Sandhurst, Ringle Crouch Green
S. Sandwich (White Mill)
S. Sarre
P. Shorne (Shorne Hill Mill)
S. Sissinghurst (Crampton's Mill)
P. Smarden (West Mill)
S. ,, (East Mill)
S. Stelling Minnis (Davison's Mill)
S. Sutton Valence
S. Uphill, near Folkestone[1]
S. Waltham (Cloke's Mill)[1]
S. Whitstable (Black Mill)
T. Wingham, Wingham Well
P. Wittersham (The Stocks Mill)
S. Woodchurch (Upper Mill)
S. ,, (Lower Mill)

[1] Since this list was compiled three of the fifty-three mills have disappeared—Adisham (Bekesbourne Mill), which was burnt down on August 29th, 1933 ; Uphill Mill, which was pulled down in May, 1931 ; and Waltham (Cloke's Mill), which collapsed on February 25th, 1931, and of which a base alone remains.

WINDMILL BASES ONLY, 1930

Aldington
Appledore Heath
Bethersden (Black Mill)
Blean (Old Mill)
Bluebell Hill, near Rochester
Great Chart, near Ashford
Cobham (Darnley's Mill)—now a
    dwelling
Egerton, Stone Hill
Elmsted (Bodsham Green Mill)
Erith, Northumberland Heath
Folkestone, Cheriton (Ashley Mill)
Frindsbury (Prospect Hill)—now
    cottages
Guilton, near Ash
Higham (Rose's Mill)
High Halden

Kingsnorth—base heightened and now
    a labourer's cottage
Lenham Heath
Margate (Little Drapers' Mill)
Newchurch
Plumstead Common (The Old Mill)
Ramsgate, Grange Road
Sheerness (The Great Mill or Ride's
    Mill)
    ,,   Marine Town (The 100-Acre
    Windmill)
Southfleet, Betsham
Staplehurst
Upchurch (Wakeley's Mill)
Wye

NOTE.—Since 1930 Waltham (Cloke's Mill) has joined the bases (see facing
p. 145).

MAP

1596 to 1930

The last map to place before the reader shows the sites of the four hundred and four windmills known to have been standing in Kent between 1596 and 1930 (facing p. 160).[1]

It clearly indicates how, from the small beginning in 1596, when but thirty-nine post mills could be counted, to the cessation of their construction in the middle of the nineteenth century, at least four hundred and four post, tower and smock mills have been accounted for, all of ingenious construction and very many of imposing and picturesque appearance.

---

[1] Since the completion of this map a further six mills have been traced, making a total of 410 windmills known to have stood in the County.

CHAPTER XI

HISTORICAL NOTES

In regard to mills at Blackheath, Charlton, Deptford, Eltham, Greenwich, Lee, Plumstead, Sydenham and Woolwich, it was wondered whether these should be included as Kentish mills. The following extract from a letter from A. J. Golding, Esq., Curator and Librarian of the Museum and Public Library, Maidstone, settles the matter :

These places were formerly in the County of Kent, and for Historical and Archaeological purposes we still recognise them as being in the County. Under the provisions of the Local Government Act, 1888, they are included in the County of London.

* Signifies that an illustration is given in the book (see list on pp. 16-20).

ACRISE

(NEAR CANTERBURY)

Elham Mill.* ¾ *mile W. of Acrise Church.* 1596, 1610, 1736, 1769, 1819–43, 1858–72, 1903–10.

Until about 1876 an old post mill, known as the Manor Mill, stood at the position above noted. It might have been the very same mill that is noted on Phil. Symonson's map of 1596 and J. Speed's map of 1610.

This old mill was taken over by Edward May in 1864. About twelve years later it was blown down in a high wind. On the day of the collapse, the weather being mild, it was left unattended, with the cloth sails spread on the sweeps, the mill facing south, when suddenly a heavy squall arose from the north-west. In this unexpected change in the wind the mill was caught broadside, and over she went.

To replace the old post mill a small smock mill was built in 1878 on the same site by John Hogben, a carpenter of Lyminge. There was no stage to the new mill—its sweeps came close to the ground. Two pairs of stones were fitted, and it is interesting to note that the iron windshaft came out of Herne Bay windmill, which was at that time being dismantled.

The mill withstood some terrible winds, one of the worst being on November 11th, 1891, when the full-rigged ship, the *Benvenue*, was wrecked off Sandgate. On that occasion it was impossible to stop the mill, the brake being powerless. Fortunately the gale did not last long, but at its height some of the shutters of the sweeps were blown off and carried a distance of three quarters of a mile, being found later in the stackyard at Wick Farm.

The mill was last worked in June, 1916, the tenant being James May, who had taken over from his father in 1888. Latterly no flour had been made. Its trade had been in grinding pig corn and poultry food. No auxiliary power had been installed in the mill—it had worked entirely by wind.

During the Great War the mill was used by troops as an observation post, a commanding view being obtained for miles around. It was also a favourite meeting-place for the East Kent Foxhounds.

The structure gradually fell into disrepair and was considered unsafe, owing to rotted timbers, and dangerous to the sheep that grazed around. It was, therefore, pulled down on July 6th, 1919, having stood for forty-one years. Nothing remains of the mill to-day.

Standing at one mile south of Elham Church, the early post mill, and, later, the smock mill, were sometimes known as Elham Mill. On the 1769 map it is referred to as Elham Down Mill, and as Elham Mill on the 1819-43 Ordnance Map.

7 furlongs SE. of Church. 1769.

This was evidently one of the old post mills of which no trace remains, and about which no information is available.

ADISHAM
(NEAR CANTERBURY)

*Bekesbourne Mill.** 1¼ *miles W. of Adisham Church. Standing to-day, derelict.*
1819–43, 1903–10.

Although this mill has been known for many years as Bekesbourne Mill, it is noted as Adisham Mill on the 1819–43 Ordnance Map.

The dilapidated structure that remains to-day looks as if it will not withstand many more wintry gales. It has a weakened cant post, causing it to lean over slightly, and one of its sweeps is stripped of framing and shuttering, as a result of the mill having been tail-winded in about 1922. The structure is infested with rats, the cant posts being full of rat holes. A portion of the weather-board has been torn away between the cant post and the door facing the road so that it is possible to enter the mill and examine the interior. The stones, two pairs of Peak and one pair of burr, and much of the machinery, are still intact. It is doubtless a very old mill— perhaps one of the earliest smock mills of the county.

After the mill was struck by lightning on June 28th, 1892, two new sweeps were supplied at a cost of £42 (a very reasonable price). Then, in about 1906, a new set of four sweeps was fitted as well as a new fan.

Edward Jarvis had the mill in 1878 and a succeeding tenant was George Sheaff. It was last worked by the owner, Mr. Ernest W. Baker.

I remember visiting this mill in 1905 in its working days, when apparently it was in good running order ; upon re-visiting it recently I found it difficult to reconcile the idle wreck with the once busy grinder.

(See also Addenda, p. 311)

ALDINGTON
(NEAR ASHFORD)

1 *mile* 1 *furlong W. of Church.** *A brick base remaining to-day.* 1903-10.

The mill at Aldington was badly in need of repair and considered unsafe. It was therefore pulled down in about 1910. Mr. George Jarvis, of Bethersden, undertook the work, and was given the material of which the mill consisted as payment for his work of demolition. The brick base was left and subsequently roofed over as a store, for which purpose it is used to-day.

Mr. George Prebble, who came to Aldington Mill from Newchurch in 1899, was the last to work the mill. Previous owners were T. Bills, a Mr. Gasston, Edward Marchant (1878), and, earlier still, B. Hobbs—the originator of the firm of auctioneers at Ashford, Messrs. W. & B. Hobbs—who was born in the Mill House at Aldington and later owned and worked the mill. Mr. Hobbs was a lover of horses, and it is said that the large buildings close by the mill, now a granary, were originally the stables for Mr. Hobbs' six horses.

The mill had three pairs of stones—two French burr and one Peak. All four sweeps were on the mill when demolished—they had stood still for about two years previously. When Mr. Jarvis took the mill down he transferred the sweeps to High Halden post mill and, later, when he demolished that mill the same sweeps were taken to the Lower Mill, Woodchurch, on which mill they are still to be seen.

Aldington Mill, like Pluckley and Biddenden, at one time had its fantail painted red, white and blue.

APPLEDORE

(NEAR ASHFORD)

Horne Place, 7 *furlongs NNE. of Church.* 1596, 1736.
Court Lodge 3 *furlongs SW. of Church.* 1596.
Appledore Heath (*two mills*)*, ½ *mile N. of Church. Base of one mill remains
    standing.* 1819-43, 1903-10.

I am indebted to Dr. F. W. Cock, of Appledore, for the following information respecting the mills at Appledore. The first two old mills he mentions are evidently those shown on the 1596 Symonson map.

There have been four windmills in this parish. The two earlier were 'Manor mills.' One, on the Mill Bank on the Court Lodge Estate, was taken down about 1790 ; the other, on the Mill Bank of Horne Place, was there in some part of the seventeenth century, because it is shown on maps of the period. Both these mills were post mills. In a document in my possession the Court Lodge mill is stated to be rented, in 1675, at £6 a year. The last man to be its tenant was William Monk, who died at the end of the eighteenth century.

The next mill was a large one on Appledore Heath. This had a fantail, and it was built in 1791. This date is on a stone still existing in the brick base which is now used as a store. The other mill was a post mill which originally stood on Rye Cliff at Playden, then brought here, then taken back to Rye and finally finished here, close to its larger neighbour. They were both dismantled about 1908-9, the process being a slow one.

William Packham, the miller at the time, issued a trade token in 1794. I believe it is the only one with a mill on it, and it is a very good specimen of the artistic series which came from Birmingham. Round the edge is, "Payable at W. Packhams, Appledore." It was also used by W. Friggles of Goudhurst.

The large smock mill was built by the 'Union of Appledore.' This Union was a club of farmers who combined together to build the mill, use it themselves, and let the public also use it at fixed rates for grinding.

The Union issued a notice offering a good reward for the capture and conviction of house-breakers, horse-thieves and such like. The Great Mill was broken into more than once, so they set a 'sack trap.' This consisted of filling up the passage from the door with empty sacks. Then a watch was set, each man being armed with several sacks. The next time the thieves came, as soon as they burst open the door, the watchers ran in and threw their armfuls of sacks on to the thieves and then, when these were struggling amongst the loose material, it was easy to secure them. On one occasion one of the Ransleys, of the celebrated smugglers' gang, was thus captured. On another, the miller pursued the thief and smote off the calf of his leg, so that he died from hemorrhage.

About 1876 Mr. Crux was the miller at the Great Mill, and Mr. Turner at the post mill. Two new midlings and a complete set of sweeps were fitted on the post mill by Messrs. Hill, the Ashford millwrights, in about 1876. Both mills were then in good working order.

An 1878 Kent Directory gives George Grist as the miller at Appledore.

ASH

(NEAR SANDWICH)

Mount Ephraim Mill. 3 *furlongs ESE. of Church. Still standing, working.*
    1769, 1819–43, 1903–10.

This is a fine specimen of an active post mill. It is the only windmill of early type at work in the county to-day. There *is* another active post mill, Chillenden, but that is comparatively a modern mill, being built as recently as 1868. Thus Mount Ephraim Mill claims distinction. Originally it stood at Ringleton, in the parish of Woodnesborough, and it is shown there on the 1769 large-scale map. It was moved to its present site, about half a mile distant, in 1818.

The mill has two cloth-covered sails, commons, and two shuttered sweeps. There are two pairs of stones, one an exceptionally large pair, being a 4 ft. 10 in. French burr ; the other, a 3 ft. 8 in. Peak. A new 36 ft. pitch pine midling was fitted in about 1926.

A unique piece of engineering in connection with this mill is the windshaft which is in two sections, being joined by a flange coupling.

The mill was built in 1735, and ran without an interval up to 1877, a continuity of different tenants ; then it was idle and neglected for two years, being purchased and restored in 1879–80 by Mr. Joseph Brockman who has owned and worked it ever since, keeping it in constant repair.

One of the earliest occupants and owners was Zachariah Hudson, great-grandfather to the head of the firm of that name now carrying on business at the Isle of Thanet Steam Flour Mills at Ramsgate.

3 furlongs ESE. of Ash Church. No map reference.

I learn from Mr. William Holman, an authority on Kentish mills, par-ticularly those in East Kent, that a windmill once stood on the edge of the sandpit behind the Red Lion Inn at Ash. In confirmation of this, Mr. J. Brockman writes that there was a companion mill to his mill at Mount Ephraim but that it was taken down prior to his coming to Ash in 1879. It was only used for grinding cattle corn, Mr. Brockman's mill being the flour mill. Both mills were worked by Zachariah Hudson and by successive owners of Mount Ephraim Mill.

¾ mile N. of Ash Church. 1736 map.

E. Bowen's map of 1736 plainly shows a windmill north-west of Knell Farm, at the position above noted. It is named Ash Mill, and is evidently one of the lost old post mills of the county.

ASHFORD

¼ mile W. of Parish Church.* No map reference.

The mill now standing derelict at Badlesmere, near Faversham, originally stood in Regent's Place, Ashford, and was removed in 1872 by Messrs. Hill, the millwrights. The Mill Cottage facing on to Regent's Place, is still standing.

I am indebted to "X. Willis" of the *Kentish Express* for the following note :

> The mill stood on rising ground at the rear of the Coach and Horses Inn and immediately behind the old Friends' Meeting House. It was occupied by a miller named Sharp, dismantled about 1872 and bought by a Mr. Matcham of Throwley, afterwards being put up at Badlesmere, where the remains are still to be seen.

Confirming "X. Willis's" statement, a directory of 1870 has the following entry :

> Stephen Sharp, miller, 1 Regent's Place, Ashford.

An old lady (Mrs. Nicholls) when recently celebrating her ninety-fourth birthday referred, among her reminiscences of the past, to "a fine old windmill standing in what is now known as Regent's Place." To her, times must indeed have changed at Ashford, for she says :

> There was no police station when I was a girl, but at the top of New Rents there was a small square building that we called 'The Cage,' where offenders were locked up.

It was a four-mile journey to get the *Kentish Express* which, when read, was passed all round the village. Mrs. Nicholls lives alone, does her own housework, attends the garden, reads much—often without the aid of glasses. She has seven children living, twenty grandchildren and ten great-grandchildren.

BADLESMERE
(NEAR FAVERSHAM)

Boundgate Mill.* 1¼ miles SSW. of Church. Standing to-day disused. 1903-10.

This must have been a conspicuous figure in the hey-day of its utility, being a tall smock mill, with two brick floors under the stage.

The sweeps were removed in about 1921, and the fan and stage have also gone.

(See also ASHFORD, page 155)

BADLESMERE LEES
(NEAR FAVERSHAM)

Approx. 1 mile SSW. of Badlesmere Church. 1695, 1736.

A windmill is shown at Badlesmere Lees on Robt. Morden's map of 1695 and E. Bowen's map of 1736. It was evidently a post mill and not succeeded by another mill, for one is not shown here on the 1769 and later maps. It is difficult to decide the actual position of the mill from the above maps, but it would appear to have been situated about a quarter of a mile to the north-west of the one now standing at Boundgate, and to the west of the main road to Faversham.

BAPCHILD
(NEAR SITTINGBOURNE)

½ mile E. of Church. 1819-43.

This mill is shown as standing at the junction of Watling Street (south side) with the road leading to 'Westons'. I have been able to glean nothing of its history. It must have been cleared away before 1865, for I understand from an elderly resident who knew the district well that it was not standing at that date.

BARFRESTON
(NEAR DOVER)

¼ mile NW. of Church.* 2 mills—1769, 1819–43. 1 mill—1858–72.

Two mills, a pair together, are shown on the 1769 and 1819–43 maps, but only one appears on the 1858–72 map. A correspondent writes :

> I have found a person who, seventy years ago, lived in the base of a mill which was converted into a cottage at Barfreston, and from information gleaned I think there was a smock mill there over eighty years ago (1852), said to have been pulled down because a plantation of trees grew and obstructed the wind.

BARHAM
(NEAR CANTERBURY)

Black Mill. * 5 *furlongs NNE. of Church. Standing to-day, active.* 1596, 1695, 1736, 1819–43, 1858–72, 1903–10.

There were probably two previous mills on the site of the present mill at Barham, as evidenced by the maps of 1596, 1695, 1736 and 1819–43. No mill is shown on the 1769 map, which seems to show that the earlier post mill of 1596 had vanished by then and that the mill shown on the 1819–43 map is a later mill which, in its turn, was cleared away and succeeded by the present mill, which was built in 1834.

This mill is known as Barham Downs Mill, or Black Mill—being covered by tarred sheeting. I took a picture about 1905, and on comparing it with one taken recently, I find the mill is so well preserved that there is no change in its appearance, despite the fact that it has weathered and worked through a further quarter of a century.

It was built by John Holman, of Canterbury, in a good wheat-growing district, and conveniently placed for deliveries to Dover, Deal, Canterbury and Folkestone. The present head of the firm of Holman's tells me that the mill was struck by lightning on the afternoon of Sunday, June 17th, 1878, when considerable damage was done, necessitating an expenditure of £150 in repairs. One sweep of the mill was rent asunder, shutters torn out and broken, and the ironwork damaged, weather-board sheeting ripped off, several of the quarters damaged, glass broken, doors wrenched from their hinges, and the brickwork of the foundations displaced. Mr. Holman further adds : "She is the finest mill in Kent and the hardest worker, driving four pairs of stones."

The sweeps were at one time of exceptional length, having a span of eighty feet. These were later shortened.

It is interesting to note that Henry Sturgess Pledge, who originated the steam milling business of that name at Ashford, began his milling career in Barham Mill about 1850, and later went to Kennington Mill.

The mill is at present owned and worked by Messrs. T. Denne & Sons, Ltd. Previously it was worked for half a century by R. Walter.

About 150 years ago a predecessor of the Black Mill was moved a short distance, as the following extract shows :

Dr. Stukely, in his *Itinerarium Curiosum*, says : "To Dover from Canterbury the Watling Street is still the common way ; it is left entire over Barham Down, with a high ridge strait pointing to Canterbury Cathedral tower ; as soon as it enters the Down it traverses a group of Celtic barrows, then leaves a small camp of Cæsar's ; farther on it has been inclosed through two fields, and levelled with ploughing ; then it passes a single barrow, whereon stood the mill, which is now removed higher up ; then it ascends the hill to a hedge corner, where are three barrows, a great one between two little ones, all inclosed with a double square entrenchment of no great bulk : I fancy them Roman, because parallel to, and close by, the Roman road."[1]

[1] *The Kentish Traveller's Companion,* 1787, p. 316.

½ *mile ESE. of Church.* 1819-43.

Although shown on the 1819–43 Ordnance Map, no information concerning this mill could be obtained at Barham, recent enquiries proving futile.

*Breach Downs Mill.** 5 *furlongs SSW. of Church.* 1858-72.

Breach Downs Mill, on Derringstone Hill, was of smock type, without a stage. The four sweeps last on the mill came from Herne Bay Mill in 1878. The mill could not, however, have worked for many years after that, for it was demolished about 1900 and had then been standing derelict for some years.

R. Walter, who ran Barham Black Mill for fifty years, began his milling career at this mill. John B. White bought the mill from Mr. Walter and worked it latterly. In about 1875 D. Baker occupied the mill.

¼ *mile WSW. of Church. No map reference.*

I have it on good authority that one of the Drapers' Mills at Margate came from Barham, having originally stood near where Barham Railway Station is now situated. The removal took place about 1869.

BARMING
(NEAR MAIDSTONE)

Barming Heath. 1 *mile NE. of Church.* 1829.

Although not shown on the one-inch scale Ordnance Map of 1819, a mill stood at the above position, near the site of the Asylum, early in the nineteenth century, as evidenced by Greenwood & Co.'s map of 1829. Four dwellings, named The Mill Cottages, stand to-day and are reminiscent of the mill.

By the courtesy of the Rev. W. C. Granville Sharp, M.A., the present Rector of Barming Parish, and Mrs. E. M. Carr, widow of the Rev. T. W. Carr (Rector of the Parish for forty-six years), I was privileged to examine a manuscript copied by the Rev. T. W. Carr from the original writings (an unpublished *History of Barming*) of a former Rector, the Rev. Mark Noble who, as the record indicates, commenced the compilation of the history of the Parish when he came to Barming in 1786.

The following is an extract from the account given of the windmill :

There being a general complaint of the impositions practised by the millers, many windmills were erected about 1800. Mr. Carter, tenant of Steed's house on the Heath, understanding the business of a miller, was desirous of building one. . . . Mr. Pope, of Hollingbourne, it is supposed, advanced the money. The Rev. Mark Noble, as Rector of the Parish, and Lord of the Manor of the Glebe Farm, was asked for his consent. His answer was that if the Hon. Philip Pusey would give leave he should. He therefore wrote, by Carter's desire, to Mr. Pusey, who, as the parishioners had wished it, complied. . . . The architect was Mr. Thos. Sweetlove, millwright of Sutton Valence. The expense was about £700. It was a convenience and an ornament. Mr. Pope died soon after it was built and Carter, becoming insolvent, sold his share. As if misfortune were to attend the undertaking on Mr. Pope, jun., the windmill, by the friction of the work, was set on fire, and in less than an hour was entirely consumed. . . . It was rebuilt in 1805, but in 1810 it was finally taken down, and the woodwork and machinery sent to be used somewhere near Rochester. The loss of its picturesqueness in the scenery must ever be deplored. There has been another windmill built upon the site and an house near it for the miller. The owner is Mr. Bennet, who resides in the house.

Unfortunately these old records do not trace the matter further.

By examination of the old deeds of the property, however, further light is thrown on the matter. One of the documents, dated August 26th, 1805, confirms that the windmill was rebuilt by Thomas Sweetlove, millwright of Maidstone, for Francis and George Pope. Reference is made to the mill as being "erected upon or near the site of the lately destroyed mill by fire."

In 1810 the mill was leased to Robt. Mace for a year. In 1833 Wm. Jefferys leased the mill to Stephen Bowles for one year. A document dated 1845 gives evidence of the mill's existence then, but one dated 1853 includes reference to "the site of a corn windmill and stables now pulled down."

In 1846 John Palmer granted John Beal Jude a fourteen years' lease of two mill cottages at £16 a year. As there is no mention of mill cottages in the earlier documents, it seems that they were non-existent at the time of the mill. It is believed that the windmill was demolished in 1846 and that the two cottages were erected on the site and named after it ; two more cottages were added some years later, making the four that stand to-day and still bear the name of Mill Cottages.

BEARSTED
(NEAR MAIDSTONE)

3 furlongs NW. of Church. 1819-43.

A directory of a century ago shows that Thomas Tuddenham was the miller at Bearsted. The windmill, of smock type, stood on a steep incline, almost opposite the position of Bearsted Station, a little to the left of the road (Sandy Lane) to Rose Acre, and a little way from the main road. The site to-day is part of a chestnut plantation.

From conversations with elderly residents I learn that the mill certainly disappeared prior to 1873—probably many years before that.

It has been suggested to me that a house, known as Sandy Mount, on the corner of Sandy Lane, might have originally been the Mill House, but I have no definite confirmation of this. On visiting the house, which is to-day a dairy farm, I learned that the present owners, a family by the name of Foster, have been here for forty-one years, but the only windmill they have heard of near the spot was a wind-pump erected by the late Dr. Adams many years ago to pump water for his house (now St. Faith's Girls' Home) which is very near the site of the mill. An inscription above Sandy Mount gives the date 1812.

BENENDEN
(NEAR CRANBROOK)

Beacon Mill. ¾ mile E. of Church. Standing to-day, disused. 2 mills—1819-43.
　1 mill—1903-10.*

Beacon Mill, on Beacon Hill, Benenden, is an octagonal smock and stage mill on a brick base, and is one of a pair of mills that stood together on the site, as indicated by the Ordnance Map of 1819-43. There is no trace to-day of the other mill and, except that local people have *heard* that there were once two mills, no definite confirmation can be given.

Mr. Walter Neve, of Cranbrook, writes :

> My father lived at the Beacon House from 1850 till 1855. I never heard him speak of there being two windmills there.

The mill now standing is known to have been worked by Thomas Collins (son of the Sandhurst miller) for some years, in the 1870's. It ceased work about 1921, Mr. Burgess being the last to use it. The sweeps were removed in March 1923 and the machinery disposed of. Two of the sweeps are now on Headcorn Mill. The other two were sold to Mr. J. Russell of Cranbrook but they did not prove suitable for erection on the Cranbrook Mill. There were three sets of stones and of these a 4 ft. French pair went to Cranbrook Mill.

East End. 2 miles 3 furlongs NE. of Church. No map reference.

The late Mr. William Warren, the millwright of Hawkhurst, well remembered a mill standing near where Benenden Sanatorium is now situated. To-day there remains a mound on which the mill stood and this is occupied by the Sanatorium's water tanks. A pair of cottages close by are still known as Windmill Cottages.

Further enquiries in the district elicit the fact that the mill was an old black post mill and was pulled down about 1870.

BETHERSDEN
(NEAR ASHFORD)

Old Post Mill. 3 furlongs E. of Church. 1596, 1610, 1736, 1769.

As evidenced by the above maps there was an old mill at Bethersden about the site of the White Mill that now stands derelict. It is believed that this old mill was moved to Biddenden, where it later became known as Paul Sharpe's Mill, and that the White Mill, of smock type, next described, was built in its stead.

White Mill. 3 furlongs E. of Church. Standing to-day, derelict. 1819-43,
　1903-10.*

This smock mill was built for the grandfather of Mr. J. T. Adams (the present owner of the mill), by the millwrights, Messrs. Hill of Ashford, at a

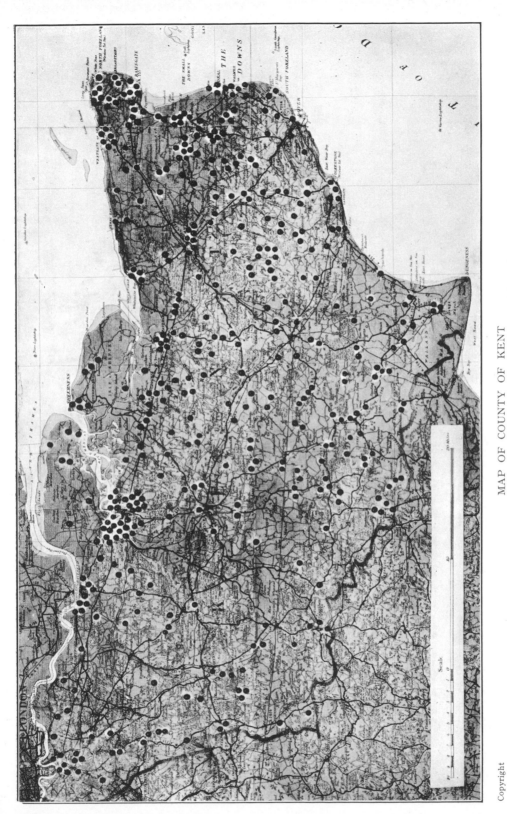

MAP OF COUNTY OF KENT

Showing sites of 404 Windmills known to have been standing between 1596 and 1930.

See page 150

Facing page 160

DARTFORD (The Brent Mill)   S. K. Keyes

See page 191

DEPTFORD (Grand Surrey Canal)
From *Reminiscences of Old Deptford*, by Thankful Sturdee.
See page 194

DEPTFORD (Tanner's Hill)
From *Reminiscences of Old Deptford*, by Thankful Sturdee.
See page 195

cost of £1200. It has always been in the Adams family, although tenanted by various millers, the chief of whom perhaps was James Wood who ran the mill for about thirty years, working it last in 1923.

The mill drove three pairs of stones. During the last two years of its milling career, it worked with only two sweeps, one having been blown down in a high wind in 1921, and the other removed. One of the corner posts was once rotted through, and Mr. George Jarvis undertook the work of cutting away the base of the post and replacing with about ten feet of new timber.

Practically all the 'tackle,' including the three sets of stones, is still intact in the mill, although the structure itself is rapidly decaying and gaps are appearing in the weather-beaten timbers. The floor boards do not provide a very sure foothold, and, mounting the rickety stairways, one's impression is that the mill will not stand many more wintry gales, that one day the whole fabric will be blown down.

(See also page 93)

Little Mill. ¼ mile NNE. of Church. No map reference.

Bethersden was the fourth home of a little timber-sawing windmill of six sweeps originally built by J. Padgham at Great Chart and the predecessor of a similar mill there, of which the base alone remains to-day. It was moved from Great Chart to Sandgate, being purchased by the builder, Mr. Brissenden. It worked there for many years but, as Sandgate grew, the mill was hemmed in by houses and it became impossible to use it satisfactorily.

It was then purchased for £20 by Mr. George Jarvis and removed to Bethersden, where it was re-erected near his carpenter's shop, to the rear of Boorman's Stores. Later he moved it to the other side of Bethersden village, where later the larger Black Mill was erected. It did further useful service there as a timber saw mill and was pulled down in about 1896.

(See also page 66)

Black Mill.* ¼ mile NNE. of Church. Portion of brick base alone remains.
1903-10.

This mill replaced the Little Mill at Bethersden. Until about 1886 it stood at Millfield, Folkestone, when it was moved to Bethersden and re-erected in Jarvis's sawmills. At Folkestone it had always been a corn grinding mill but at Bethersden it was used mainly for timber sawing. Occasionally it was hired for corn grinding by the miller at the White Mill, Bethersden, when he was extra busy at his own mill. At Bethersden the mill was tarred, hence its name ; but at Folkestone it had always been painted white.

After some years, wind power being variable and unreliable, a suction gas plant was installed. The sweeps were then discarded and later removed. The windshaft, which weighed 32 cwt., was made into a crane for lifting timber and is still in use at the sawmills.

The body of the mill remained intact for many years but gradually the upper portion was removed, the base built round and merged into the

L

other buildings in the timber yard. To-day only a small portion of the brick base of the actual mill remains.

It is worthy of note that Mr. Jarvis, when dismantling the mill at Folkestone, found that all the cant posts had been renewed at some time, which seems to indicate that the mill was not originally built at Millfield but rebuilt there, new cant posts being installed at the time of its re-erection.

(See also pp. 64 and 67; FOLKESTONE (Millfield), p. 205; and PENENDEN HEATH, p. 255).

BETTESHANGER
(NEAR DEAL)

NW. of Church. 1596.

The 1596 map is my only authority for this mill.

BEXLEY HEATH

May Place Mill. * 1¼ *miles N. of Bexley Church.* 1769, 1819-43.

This old post mill "stood in a field at the corner of Erith Road and May Place Road, close to the house known as Millfields, occupied by Miss Beadle."

The earliest reference I have traced of the mill is the 1769 large-scale map on which it is clearly drawn as at 1¼ miles north of Bexley Church. Hasted's map of 1778 also shows the mill.

The next reference is of 1787, for which date I have the following extract :

> When there is much dust, and the draught heavy for the horses, it is not unusual for travellers, soon after they enter upon the Heath, to bear rather to the north of the main road ; the windmill is the point of direction, as it lies very little to the left of the tract ; by pursuing which, they will likewise avoid one hill, and have the further satisfaction of passing thro' a shady lane that will lead them within a few yards distance of May-place.[1]

The Ordnance Survey Maps of the early nineteenth century show the mill. As early as 1830 it is known to have been in the possession of Mr. John Dann, for among the plans of Freehold Estates belonging to him, prepared by a Surveyor, Mr. W. Hubbard, is "a plan of the windmill land and premises situate at Bexley Heath in Crayford Parish, surveyed in 1830." I understand from Mr. Henry Dann, of Dartford, a descendant of the family, that Mr. John Dann, in his younger days, used to go to the top of the windmill to see how far his donkeys and horses had strayed on Bexley Heath !

Mr. Henry Dann writes :

> I do not think the mill was *built* by a Dann, as the first Dann who came to Bexley from Brookland in Romney Marsh, was born in 1757.

Mr. Harold A. Strickland, who was born at the Mill House in 1857, tells me that at that date his father, Mr. Samuel Strickland, was in occupation

[1] *The Kentish Traveller's Companion*, 1787, p. 35.

and had been so for a number of years, and that the mill was worked by him up till 1858, when the lease expired and he purchased another windmill, at Northumberland Heath, Erith, a little over a mile away, and removed his business there.

The mill was last owned by the late Mr. Stephen Cannon, the founder of the firm of Messrs. Cannon & Gaze, the large flour millers of Erith and Strood. For many years after he ceased to use it he kept it in excellent repair, as a mark of respect for the faithful service it had rendered him in starting him on his prosperous career.

The old structure was probably demolished about 1867.

BICKNOR
(NEAR SITTINGBOURNE)

½ *mile SSW. of Church.* 1769.

This is one of the long lost mills—probably an early post mill. It must have disappeared before 1865, for it is not remembered by elderly residents.

BIDBOROUGH
(NEAR TUNBRIDGE WELLS)

¼ *mile WNW. of Church.* Standing to-day, derelict.* 1769, 1819-43, 1903-10.

Bidborough Mill, in its prime, must have been a splendid specimen of a brick tower mill. The derelict, sweepless body of the mill remains to-day and is in a fair state of repair, although the cement facing of the brickwork has broken away in places.

During a storm about 1900 the mill was struck by lightning and two of the sweeps fell. This was the beginning of the end, for the mill worked no more. As with many of its contemporaries, there was not sufficient trade at the mill to justify the expense of replacing the sweeps or of carrying out any substantial repair. Thus, a little later, the remaining sweeps were removed, likewise the fan, and the body of the mill became neglected.

An 1878 Kent Directory states that George Wood was the miller at Bidborough at that date.

The mill was owned for many years by Mr. J. F. W. Deacon, D.L., J.P., a prominent landowner of the district, but has lately been acquired by Sir Thomas O. Callender, J.P., of Bidborough Court.

I understand that it had recently been proposed to sink a well at the mill, install water tanks in the tower and to use its height for the purpose of a wind pump. A similar undertaking has been carried out at Sandhurst Mill but in that case the wind pump has been erected alongside the mill as a separate structure, the mill itself being used only as a reservoir. In the case of Bidborough, however, the wind pump was to have been carried up through the interior of the mill and the wind fan affixed to the top of the tower, presumably replacing the present wooden cupola.

I believe the scheme had been abandoned, and it has been whispered locally that Sir Thomas O. Callender, instead, *may* see his way to restore the structure and renew the sweeps, so that once more a beautiful mill may here grace the landscape. It would be an expensive undertaking merely to satisfy artistic taste—although all true lovers of our windmills will hope that the splendid and generous thing will come to pass. Apart from making the village of Bidborough more attractive, the County of Kent badly needs a few generous, public-spirited folk to take a windmill 'under their wing,' so that at least a few of our Kentish mills may be preserved and handed down to posterity as specimens of a worthy and time-honoured industry.

BIDDENDEN
(NEAR ASHFORD)

*Beacon Hill Mill, or Paul Sharpe's Mill.** ¾ *mile S. of Church.* 1736, 1769, 1819-43, 1903-10.

This old post mill is believed to have replaced a previous mill on the same site, and to have originally stood at Bethersden, being the predecessor of the White Mill there, and moved to Biddenden when the White Mill was built early in the nineteenth century.

The mill's original name was Beacon Hill Mill, but it later became known as Paul Sharpe's Mill, after its occupier. It is reputed to have been the oldest mill in Kent, dating back to 1555. It was one of the now rare 'open trestle post mills' or 'tripod post mills.' Unfortunately nothing now remains of it, holes in the ground being all that denotes the site.

The mill was sold for demolition in 1912. There was some fine old oak in it and much of this was sawn up on the spot and made into a complete billiard room outfit—billiard table, chairs, etc.

Messrs. Hill of Ashford carried out some repairs to the mill in 1875 during the time Frederick Field was the tenant under the owner, Squire Schreiber. I understand that Mr. Field was the last miller to work the mill for corn grinding in 1882.

(See also page 72)

*Three Chimneys, Cherry Clack Mill.** 1½ *miles W. of Church. No map reference.*

On the road from Sissinghurst to Biddenden, after crossing the mill stream at Hammer Mill, the ground rises and, at the top of the hill on the left side of the road, is a disused sandpit. Just near this sandpit stood a windmill of the smock type.

The district is known as Three Chimneys, and elderly residents say that the mill was called Three Chimneys Mill, to distinguish it from Paul Sharpe's

Basil Schon

DEAL (Upper Deal Mill)

See page 192

C. W. Chitty

DEAL (North End or Great Mill)

See page 193

C. W. Chitty

DEAL (Sandown Mill)

See page 193

C. W. Chitty

DEAL (Wellington Mill)

See page 192

Facing page 164

EASTRY, 1905
The then two remaining mills of a group of four that once stood here.

EASTRY (The sole survivor)

See page 198

Mill and the Town Mill, the other two Biddenden mills. Cherry Clack Mill is, however, the name by which Warren, the millwright, knew it. It was run in conjunction with Hammer Mill (watermill) by Mr. Harris.

Nothing remains on the spot to denote a windmill ever stood there, for the structure was taken down in 1856 and removed, by wagon and team, to Punnetts Town, Heathfield, Sussex, where it was re-erected to replace a mill that had been burnt down.

The mill, now owned by Messrs. Dallaway Bros., still stands at Punnetts Town, and was working by wind till about 1927. Its sweeps have been removed and to-day it is worked by an oil engine.

Town Mill. 1 *furlong SSE. of Church. Standing to-day, derelict.* 1819-43, 1903-10.

Many years ago this mill was taken over from the West family by Charles Homewood, who worked it up to his death and willed it to Albert Dean. The latter did very little grinding at the mill and it was last worked in 1914.

It is perhaps one of the earliest smock mills built in Kent. Originally the sweeps reached to the ground but the mill was later raised on a two-storied brick base and a stage added. The base is now used as a dwelling by Mr. Dean but the structure of the mill proper is very dilapidated.

The cap is of uncommon shape and overhangs the body of the mill much more than is usual.

Warren, the Hawkhurst millwright, fitted a new fantail about 1907 and this is probably the fan that blew off in 1930. The fantail was at one time painted red, white and blue.

(See also page 92)

BIRCHINGTON

E. of Church. 1596, 1695, 1719.

A windmill, evidently of post type, is shown on the early maps above quoted but as these are of such small scale, it is only possible to give approximate positions for the earlier mills.

NE. of Church. 1610, 1695.

J. Speed's map of 1610 and Robt. Morden's map of 1695 show a mill at Dentdelion (Dandelion). No mill is shown here on later maps.

7 furlongs SE. of Church. 1736, 1769, 1819-43.

This mill was situated at the corner of Quex Park, marked as Queeks on the older maps. Bowen's 1736 map calls it Birchington Mill. No information is available regarding its history, unless, as local people suggest, it was moved and is the same mill as Hudson's Mill, described later.

1 furlong WNW. of Church. 1769.

This mill apparently stood near the coast, at ¼ mile north-east of Grove End.

3 furlongs N. of Church. 1819-43.

On the 1819-43 map this mill is noted as a Seed Mill. It evidently stood near the Railway Station. I have no particulars of it.

Hudson's Mill. 3 furlongs SW. of Church. 1819-43, 1858-72.

It is thought that this mill originally stood on the east side of Quex Park, Birchington, but was removed to the position above noted owing to the trees of the Park obstructing the wind.

It was a large smock mill raised, in about 1850, fifteen to twenty feet higher and staging added round it. There were five floors in addition to the increased storage accommodation in the base that resulted from the structure having been heightened. Three pairs of stones were worked by wind and latterly there were an additional two pairs of stones driven by steam.

The name of the mill is due to its having been in the Hudson family for about sixty years. Mr. Wilfred P. Hudson tells me that James Hudson came here in the '30's, his father, Zachariah Hudson (who had Mount Ephraim Mill, Ash, for many years) having bought this mill for him. James Hudson's son, Charles James Hudson (who was born at the mill), took it over from his father in 1873 and carried it on till 1891. During the later years of his occupation he introduced several roller mills, which were run in conjunction with the stones. A regular flour trade was maintained and the mill kept running, till 11 p.m. all the week, the flour being sold in the neighbouring towns of Margate, Broadstairs and Ramsgate. Later he purchased the Isle of Thanet Steam Flour Mills at Ramsgate, and this is the business that bears his name to-day—a large establishment equipped with all the modern machinery necessary for the present-day milling trade.

When C. J. Hudson left the Birchington Mill he sold it to James Fright, who let it for a short period to Stone & Roberts. Edwin Smith was, however, the last owner. The mill was unoccupied for a few years and finally pulled down about 1900. Nothing remains of it to-day; there is just the house and few outbuildings on the spot.

Various repairs were carried out at the mill by Messrs. Holman Bros. of Canterbury. Two new sweeps were fitted, in 1876, at a cost of £25; in 1879 a new silk dressing machine was installed, costing £75; in 1884 two midlings were replaced and in 1887 the tower of the mill was strengthened, evidently when James Fright purchased the mill. There is a record of a millwright working at the mill for five weeks in 1891, which seems to show that substantial repairs were carried out and that when the mill was demolished in about 1900 it could not have been a derelict.

BLACKHEATH[1]

(Four windmills).* Approx. 1 mile NNE. of Lewisham Church. 1 mill—1769 ; 2 mills—1819-43.

In connection with the mills at Blackheath I am indebted to Mr. H. Whitelocke, Chief Librarian of the Central Library at Lewisham, who has kindly referred me to Duncan's *History of the Borough of Lewisham* from which I take the following :

The most conspicuous objects on the Heath from the seventeenth century onwards must have been the windmills, of which four appear to have existed at one time or another. Of these the oldest was situated at the top of Lewisham Hill, where Holly Hedge House (the Territorial Force Headquarters) now stands. This mill is shown on maps of 1695 and 1745, and in the latter map another mill is shown a little to the west at the top of Morden Hill. This is the mill which is apparently shown in the picture entitled, *A View of Blackheath towards Lewisham,** engraved by J. Couse, who flourished about 1750. The mills are mentioned in the parish registers, entries occurring as follows :

Burials :   1716, Sept. 15. Mr. Thomas Baizdon, miller on Blackheath.
1729/30, March 2. Elizabeth, wife of James Marlow, from the Windmill, Blackheath.
1734, Aug. 1. Elizabeth Saxby, from the Windmill.
1737, Oct. 30. William Baizdon, miller from Blackheath.

Baptisms : 1738, Nov. 26.   Jane, daughter of John Lamer, from Blackheath Windmill.
1741, Nov. 29. John, son of Wm. Hubbert, from Windmill, Blackheath.

These two seem to have disappeared by the end of the century, and others were erected near the centre of the Heath, one where Mill House now stands, and another close by on the ground now occupied by Talbot Place. Of these two mills several drawings were made. The earliest in date was published by Carrington Bowles in 1770. It is entitled, *A View of a Windmill near Blackheath by Moonlight,** and is one of a series of six views of this neighbourhood, each bearing titles in English and French. There is a view showing both mills, etched by S. Prout, R.A., dated 1815.* Another view occurs in *Blackheath, a poem*, by Noble, published in 1810.* A sketch made by Sir John Gilbert shows both the mills (a copy of this is in the possession of Mr. H. T. Wood, of Hollington).[2]

I cannot trace any mill at Blackheath on later maps than that of the 1819-43 Ordnance Survey.

BLEAN

(NEAR CANTERBURY)

Glover's Mills.* ¼ mile W. of Church. One brick base remaining. Old Mill—1819-43, 1903-10. New Mill—1903-10.

---

[1] See note on page 151.
[2] *History of the Borough of Lewisham*, by Leland L. Duncan, M.V.O., F.S.A., Blackheath Press, 1908, p. 62.

The district in which the two Blean Mills stood has an unusual and high-sounding name—St. Cosmus and St. Damien in the Blean.

The Old Mill and the New Mill stood close to each other, about a hundred yards from the Peacock Inn, some distance down the lane to Tylerhill and Blean Halt, which leads off by the Clock Tower to the right of the main road from Canterbury to Whitstable.

The base of the Old Mill still stands. It has been roofed over and is now used as a playground by the children of the occupier of Mill House, to which it is adjacent. The children look upon the base of the mill as their own domain and one of them has chalked up the words "Mill Cottage" on the door.

Nothing remains above ground of the New Mill. The site, however, can be seen by a circular foundation of brickwork, level with the ground, over which pigs wallow.

Both mills were built by J. J. & T. R. Holman of Canterbury. The Old Mill is noted on the 1819-43 Ordnance Map, but the New Mill was not erected until 1868.

The mills were of the usual type of weather-boarded smock, with brick base and a stage ; both had tarred caps and bodies but white fantail and sweeps.

It is stated locally that the Old Mill originally stood on St. Martin's Hill, Canterbury and was re-erected at Blean for Thomas Glover. This is not strictly correct. When the Black Mill on St. Martin's Hill, Canterbury, was pulled down in 1868, the sweeps, windshaft and some of the machinery were utilised in the building of the New Mill at Blean. Thomas Glover had owned and worked the Old Mill for many years and apparently had worked up such a good business at Blean that he needed another windmill to cope with the work. Thus the New Mill was built.

There was no auxiliary power of any kind installed in either mill. They worked entirely by wind.

William K. Glover succeeded his father at the mills. Later owners were : C. T. Stanley, Wallis & Field, and Charles Phillips. Both mills were still in working order when Mr. Phillips came into possession.

In conjunction with the milling trade there was a bakery, the baking being carried on in part of the Mill House. This side of the business, however, was transferred to Canterbury by Mr. Phillips.

The Old Mill was the first to be pulled down, but demolition was gradual. Both retained their sweeps to the last, although somewhat dilapidated. It is known definitely that the New Mill was standing in more or less complete order in 1922 (when I understand it was last worked). It was sold and pulled down in 1924 in order to make use of the iron and brass from it. The mill was not really in a bad condition. "Trade was gone"—that sealed the fate of this mill as of many others.

I understand the New Mill was used as an observation post by the military during the Great War.

BLUEBELL HILL

(NEAR ROCHESTER)

1 furlong E. of Upper Bell Inn.* Base alone remains. 1833 Froggett map.

This mill stood off the Rochester-Maidstone road, on the crest of the Downs, overlooking Maidstone and the Weald of Kent, one of the grandest views of the county.

The mill had been idle for many years and was a sad derelict. As it stood about 600 feet above sea level, it is little wonder that an easterly gale in July 1890, catching the mill 'tail-winded,' completely destroyed it. The brick base alone remained and this was converted into a shed for cattle. It stands fulfilling the same useful purpose to-day, save that the briars and brambles are creeping over the old mill-stones, covering with a tender cloak of green the wreckage caused by the gale of forty years ago. The weather-worn Miller's Cottage still tells the traveller that here the miller of Bluebell Mill lived.

Walter Skinner (who came from the Star Mill, Chatham) was the miller here in 1879 and was probably the last to work it. Previously it was held by Mr. Kingsnorth for many years. It was a smock and stage mill, working two pairs of stones and driven by gearing beneath them, known as 'under-drift.' A milling friend tells me the mill was fitted with very good machinery.

BOBBING

(NEAR SITTINGBOURNE)

Key Street, Goord's Mill. 5 furlongs SW. of Church. 1819-43, 1858-72.

Gore Hill, at the junction of Watling Street and the road to Bobbing, was the situation of this mill—a black smock mill, with two floors of brickwork under the stage. At one time it was kept in splendid repair. There were three pairs of stones. The miller was Henry Goord, preceded by John Goord.

The mill was pulled down about 1902, when a pair of Peak stones went to the Great Mill at Sheerness to replace a pair bought some years previously from Borstal Mill, Rochester.

George Ride, who later had the Great Mill at Sheerness, came here to work under Mr. Goord in about 1857. It was his first place after learning his trade with his brother at Sheerness.

It is very interesting to note that Mr. Goord also owned a Tide Mill at Milton-next-Sittingbourne, and a son of Mr. Ride recalls that his father used to have to go to the Tide Mill when the wind was not favourable to work the Key Street Mill.

BOUGHTON MONCHELSEA

(NEAR MAIDSTONE)

Haste Hill. 7 furlongs NNW. of Church. 1819-43.

The present Haste Hill House was built in 1864 on or about the site of a smock windmill that was destroyed by fire in 1858.

The mill was worked by the Day family for many years, David Day, who lived to the age of 86, being the last to use it. He lived in the one-storied Mill House, which still stands, and is known by the name of Haste Hill Cottage. Mr. T. Gates, aged 65, the gardener at Haste Hill House, lives there to-day. He has lived at Boughton Monchelsea for forty-three years and used to work for Mr. Day, although of course the mill was not standing at that time.

At the back door of the cottage is one of the old mill-stones, worn so smooth that there is hardly a mark of a furrow on it. Another stone, in better condition, is to be seen at the side door of Haste Hill House. Except for these stones, not a vestige remains of the old mill.

BOUGHTON-UNDER-BLEAN

(NEAR FAVERSHAM)

7 furlongs NE. of Church. 2 mills—1819-43.

Four windmills are shown, almost in a line, on the 1819-43 map. Of the above two I have little to say, except that Mrs. Miles, now 83 years of age, remembers one of them and says it stood at the north end of the street, in Bounds Lane, and was known, because of its being tarred, as the Black Mill. The other mill must have disappeared before living memory.

Miles' Mill.* 7 furlongs NE. of Church. Standing to-day, idle. 1819-43, 1903-10.

Boughton-Blean Mill, or Miles' Mill, is believed to be about 140 years old and is a fine mill of five storeys, with a stout body and an exceptionally large cap. It is considered to be the broadest mill in Kent.

It ran three pairs of 4 ft. 6 in. stones—two French burr and one Derby Peak. The sweeps and fan were taken down in 1929. I understand, however, that they were then in good condition and were stored, so that should a miller take over the mill (it was then for sale), they could be replaced.

For five years, up till March 1931, when the mill was closed down, it was worked by a 15 h.p. Blackstone engine. For some years prior to that, steam had been an auxiliary power at the mill.

*Richardson's Mill.** 7 furlongs NE of Church. Standing to-day, derelict.* 1769, 1819-43, 1903-10.

The weather-boarded tower is all that remains to-day of the mill in Bull Lane, Boughton, and the base is used as a garage. It was known as Richardson's Mill, after I. K. Richardson who worked it for many years.

It is understood that the mill had to be closed down through lack of money to carry out the necessary repairs. The mill-stones were removed to Miles' Mill. This lightened the mill considerably and a story has it that in a certain storm, the weight being gone, the brake would not hold the sweeps against the gale, and they began to race uncontrolled. Had it not been for the resourcefulness of the miller, who thrust a steel bar into the gearing and checked the runaway sweeps, the mill would have fired, so great was the speed at which she was running. A miller friend to whom I related the incident made the comment, "Very unlikely—not a miller's tale!"

The mill was of very low gear and its fast revolving sails must have been a pretty sight, especially when working in conjunction with the other three mills that at one time stood near by.

It was one of the few mills in Kent that had a 'bee-hive' cap—which was removed in 1925.

BOXLEY
(NEAR MAIDSTONE)

The Pilgrim's Way. ½ *mile NNW. of Church.* 1819-43.

The site of this mill was close to the steep escarpment of the North Downs, near Boxley Hill, on the borders of that ancient British trackway now known as The Pilgrim's Way. As a lover of the old Way, I can conjure up a picture of the white sails of a windmill revolving and bickering in the sunlight against a background dark with yew trees.

I doubt if many are aware of this site of a vanished mill. Half a century ago, as a youth, I and my companions haunted every hill and glade of that section of the Way, searching for the first violet and the first bird's nest ; for glow-worms, efts and snakes ; at the season's end, for the wild fruits that abound there ; but never a fragment of an old windmill or portion of a mill-stone came before our prying eyes.

The 1819-43 map, however, is indisputable evidence that early in the nineteenth century a windmill stood there, to grind corn for those who lived in the surrounding scattered dwellings.

(See also Addenda, page 311)

BRABOURNE
(NEAR ASHFORD)

1 *mile SW. of Church.* 1819-43.

This smock mill stood near the Tile Works at Brabourne Lees, in a good position for the wind. It was last worked about 1870. Alfred Mummery had worked it for a short time about 1867, and Charles Hancock (a son of Charles Hancock who owned Harbledown Mill) also had some slight connection with it. Mr. Hancock came to Brabourne from Shorne Mill, near Gravesend, and purchased East Brabourne watermill and lived there until 1881. It is believed that he had the Brabourne windmill for a short time but he was not the owner. At any rate, it is known that he decided to build a windmill for himself in the meadow belonging to the watermill, in order to deal with the flour milling trade he was working up. The mill, a very small one with a narrow base, was built but, not having a sound enough foundation and unskilled labour having been used, it was in danger from the first. It stood only a few years and no trace remained of it in 1883. The structure, as a windmill, was almost an abortion and cannot therefore be seriously considered as a Kentish mill.

The original Brabourne windmill at Brabourne Lees was burnt down about 1871. The Mill House still stands near the site.

BREDGAR
(NEAR SITTINGBOURNE)

*Dean's Hill Mill.** 1 *mile WNW. of Church.* 1769, 1819-43, 1858-72, 1903-10.

When I visited this mill in 1909 it was standing in a state of ruin. The sweeps and fan were already gone and the elements had perhaps worked this preliminary destruction but it was the handiwork of man which had started the demolition of the mill-cap and body. The fact is, it was required for fire-wood. This part of the transaction was going on in a most business-like way at the time of my visit. A typical British tar was on the job and there appeared to be no half-measures about him. He had so far stripped the outside boarding that much of the interior of the mill could be seen intact. At the time, I wrote :

> I fear I am giving away family secrets but I gleaned he was courting the miller's daughter ; and also that the firewood somehow formed part of the matrimonial bargains. I presumed from what I saw, that while on furlough this amorous tar divided his energies between courting and (with true nautical interest) looking out for rough weather by providing against it by pulling down and storing this grand old windmill ; truly a herculean task for even an energetic lover single-handed.
> I trust there was no slip between the cup and the lip, and that our sturdy son of the sea got both the bride and the firewood, and that the former truly cheered him and the latter warmed both through the next and subsequent winters.
> Should this meet their eyes, I hope they will deal leniently with the person who did not confine his attention exclusively to photographing the fine old mill but gathered up a few stray threads of what was happening sympathetically, as well as practically, in connection with this old mill.

In 1878 the miller was William Moore. Prior to his occupation, James Wiles, a farmer, was the owner and miller. It is said that Mr. Wiles did not believe in night work ! But it is also said that the hours of duty for his workmen were from six a.m. till ten p.m. and often, if the wind was still favourable as it neared ten o'clock, he would tell his men to carry on until he

CHARING (Field Mill)

W.C.F.

DOVER (Buckland)

See page 179

See page 196

W.C.F.

Lambert Weston & Son, Ltd., Folkestone

(?) FOLKESTONE (Old Mill)

FOLKESTONE (Dawson's Mill, Millfield)
Removed to Bethersden in 1885 (see Black Mill)

See page 205

G. E. Ride

Facing page 172

W.C.F.

FOLKESTONE (ASHLEY MILL, CHERITON)

W. Martin

See page 204

told them to stop. He himself would then return to the Mill House, dose in a comfy chair and awake *with much surprise* to find it was two o'clock or more, and then hurry into the mill to express his earnest regret at having lost count of time. He did not think to tell his men not to come into the mill and start work again until later in the day, to make up for lost sleep. Although they did not leave the mill until after two o'clock they would be back again at six, ready for another long day's grind.

Dean's Hill Mill was quite a small mill, without a stage. It worked four 'patent' sweeps and two pairs of stones, with the usual flour dressing machine. An unusual thing about the mill is that it had sunk a little to one side, low enough to put the spur wheel out of gear of the stones. To overcome the difficulty a shaft was carried down to the stone floor and the stones driven 'underdrift.'

BREDHURST
(NEAR CHATHAM)

Dunn Street, Naylor's Mill.* ½ mile SW. of Church. 1903-10.

Mr. George Naylor, who lives at the Mill House at Bredhurst, tells me that it is quite half a century since this old mill was in use as a windmill. During that time it was used as a store, for the most part sweepless.

The mill was in a sorry condition when first I visited it in 1905, sweepless, fanless, and the body and cap falling to pieces. I am not surprised to learn that the old mill had become so shaky that had it not been pulled over by a wire rope in or about 1914, it would very soon have tumbled down of its own accord.

It was a smock mill, on a brick base, with a stage, working two pairs of stones. John Wyles was the miller as far back as 1845 and, later (1860) a Mr. Boucher.

BRENCHLEY
(NEAR PADDOCK WOOD)

¼ mile N. of Church.* 1769, 1819-43.

An old post mill at one time stood on Pixett Hill, Brenchley, and the Vicar of Brenchley, the Rev. Percy S. Whelan, M.A., writes about it as follows :

I called on the oldest man in this village, by name Walter Fairman, who lives on Hill Top.[1] He tells me that seventy or eighty years ago he used to work the old mill that was then going strong. He is now ninety-six years of age. He says that he often used to have to get out of his bed at an unearthly hour in order to get a move on in the mill. As far as Fairman knows, the old mill was always there !

Mr. T. Else, of Paddock Wood, also writes :

My father occupied the Brenchley Mill about 1840 and I believe hired it from Mr. E. Clemetson of Goudhurst. It was pulled down soon after that date, but the old Mill House is still standing (half timber built) and in part of this Fairman is living.

[1] Mr. Fairman passed away in May, 1933.

who, you say, worked in the mill. He was a postman when I was a boy at Brenchley in 1865, walking with letters daily to Paddock Wood.

The hill from Brenchley village is still called "Windmill Hill" and I remember an inn close by called Windmill Inn, now a cottage.

My father has told me that from the upper stage of the mill he could see the sea at Hythe and that it was a 'sea mark.' It could also be seen all down the railway line from Tonbridge to Ashford, as this hill stands about 350 feet above the Wealden plain.

Mr. E. Clemetson, of Hope Mill (watermill) Goudhurst, tells me that his grandfather came to Goudhurst from Brenchley in 1837.

BRENZETT
(NEAR ASHFORD)

*3 furlongs SW. of Church.** 1596, 1610, 1819-43, 1903-10.

The post mill that stood at Brenzett Corner, on the New Romney road, was taken down, for its timber, on February 5th, 1925. It had not been idle long, for it was working in 1924. It was built in 1776 and replaced an earlier post mill which is shown on the maps of 1596 and 1610. It worked two pairs of stones.

It was a fine specimen when I visited it in 1905 and in working order.

In the 1870's it was owned by Thomas Nash, later by a Mr. Small, from whom it was hired and worked by George Nash who last used it.

In connection with this mill Dr. F. W. Cock, of Appledore, writes :

The Brenzett post mill was used to within a little of its demolition for grinding hog meal and such like material. I believe the last time it ground wheat was about 1897 or 1898 when my uncle, the late Edwin Cock, sent a couple of bushels to be made into flour.

The model of a cockerel, perched on top of the mill, did duty as a weather-vane right up to the time the mill was pulled down.

BRIDGE
(NEAR CANTERBURY)

¼ *mile E. of Church.* 1596, 1719, 1829.

There must have been one of the old post mills at Bridge, for Symonson shows one east of the Church on his 1596 map.

Dr. Harris also gives a mill at this spot on his County Map of 1719 but no mill is shown on the 1769 map.

The mill shown on a map dated 1829, accompanying *Paterson's Roads*, is probably a smock mill that replaced the mill of earlier type.

*3 furlongs NW. of Church.** *Standing to-day, derelict.* 1819-43, 1903-10.

This is quite a small smock mill and used to work two pairs of stones. It is quite a derelict now ; only the midlings of two of its sweeps remain, and it has lost its fan. It was run from 1900 to 1907 by Mr. William Manwaring, who now owns Willesborough Mill. Mr. Manwaring had a Blackstone oil engine installed in an outside store, to run another pair of stones.

Mr. Jack Holman tells me that in 1879 the mill was taken over from George Fryer by Messrs. Johnson (who had at one time the Barton watermills at Canterbury). In 1880 the mill changed hands again, a Mr. White succeeding Messrs. Johnson.

(See also Addenda, page 313)

BROADSTAIRS

Reading Street, St. Peter's Mill. ¾ *mile NNE. of St. Peter's Church.* 1695, 1736, 1819-43.

I cannot say whether this mill, noted on the 1819-43 map, is the same as that shown on the 1695 and 1736 maps. The 1736 map calls it St. Peter's Mill. There is no mill shown on the 1769 large-scale map.

¾ *mile SE. of St. Peter's Church.* 1 *mill*—1596, 1610, 1719, 1736, 1769; 2 *mills*—1819-43 ; 1 *mill*—1903-10.

There was a mill at about this position as far back as 1596, as evidenced by Symonson's map. It is also shown by J. Speed in 1610. E. Bowen's map of 1736 shows it clearly as situated just north-east of Upton, and he calls it Broadstairs Mill. It appears again on the 1769 map. The 1819-43 map however, gives *two* mills together, and the words 'Clairmont House' marked close by.

The mill that stood latterly and is noted on the 1903-10 map is remembered by Messrs. Holman Bros. as being a smock mill that used to belong to Mr. Goodson of Upton. Mr. T. R. Holman fitted a new brakewheel in 1881 at a cost of £62, following damage done to the old wheel when the mill 'ran away.' It was in the Hodgman family for a great number of years and, later, the Hills. Mrs. Hills and William Hills are noted as the millers in an 1878 directory. The mill was pulled down about 1908, having ceased to work about 1907.

BROMLEY

¼ *mile NW. of Bromley College.* * 1769, 1819-43.

By kind permission of Mr. R. F. Brain, I am able to give a picture, dated 1785, of two post mills at Bromley. Strangely enough I have no confirmation of the existence of *two* mills at Bromley, one only being shown on all the maps I have examined.

By the courtesy of Herbert Alderton, Esq., F.L.A., the Librarian of the Bromley Public Library, I am able to give the following extract from a recently published *History of Bromley* :

This windmill came into existence about 1600 by the act of Edmund Style, who, in his will, dated 1614, speaks of "a Mill I have erected in the Parish of Bromleighe." The particular windmill in question stood a short distance west of the London Road, and about a quarter of a mile north-west of the College—its position is marked in Rocques' map of 1763. The mill not only survived but continued in active use until the nineteenth century was well advanced. Somewhere between 1835 and 1840 it was demolished.

Mr. Alderton adds :

The *Annual Register* for 1768 (Vol. XI, p. 164) records the removal of the mill a distance of some 400 yards by means of 'capsterns.' This might account for the belief that there were *two* mills on Bromley Hill.

The old Registers at Bromley Parish Church give the following entries of deaths at Bromley post mill :

Dec. 3, 1669. A man child that the windmiller nursed.
April 23, 1676. Matthew Janwood of the Windmill.
1704. William Lets from the Windmill.
1726. Sarah, daughter of William Bar from the Windmill.

BROOK

(NEAR ASHFORD)

Spelder's Hill. ½ *mile SW. of Church.* 1858-72, 1903-10.

This was a small tarred smock and stage mill, probably built about 1800-20. It had one floor under the stage and two above ; it worked three pairs of stones ; two cloth sails and two spring sweeps were used ; no auxiliary power of any kind was installed.

It was owned by Walter Cook, who also had the Brook watermill. A local story has it that when found shooting in or near a neighbouring preserve and asked for his name his reply was : "I am Mr. Cook, the Miller of Brook, wind and water combined, my lord."

From 1885 to 1894 the mill was occupied by F. Hammon and then passed to the tenancy of Marcus Hancock who held it until October 1902, which is also the date when it last worked. The mill was, however, in good condition when Mr. Hancock terminated his occupation ; his chief reason for giving it up was that his trade had been handicapped owing to the windmill yard and buildings being let by the owner for greyhound stables.

In about 1912 the mill was ruthlessly destroyed, being pulled over by a wire rope ; a traction engine was hired for the purpose. The base alone was left and this was roofed over and used for some years as a store.

A local inn goes by the name of The Honest Miller. Wondering if the name had any connection with the mill, I wrote to the landlord, Mr. H. Hayward, but in his reply he regretted he could not give me the origin of the name.

A. W. Tiffin

EDENBRIDGE

See page 199

W.C.F.

ELHAM (Cullen's Hill)

See page 200

A. W. Tiffin

GOUDHURST (Town Mill)

See page 211

Ridley's Studios, Tenterden

HAWKHURST

(Nightingale's Mill, Four Throws)

See page 218

Facing page 176

Henry Smetham

FRINDSBURY (Prospect Hill Mills)

See page 206

W.C.F.

W.C.F.

FRINDSBURY (House Mill)

See page 206

Facing page 177

CANTERBURY

*St. Martin's Mill.** 1 *furlong E. of St. Martin's Church. Standing to-day.*
1819-43, 1903-10.

The stone tower mill on St. Martin's Hill was built in 1817 by John Adams and worked continually until 1890. In the early days of its history it was known as Buck Windmill.

I first visited the mill in 1905 when it was well advanced along the road to abandonment and neglect. I was pleased to find on a recent visit that the body of the mill was being carefully preserved. Mr. Cozens, a Canterbury builder, bought it in 1920 and, by additions, had converted it into a delightful residence, now known as 'Querns.' It stands in a splendidly designed garden.

The original 'Miller's House' has been preserved as a separate house— this stands in front of the Mill. Mrs. D. E. Drew writes :

> Mr. Cozens was a great collector of old things, the mill being full of old pictures, etc., and the garden full of priceless old stones, etc. The mill-stones are put down in the garden as the stars 'The Horse and Wagon'—the four and the three.

During a storm one night many years ago, the mill, being struck by lightning, was thought to be on fire. A crowd soon gathered but all they saw in connection with a fire were two firemen running about with *lanterns* looking for it !

St. Martin's Hill, Black Mill. ¼ *mile E. of St. Martin's Church.* 1819-43.

This mill stood on the south side of the Sandwich road, nearly opposite St. Martin's Mill. I learn from Mr. Jack Holman that it was known as St. Martin's Black Mill, that it stood near where the Mill Inn stands and, further, that it was pulled down and parts of it used to build one of the Blean Mills in 1868. Mr. Holman has the original estimate, dated December 16th, 1867, signed by his grandfather, Thomas Holman, and Thomas Glover, for whom the Blean Mill was built. The following tackle was used from the Black Mill :

> Sweeps with striking tackle
> Midlings
> Fan tackle
> Windshaft
> Spur wheel
> Flour machines, etc.

St. Lawrence Mill. 5 *furlongs SSW. of St. Martin's Church.* 1819-43.

On the 1819-43 map this mill is shown as being on the south-western side of the Old Dover Road, three furlongs south-east of the Cattle Market, near the site of the St. Lawrence Leper Hospital and the County Cricket Ground. It was a large black smock mill. There was no stage—the sweeps came very close to the ground. It worked almost to the time of its destruction— and was burnt down on May 15th, 1873.

M

A painting of the mill may be seen on the walls of the Reference Library at the Beaney Institute.

Dane John Mill. *No map reference.*

Although I can give no map reference for a mill on the Dane John, one certainly crowned that mound. In 1731 it was advertised in the *Kentish Post* : "To be sold—a great pennyworth !"

I have been in touch with the great-grandson (born in 1855) of Mr. James Simmonds who, in 1790, rebuilt the Dane John Mill. Mr. James Simmonds was, I understand, for many years Mayor of Canterbury and a Member of Parliament, and he was buried in the Cloisters of Canterbury Cathedral.

Franciscan Gardens. *1/5th mile NW. of Castle.* 1846 *Print.*

An old print of 1846 shows this smock mill, and I learn from Mr. Jack Holman that it stood beside the watermill, at the junction of the River Stour, at the corner of the Franciscan Gardens.

St. Thomas' Hill. *No map reference.*

Prints of 1816, 1835 and 1856 show this mill, and I understand from my millwright friends that it stood on the south-western side of St. Thomas' Hill.

CHALLOCK LEES
(NEAR ASHFORD)

1 *mile NNW. of Challock Church.* 1769, 1819-43, 1858-72, 1903-10.

This mill stood near the junction of the four cross-roads on the Charing to Chilham road. It was a smock mill on a very low brick base. John Chapman was miller at one time and there was a good baking business as well. The following extract from the *Kentish Express* is of interest :

February 8th, 1906. In a storm the spire of Westwell Church, near Ashford, was set on fire, a cottage was damaged at Chartham, and a Challock mill was destroyed.

Prior to its destruction the mill had not worked for many years. Mr. George Jarvis was given the windshaft from the mill as payment for his supervising the work of clearing the debris. The windshaft was subsequently used for a long time in the timber yard at Bethersden, embedded vertically in the ground and supporting an overhead run for hauling in the timbers.

In the meadow where the mill stood nothing remains to mark the spot save a slight grass-covered bump dominated by cockerels and their clucking hens.

(See also Addenda, page 313)

CHARING
(NEAR ASHFORD)

Field Mill.* 5 furlongs NNE. of Church. Standing to-day. 1819-43, 1903-10.

For a short time, about 1867, the occupier of this mill on Charing Hill was Alfred Sidders. In 1878 the miller was Robt. Millgate. Later occupiers include the names of Pope, Smith, and Pay. Finally it was held by Walter Hicks, by whom it was last worked—about 1892. The mill had two spring sweeps and two 'commons.' Two new 'common' sails were put up in 1890 by T. R. Holman.

After Mr. Hicks gave up the mill the next owner of the property had the machinery removed from the mill and the main floor converted into a studio. A subsequent purchaser turned the main floor into a billiard room.

The sweeps were removed in 1917. They had been much damaged by a high wind and were regarded as dangerous.

The body of the mill remains, the lower floors of which are furnished as study, lounge, etc., and the upper floor serves as an observatory. The brick base has now been converted into a store. Viewed from the Ashford road, the white mill-cap only can be seen peeping above the dark trees which line the crest of the Downs and, when seen thus from a distance, with a small stretch of imagination, it reminds one of a huge white owl surveying the surroundings fron the tree-tops.

I recall with great pleasure my visit to Old Mill House, Charing, the delightful home, constructed with artistic skill and ingenuity, embodying the old miller's house as part of the new structure. I shall ever be grateful to our hostess, Mrs. G. M. Clarke, for her gracious welcome. The wingless body of the brave old mill, the delightful terraced garden, alight with gorgeous flowers, and the lovely expansive view, will not readily be forgotten.

CHARING HEATH
(NEAR ASHFORD)

1½ miles W. of Charing Church. 1858-72.

Enquiries on the very site of this mill were fruitless, and the oldest residents have no knowledge of it, which seems to indicate that the mill disappeared entirely before, say, 1870. One elderly miller friend who has known the district well all his life disputes its very existence. He thought the mill at *Lenham* Heath must be the one referred to, and he was much astonished when I showed him a section of the 1858-72 Ordnance Map on which the mill is clearly drawn as at Charing Heath and, by tracing the position, proves to be near the Red Lion Inn. "Well," said my friend, "all I can say is that it is very strange *I've* never heard tell of a mill there."

The evidence of the Ordnance Map must, of course, be accepted as indisputable. I was pleased later, however, to discover that Mr. William

Holman had heard of the mill and that he had understood it was of smock type, a 'squab' specimen, that is, very fat and short, and that there was scarcely any brick base to it and no stage.

CHARLTON[1]
(NEAR WOOLWICH)

Near Church. No map reference.

I have not traced this mill on any map and must, therefore, rely upon Vincent's *Records of the Woolwich District* as my authority for its existence. The following are two references to this mill which are of unusual interest :

> Where the great tree stands opposite the old church, it is said, there once stood a mill, and in the mill dwelt a burly miller and his dainty wife. In one of his hunting excursions from Eltham, King John is supposed to have entered the mill for refreshment, and, surprising the young wife alone, he is presumed to have made love with such indiscretion that he did not notice the return of the miller. The infuriated husband threatened the life of the intruder, and, to save his skin, the king discovered himself, and satisfied the miller with a promise to give him all the land he could see from the mill-door. This, according to the story, made him lord of a manor stretching from Cuckold's Point at Rotherhithe to Woolwich town.[2]
>
> In 1660 King Charles II received a memorial on behalf of Mr. Dobeson, "a loyal sufferer for the late King" (Charles I). To show his joy for the restoration Mr. Dobeson "would needs burn down his windmill at Charlton to make a bonfire."[3]

GREAT CHART
(NEAR ASHFORD)

1 furlong NE. of Church. *Base remains, as store.* 1903-10.

This mill did not grind corn ; it was used for timber sawing, being built for this purpose by J. Padgham, a builder, at Pluckley, but, on being sold to his brother at Great Chart, was removed to its present site.

It was an octagonal smock mill with six sweeps. This, and another little mill of six sweeps (see Bethersden, Little Mill) are the only mills known to have been built in Kent with six sweeps.

I cannot say when the mill was last worked, although it was known to be working in 1888. It stood without its sweeps for about twenty years and was pulled down in 1928 and the base roofed over for a workshop and store.

CHARTHAM
(NEAR CANTERBURY)

Near Hatch Green. 1 mile NNW. of Church. 1819-43.

This mill is noted on the 1819-43 map but there is no other information available.

[1] See note on page 151.
[2] *Records of the Woolwich District*, by W. T. Vincent, 1890, p. 670.
[3] ibid., p. 682.

Facing page 180

GRAVESEND

Windmill Hill and the Thames

See page 213

Invicta Mag., Vol. II, p. 94

Facing page 181

THE OLD DERELICT

GRAVESEND

Homeland Handbook, Vol. 53

THE OLD WINDMILL AND BELLE VUE

See page 213

CHATHAM

*Upberry Mill.** ½ *mile NW. of Luton Church.* 1596, 1695, 1736, 1769, 1819-43.

This mill, probably the earliest in Chatham, was known as Gilbert's Mill, after John Gilbert, an early owner, but later as Upberry Mill. It was also known as Lower Chatham Hill Mill. It stood on Windmill Road, which branches off Chatham Hill in the direction of Gillingham.

The sweeps swept dangerously near the footpath and a woman was killed by them. It is also stated that a donkey was once tethered to one of the sweeps while the owner was making a purchase of flour. The miller, being unaware of this, released the brake and started the mill. . . . !

I understand that George Manwaring, late of Preston Mill, near Wingham, grandfather of William Manwaring, now of Willesborough Mill, had the Upberry Mill about 1834. A Mr. Wyatt had it about 1885. It is said that because he could not get enough trade to make a living at the mill he used to go out stone dressing, at which art he was very proficient and thus able to supplement his income.

The mill was pulled down in the autumn of 1897.

*Star Mill.** 3 *furlongs E. of Luton Church.* 1819-43, 1903-10.

Star Mill, sometimes also known as the Upper Chatham Hill Mill, was originally called Austin's Mill, at least seventy-one years ago. Austin was a corn factor and miller with business premises next to Hill's Coal Office in the High Street. John Webb was the miller in 1878. Prior to his occupation the mill was worked by Walter Skinner, who went from it to the mill on Bluebell Hill.

Writing of this old mill in 1925, I said :

> Chatham cannot now claim even one active mill. The sole survivor at the time of writing is Star Mill, near the Rainham Road (Watling Street). Though two sweeps revolve to grind the last sack of corn, most of the interior is already removed, for even now it is unsafe to work, the whole structure being rotten with age. This mill is referred to in Percy Young's *The Tide Mill Secret* as Darland Mill. It is occupied by Messrs. R. & F. Pain and is owned by the local Water Company who purchased it from the War Department.

Shortly after the above was written, it became my duty, as Engineer of the said Company, to take the mill down. As it stood near my home I hoped to save a part of the body and the base to convert into a summer retreat. It was beyond salving, however, and had to be destroyed in 1925.

Cherry Tree Hall Mill. 1 *furlong WSW. of St. Paul's Church.* 1819-43.

This mill stood at The Mount—a lane opposite the *Stag and Hounds* in Old Road, a stone's throw from New Road. It was destroyed about 1875, when the base was converted into a store. Later, about 1900, this base was removed. To-day the actual site of the mill is occupied by two modern dwellings known as Nos. 1 and 2 Mill Cottages. Since the demolition of the mill the old farm buildings, with which the mill was associated, were burnt down ; fragments of walls and foundations are still to be seen. Five acres of 'Very Desirable Building Land' separate the mill site from Southill Barracks.

My veteran miller friend of eighty-one years of age, John J. Freeman, whose ancestry is linked with the local mills, knew this mill well, living as he did in Cherry Tree Hall Cottage near by. From him I learned that it was a smock mill, standing on a brick base, with a stage. It was working prior to 1860, when it was occupied by Warner Joy, a corn factor in the High Street. About 1870 it was taken over by a man named Higgins and used for grinding cork, for what use I could not gather.

John J. Freeman's grandfather, Thomas Freeman, built the House Mill at Frindsbury, which is described later in these notes. His grandmother was the mother of twenty-six children ; she lived to 101 years of age and was "a veritable Amazon," a masterful woman of wonderful personality.

From John J. Freeman I gleaned much information about Chatham mills, and I never saw eighty-one years set more happily on a man than they did upon him—active, robust and with a memory far more ready than my own in recalling the past.

Chalk-pit Hill, Field's Mill. ¼ *mile S. of St. Paul's Church.* (*Two mills*). 1819-43.

There were two mills on Chalk-pit Hill, according to the 1819-43 map, but I can only trace particulars of one—Field's Mill. The site of this mill is now occupied by dwellings known as Nos. 41 and 42 Chalk-pit Hill. The Mill House still stands and is to-day No. 1 Palmerston Road, at the corner of Albert Road.

It was a smock mill on a square base, with two floors of brickwork under the stage—a similar mill to Delce Mill, Rochester, except that it had an extra storey in its base. It was worked by four 'patent' sweeps and the usual fantail gear ; three pairs of stones were used.

It was built in 1837 by John Stedman for John Field to replace an earlier mill, on the same spot, that was burnt down in 1836. The mill, apparently, had always been in the Field family. John S. Field succeeded his father and lived to the grand old age of eighty-five. He died about ten years ago.

The earlier mill that fell to the flames was somewhat smaller. Its two upper stories were so slender that they could only be reached from the outside, a ladder being fixed in front of the cap and entrance effected under the fantail. Its successor was a lofty, powerful mill. An elderly man, with whom I had a chat, recalled that in 1867 he "assisted with sixteen quarter of wheat, with four horses, up Chalk-pit Hill, to the mill."

Mr. E. F. Daniels, who worked in the mill last, having been the miller under Mr. Field for about nine years prior to its demolition, informs me that it was in splendid order at the time of its destruction and in use right to the last. The mill was not given the chance to become in any way derelict for it was pulled down by James Boyer Stedman almost immediately after it was sold in 1887.

Mr. Daniel's predecessor in the mill, a Mr. Busbidge, was the miller for no less than half a century.

*New Road, Feather Mill.** 1 furlong W. of St. Bartholomew Church. Base shown on 1898 Ordnance Map.*

In Ireland's *History of Kent*, Vol. IV, page 439, there is a print of Chatham Dockyard from Fort Pitt and in it, as in other prints of the period, a windmill is shown, in the direction of New Road, poised high upon a substantial brick base.

I learn from John J. Freeman that his parents frequently spoke of the mill in New Road, and he knew the site, fixing its position by the fact that it stood in line with the Chest Arms Hotel, now the site of the Empire Theatre. The present garage of the Empire is the site of the Chest Arms Tap at Chest Arms Hard, where the boats from the shipping in the Medway ran ashore. The Tap was the *rendezvous* of the common seamen, and the Hotel for those 'superior' persons who joined the townsfolk in their carousal.

From all I could gather, it was indeed a rough spot, but it is well to leave what that meant to the fertile brain of those versed in the history of such ports, say, a century ago. The point of interest here is that, in coming ashore and traversing the road that still leads to the High Street, at the side of the Empire Theatre, one could not have failed to see the old mill, perched high up on the bank in New Road.

Pursuing my enquiries further, I found a lady who, when a girl, some seventy years ago, daily went past this mill on the way to school, and she referred to it as being a 'Feather Mill.' I then recalled that, many years ago, I casually learned that the mill was used for preparing feathers for domestic use—beds, pillow-cases, etc.—but I cannot remember the authority, and my friend Freeman had never heard of the suggestion.

On tracing the actual site of the mill with the help of the 1898 Ordnance Map, on which the remaining brick base was noted, I find the mill stood at the back of No. 46 High Street, mid-way between the High Street and the New Road, exactly as described by my friend Freeman. These premises are in the occupation of Mr. Horace H. Joyce, who not only assured me of the correctness of the discovery but also called my attention to the remains of the large, high, brick structure, with the decayed timber plates which had carried the floor stages of the basement of the mill.

I understand that the mill had stood for many years without its sweeps before being pulled down about 1890 and a roof put on the base.

*Ordnance Place, Bacon's Mill or Belsey's Mill.** ¼ mile SSW. of St. John's Church.*

This was one of two mills that stood in Ordnance Place. Its timber body was dismantled about 1900 but its large, square, brick base still stands, converted into a shop and dwelling, and is now a greengrocer's (H. Kemsley) at No. 46 Ordnance Street, next door to the Mason's Arms. No. 44, now a butcher's shop (H. G. Sims) at the corner of Cannon Street, used to be a corn chandler's shop connected with the mill. There was a bakery at the back of the premises, and also the miller's house.

The mill was known as Bacon's Mill and later, as Belsey's Mill, after the names of its owners. A directory of 1858 states : "Matthew Bacon, miller, Front Row." The mill was in his possession at least as early as 1845 and held by him until his death in about 1890.

It was built originally for grinding corn but, water being a necessity, a 200-feet well was dug and the mill used for pumping water, later supplying no less than one hundred neighbouring houses regularly three times a week. A rent was paid to the miller, of course, and it is said that this brought in nearly £100 a year.

After Mr. Bacon's death the mill was used solely for pumping water but this work has long since been taken over by the local Water Company.

Mr. George E. Ride writes :

> I had a little experience with this mill. A friend of my father, Mr. E. Chapman, took the mill in 1880 and he was a delicate man and was afraid to go to the top to oil up the fantail and gear, so I used to go every Saturday afternoon and do it for him. The mill was so small at the top you could not get through to the cap; the only means was by a ladder suspended from the cap, which travelled round with it. The brake wheel was only about three feet in diameter. Although the mill had three pairs of stones and a dressing machine, she was very little used for grinding ; it seemed to take nearly all the power for pumping purposes.

Ordnance Place, Willis's Mill. ¼ mile SSW. of St. John's Church.

Willis's Mill was named after its proprietor, William Willis, who later became the proprietor of the Sun Hotel in the High Street. It stood in Ordnance Place, above Bacon's Mill, on the same side of the road. It was pulled down about 1875. To-day four houses, numbered 90, 90a, b, and c Ordnance Street, occupy its site.

For many years after Mr. Willis gave up, Thomas Goble was the miller. In the early days of the mill's history it was held by George Stoddard ; his name is given in a directory of 1839 as a miller in Ordnance Place.

It was a powerful mill with a high tower. In its later days steam power was added to the working. In addition to being a flour mill it ground spices— pepper, ginger, etc.

In common with many other smock mills, the sweeps only just cleared the ground. I am told that a daughter of Mr. Willis was struck by one of the revolving sweeps and received serious injury. A story has it that she wore a silver plate in her forehead after the accident.

In connection with this mill a miller friend relates that his father was always keen on buying all the midlings he possibly could from Mr. Goble, for Mr. Goble's midlings were almost *flour*—"nice and heavy." A bag of Mr. Goble's midlings weighed as much as a sack of flour—2½ cwt. That is, eight bushels of midlings equalled the weight of five bushels of flour, which was pretty good working for the purchaser !

Luton, Manwaring's Mill.* ½ *mile SW. of Luton Church.* 1858-72.

Slough, near Windsor, in Buckinghamshire, was the original home of this mill, where it was one of a pair known as The Two Sisters, standing on Salt Hill, and a few cottages named Mill Row commemorate their existence.

In about 1848 the mill in question was purchased by Thomas Manwaring, who came from Preston Mill, near Wingham, where he was born in 1814, his father, George Manwaring, having had that mill for many years. Accompanied by William Killick (who had one of the Strood mills), Mr. Manwaring went down to Slough to examine the mill and arrange the transaction. £100 was the purchase price and £80 the cost of transport and re-erection at Luton. These were evidently low figures even in those days and were doubtless the explanation of the mill being purchased at such a distance.

Messrs. Henry Paine & Sons, the millwrights who built the famous Delce Mill at Rochester, undertook the work of dismantling the mill at Slough and re-erecting at Luton. The structure was conveyed by barge down the Thames and then along the Medway to Chatham, where it was unloaded and conveyed by road the short distance to Luton. In order to dismantle the mill the eight corner posts were sawn down their centres, and in re-erection these were bolted together again, with tarred twine packing between the sections.

It was a tarred smock, stage and fantail mill, with two floors of brick-work under the stage and three above. When rebuilt at Luton there were only two pairs of stones—driven 'underdrift,' that is, by gearing beneath the stones, in similar manner to a watermill—but Mr. Manwaring had another pair installed, on the stage floor, driven by a 'quant.' There were also a flour dresser and a wheat smutter.

Originally there were four cloth sails, or 'commons,' and a wooden wind-shaft. In about 1853 Mr. Manwaring had two of the sweeps turned into 'patents' and for this purpose a hole had to be bored through the windshaft to take the striking rod. This hole through the shaft evidently weakened it for, during a high wind, the 'canister' was snapped off close to the shaft. When the damage was put right an iron windshaft was substituted.

Mr. Manwaring worked the mill till his death in 1884. His son, William, carried it on for the executors for about a year afterwards, when it was rented by William Burgess, by whom it was worked up till the autumn of 1887, when it was burnt down, in a high wind. The mill is supposed to have 'fired' on account of the brake not holding during the gale.

(See also page 72)

CHELSFIELD

(NEAR FARNBOROUGH)

Well Hill. 1¼ *miles ESE. of Church.* 1769.

The 1769 large-scale map is my only authority for this mill.

CHEVENING
(NEAR SEVENOAKS)

½ *mile S. of Church. No map reference.*

Chevening Mill has been gone for many years. It stood between Chipstead and Chevening, near Chipstead Halt Station, on the Dunton Green to Westerham branch line. It was at one time owned by a Mr. Hooker.

The one-storied Mill House, once the residence of the miller, still remains, and here lived Detective-Inspector Cox who captured the notorious Dougal, the Mote Farm murderer of Essex.

CHILHAM
(NEAR CANTERBURY)

1½ *miles NNE. of Church.* 1858-72.

According to the 1858-72 map a mill stood close to the railway tunnel near Lower Ensinge, south of the line. I can trace no information regarding it and have not been able to obtain local confirmation of its existence.

CHILLENDEN
(NEAR CANTERBURY)

½ *mile N. of Church.* Standing to-day, active.* 1695, 1736, 1769, 1819-43, 1903-10.

This mill is of the 'open trestle' type and is the only one of its kind remaining in Kent. Rolvenden Mill would appear, at first sight, to be of this type, but that originally had a round-house, whereas Chillenden Mill did not.

Although of such an old *type*, Chillenden is not an old mill itself. In fact, built in 1868, it is one of the latest mills erected in Kent and certainly the last post mill built in the county. It replaced an older post mill, as evidenced by the early maps, and I learn from Mr. A. H. Laker, who now works the present mill, that a seventeenth century date was discovered when it was repaired, which seems to prove that material from the old mill was incorporated with the new.

The mill is in good condition. One new midling and two new sweeps were fitted in 1927 by Messrs. Holman Bros., and the supporting beams of the trestle were repaired. Only one pair of stones is used now—for cattle corn and the like. There is another pair in the mill that was used at one time for grinding wheat for flour.

The tailpole of the mill rests on a wheel, which facilitates the moving round of the body to bring the sweeps into the wind.

CHISLEHURST

Chislehurst Common, ½ *mile W. of Church.** 1819-43.

A special point of interest in connection with this mill at Chislehurst Common is that it was originally built in 1796 for the express purpose of grinding the gleanings for the poor of the parish, on Mondays and Tuesdays of each week, 4d. per bushel being the charge for grinding. It is said that the mill and miller's house cost £2100 to build.

The mill stood facing the West Kent Cricket Ground. It was a fine smock mill, with stage and fantail, one floor under the stage and four above ; three pairs of stones were used. No auxiliary power was employed, the mill working only by wind. It was last used for corn grinding in August 1869. Mr. W. Brigden, who owned the mill for many years, possesses a fine oil painting of it.

Mr. Nicholls, who later bought Downe Mill, rented the Chislehurst Mill for a time, about the year 1855. It was pulled down about 1877. A row of modern cottages called Mill Place, now occupy the mill site, and set in the front wall of one of these cottages is a stone with a drawing of a windmill carved on it.

CHISLET
(NEAR CANTERBURY)

2¼ *miles N. of Church.* Standing to-day, derelict.* 1819-43, 1903-10.

In 1905 I took a picture of this mill in its active state and, in 1930, when I visited it again I was surprised to find that its cap, sweeps and fan had gone, the top was covered in and the body encased with sheets of rusted corrugated iron—a veritable blot on the landscape. During a storm one night in March 1916, it was tail-winded and the cap and sweeps torn off.

The mill stands on the hill above Gray's Farm, Reculver, and from it, not far distant, can be seen the famous Twin Towers of Reculver Church. The mill has sometimes been known as Reculver Mill but to Chislet it belongs, in spite of its long distance from the village.

The mill was in the Collard family for a great many years, Henry Collard being the miller in 1847. In 1878 the miller was John Wootton.

During the Great War the mill was used as an observation post for anti-aircraft guns.

CLIFFE
(NEAR ROCHESTER)

Dance's Mill. ½ *mile SSE. of Church.* 1769, 1819-43.

This black smock mill was burnt down about 1885. It had stood idle and without its sweeps for some years. Prospect Cottages now occupy its site and they bear the date 1888. Two mill-stones are all that remain of the mill and can be seen supporting the footway at the rear of the Cottages. The sweeps reached almost to the ground and, some sixty years ago, a little Frindsbury boy named Pope was struck and killed by them.

COBHAM
(NEAR GRAVESEND)

¼ mile due N. of Cobham Hall. 1596, 1610.

A mill here is shown on the Symonson map of 1596 and J. Speed's map of 1610, hence it would have been one of the earliest post mills, as at this period smock and tower mills were unknown in Kent.

Darnley's Mill.* 1 furlong W. of Church. Base converted into dwelling. 1903-10.

The brick base alone remains of this mill and it has been converted into a substantial dwelling. Originally it was a fine mill of five stories and was a splendid landmark. It had, like mills at Edenbridge, Bluebell Hill, and Boughton-under-Blean, a bee-hive cap.

Unfortunately it caught fire when struck by lightning during a storm in 1903. The brick base was roofed over after the fire and used as a store until about 1929, when it was converted to its present use.

The mill had always been in the possession of the Darnley family, being situated on Lord Darnley's Estate. For three generations it was hired by the Shearman family (William Shearman worked it in the 1870's). The succeeding tenant was a Mr. Morris, during whose occupation the mill was burnt down.

I think I am right in saying that the miller at Darnley's Mill had the mill rent free on condition that he ground all the corn required for the stock on the estate, free.

COWDEN
(NEAR EDENBRIDGE)

Polefields. About ½ mile N. of Church.

I have not been able to trace a windmill here on any map, but the Sevenoaks Librarian has kindly supplied the following information :

> Guy Ewing in his *History of Cowden* says, p. 244 : "There was a windmill at Polefields of which no record save the name of Windmill Hill in Spode Lane seems to have survived. It was not in existence when the Tithe map was made" (i.e. about 1843).
> A map of 1740 shows Great and Little Mill Crofts and the Tithe map shows Little Mill Crofts all just south-east of Beechenwood, and so near Spode Lane and not far from Polefields. It may be noted that these places are at the door of Mr. Ewing's house, Claydene. There is no mill shown on these maps. These Mill Crofts were part of Polefields farm in 1740.

CRANBROOK

¼ mile WNW. of Church. 1736, 1769.

This is doubtless the mill that gave the title to Windmill Hill and Windmill Hotel just outside the village of Cranbrook. Sir Charles Igglesden refers to it as having been situated on the site of the present Cricket Ground, but the large-scale map of 1769 would seem to indicate that the mill stood a little

Walter Stedman

GILLINGHAM (Stedman's Mill)

GILLINGHAM (Friday's Mill, Grange)

See page 210

See page 210

C. W. Welby

HERNE

HERNE BAY (The Bay Mill)

See page 221

See page 222

W. Norton

FAVERSHAM (Pumping Mill)

See page 203

W.C.F.

GUSTON (Swingate Mill)

See page 216

Rex Wailes

A. W. Tiffin

FRITTENDEN (Sinkhurst Green)

See page 209

nearer Hartley, close to one of the lodges to Angley Park, on the north side of the road known locally as the Back Lane.

It has been thought that when the mill was dismantled (in about 1814, when the Union Mill in the village was built) it was removed to Appledore and then rebuilt, but I have it on the authority of Dr. F. W. Cock, of Appledore, that no mill was ever moved there from Cranbrook. What is more likely, and this I have heard discussed locally, is that the old Cranbrook Mill was moved to Sissinghurst, where it later became known as Crampton's Mill, which is fully described later in these notes.

Satin's Hill. 1 mile 5 furlongs NE. of Church. 1769.

From a close examination of the 1769 map on which this mill is shown, it appears that it was situated on Satin's Hill, half a mile north of Sissinghurst, in the corner of a triangle formed by the junction of the Sissinghurst-Frittenden road and a by-lane (known as Spon's Lane) that leads back to the Staplehurst road.

On enquiring of the Gosden family, living at Satin's Hill Farm, which is situated a few yards from the site of the mill, I learned that they had never heard of a mill having stood there ; but as they had only lived at the farm for twenty years, they recommended me to enquire of Mr. Fred Gurr, living a little distance away, who, by reason of his having reached the grand old age of 88, and always having taken an interest in local history, would be able, if any one could, to confirm the existence of the mill and, maybe, give some information.

I called on Mr. Fred Gurr and found his memory as keen as his interest, but unfortunately, he could throw no light on the matter. He was born in 1845, and his father in 1799, both having lived in the district all their lives, and neither he nor his father (he felt sure) had ever heard of a windmill at the position shown. In spite, therefore, of the fact that his father was born in the vicinity only thirty years after the issue of the 1769 map, there is now no trace or memory of the mill remaining—truly a lost mill.

Cranbrook Common Mill. 1¾ miles NNE. of Church. 1858-72.*

This old mill on Camden Hill, of which nothing remains to-day, was an octagonal smock, and was situated about fifty yards from the north side of the Sissinghurst to Staplehurst road, to the right of the lane that now leads to the Convalescent Home. It was a fine position for a mill, on very high ground, and a good business was carried on in days gone by.

It was last held and worked by the Crampton family in about 1876. The miller for some years had been a Mr. Marsh who, after the death of William Crampton, when the mill fell into disuse, went to Sissinghurst Mill.

Cranbrook Common Mill stood idle from 1876 until it was pulled down in 1901, on the day of the coronation of King Edward VII. It was an unceremonious demolition. A traction engine was drawn up near the mill, a wire rope placed round the body, bricks in the base were removed and the whole structure pulled over. Messrs. Links and Harris of Staplehurst (a firm now extinct) undertook the work.

The last work the mill did was to grind a large quantity of acorns, for in that year there was a tremendous crop in the district; farmers had them roasted in their hop kilns and then brought to the mill to be ground for pig food. It is said that the husks of the acorns littered the mill for many years.

There was no fantail gear ; the mill cap was turned into the wind by means of a chain attached to a 'Y' wheel. The mill had the old cloth sails and, latterly, as the structure became derelict and battered by the high winds of successive winters, these old sails became ragged and would flap wildly in the wind, like a dilapidated scarecrow.

*Union Mill.** ¼ mile SE. of Church. Standing to-day, active.* 1819-43, 1858-72, 1903-10.

This is a remarkably fine specimen of a Kentish smock mill and needs but little introduction to all who know their Kent, for it towers conspicuously above its surroundings. It is quite the highest mill now standing in Kent and is often thought to be the highest in England but Mr. J. Russell, who owns it, informs me that Sutton Mill, in Norfolk, is higher, being 90 feet from the ground to the top of the cap, whereas Cranbrook is only 70 feet. Nevertheless, it is a wonderful mill and, which is even more pleasing, it is kept in splendid repair.

It is said to have cost £3,500 when it was built in 1814, for Henry Dobell, by the millwright, Humphrey, who also built mills at Goudhurst, Hythe, and Sheerness. He lived in Cranbrook and his shop and house stood where the Grammar School Lodge is now situated. He was quite a celebrated mechanic. In the Church records, on two different dates accounts were paid to him for re-hanging bells. Millwrights frequently undertook this work. Warren, the Hawkhurst millwright, re-hung Benenden and Goudhurst Church bells and probably many others.

A local story has it that when the Cranbrook Mill was built, Humphrey's son stood on the top of the cap and blew a bugle. Free drink was provided for all and there was great hilarity in celebrating the event.

Originally the mill had four cloth sweeps and no fantail. Medhurst, the millwright of Lewes, put up a new windshaft and patent sweeps in 1840, and Warren fitted the fan at the same time. Warren also, in 1880, made the present stage. Its predecessor was of wood and much wider, as was necessary to work the canvas sails. New pitch pine midlings were fitted in 1897.

The mill has been in the Russell family for a great many years. On asking Mr. Russell, who has been very willing to give all the information he could respecting his own mill and others in his locality, if he knew why his mill was called Union Mill, he replied :

I have heard that after the bankruptcy of Henry Dobell, the creditors formed a company to carry on the business, and they gave it the name Union Mill, which is supposed to have been suggested by the union of the said creditors.

The mill has seven stories, including the three-storied brick base under the stage. Three pairs of stones were driven ; now two only are used—one for rice and the other for barley. Very little flour is made at the mill to-day and for this a gas engine is used.

CUDHAM
(NEAR SEVENOAKS)

Biggin Hill, Pimlico Mill. 1½ *miles SW. of Church.* 1829.

This old post mill, owned by a Mr. Christie, stood near the Black Horse Inn and Aperfield Court, just within the Kent County boundary. It was rented and worked for some years, from 1866 onwards, by a Mr. Nicholls, who owned the mill at Downe. In 1878 the miller was T. Gillett. It was pulled down about 1885. I understand that some slight remains are still to be seen in the grounds of Mr. J. Burkin at Biggin Hill, who had the mill last.

DARTFORD

The Brent Mill.* 1 *mile ESE. of Church.* 1819-43.

The 1819-43 Ordnance Map shows this mill at Dartford Brent and situated south of Watling Street.

It was a large tarred smock mill of five stories, with a stage and fantail and working four pairs of stones. The owner was the late F. A. Pigon, Esq., of the Dartford firm of gunpowder manufacturers, Messrs. Pigon, Wilks & Laurence.

The mill was at one time occupied by Mr. John Garrard, but the last tenant was Mr. Leonard Keyes who held it from 1875 until 1886, when it was last worked.

In 1886 the business was transferred to Colyer's Mill, a water mill on the River Darent, where, in the same year, Mr. Leonard Keyes was joined by his brother, Mr. S. K. Keyes. The business was continued by the latter after the former's decease. It grew very rapidly, the premises were extended, modern machinery installed and, to-day, the firm known since about 1928 as Daren, Ltd., has a world-wide fame. Mr. S. K. Keyes is the present Governing Director.

Mr. W. Mitchell, builder, of The Brent, Dartford, states :

The mill was partly pulled down with a traction engine, by Mr. Lorenzo Fuller of Stone, about 1901. The ground floor walls were roofed over and, with the stables, used as a box manufactory and firewood bundling works by Mr. R. Sapswell, and later by Mr. W. F. Bryant. In 1930 the premises then being unused the whole was demolished by the owner of The Brent Laundry, Mr. F. May, and garages built with the material. The site is now an open yard adjoining the laundry, but may be roughly traced by a flat mill-stone at the north-west corner of the old buildings.

DEAL

*Upper Deal Mill.** ½ *mile S. of Upper Deal Church.* 1596, 1769, 1819-43, 1903-10.

This mill was situated on the hill close to Deal Waterworks. It was a fine smock mill on a stage, working three pairs of stones, built by Messrs. Sweetloves of Wingham and one of the last mills to be erected in this district—about 1855.

On this site, or close by—probably a little nearer the Waterworks Road— there was originally a post mill. This old mill is referred to in a deed dated 1701 as being bequeathed by John Holloway, a mariner of Deal, to his four daughters. Later, in 1724, it was sold for £160 to Henry Kenney. At that date it was held by William Carter. I have definite information that in 1840 it was owned by a widow, Mrs. Matson, and that the new smock mill was built for her son. This family continued to use it for a great number of years. Frederick Matson was the miller in 1878, according to a directory of that date, and he had it as late as 1894. A Mr. Barr held it in 1898, when a new midling was fitted. In 1910 Ernest Fuller hired the mill from a Mr. Parker and was probably the last to work it.

The mill was struck by lightning in 1913 and it is said that it might then have been destroyed had it not been for the splendid efforts of two men, employed in it at the time, to save it from destruction.

It was demolished in March 1929, the land being required for the erection of dwellings for the men employed in the Betteshanger Colliery. The midlings alone remained of the four sweeps when it was demolished; the fan had disappeared.

A miller friend tells me that the sweeps of Upper Deal Mill revolved very solemnly, about one revolution to twelve of the stones ; some of its neighbours ran about one to eight.

*Wellington Mill.** 3 *furlongs W. of Deal Castle.* 1819-43.

Standing in Mill Road, close to Deal Park, was this tall mill, having two floors under the stage, and owned originally by R. Chitty ; later by his son, George William Chitty, the founder of the well-known firm of that name.

Unlike most windmills, this one was devoted exclusively to the making of flour and had three pairs of stones for that purpose.

Very soon after the use of steam became general, the sweeps and fantail of Wellington Mill were dismantled, steam power was installed, three further pairs of stones were added and the mill fitted with the latest machinery for dressing flour. Then from this well-equipped converted mill much the largest business in East Kent was carried on. It was pulled down about 1890.

W.C.F. Jack Holman

HARBLEDOWN (The Old Black Mill)

See page 216

HARBLEDOWN MILL

Jack Holman

Being hauled to destruction by traction engine and cables, July 9th, 1913

See pages 96 and 216

See page 218

TUDOR HALL MILL, HAWKHURST, 1874

From the painting by M. Cazin, *Evening at Hawkhurst, Kent.*

Reproduced by courtesy of Mrs. H. Gunther, of Tongswood, Hawkhurst, who owns the original.

Facing page 193

Lower Deal Mill. ½ *mile SW. of Sandown Castle.* 1736, 1769, 1819-43.

This mill stood in Cannon Street, close to the Gas Works. It was a small smock mill, with no stage, two pairs of stones, worked in conjunction with North End Mill by T. J. Bushell.

I cannot find any one to tell much about it, as it was pulled down so long ago, about 1870. One old 'son of the soil' says that his father's pig-styes were built from its boarding. What a fate !

North End Mill or Great Mill.* ½ *mile SW. of Sandown Castle.* 1819-43.

North End Mill stood in Golf Road and is said to have been erected in 1767. As the second name infers, it was a large mill. It had two floors under the stage, used three pairs of stones, and latterly worked by spring-shuttered sweeps. For many years T. J. Bushell did a large trade here, employing three men to work the mill, in addition to carters (or loaders, as they were termed).

The large Mill House was built so close to the mill that the sweeps nearly touched the chimney pots !

About 1870 the mill passed into the hands of Mr. Chitty, who worked it to its fullest capacity until about 1880, when he gave up using wind power. A Mr. English used the mill subsequently—he had it as late as 1890. It was known to be working in 1894, for then a new midling and pair of spring sweeps were put up by T. R. Holman. Finally the mill met the fate of many other veterans, being burned down about 1896.

½ *mile SW. of Sandown Castle.* 1829.

The 1829 Greenwood map has a third mill marked at the above position, making a trio with North End Mill and Lower Deal Mill previously noted. I can trace nothing regarding this third mill. It could not have stood within the last sixty or more years.

Sandown Mill.* ¼ *mile S. of Sandown Castle.* 1695, 1819-43.

Sandown Mill was situated along the coast, very near the sea. It was a smock mill with a very low brick base and no stage ; the sweeps ran close to the ground. It worked two pairs of stones and was one of the three mills run by Mr. Chitty. A fine modern residence now occupies its site.

I am not able to say when it was pulled down but it was greatly damaged by the storm that destroyed much of Sandown Castle. The Surveyor said the mill was in a dangerous condition. It was, however, working up to the time of its demolition.

This mill, in an east wind, drew its motive power direct from the sea, and in consequence it is said to have established a record, when using four cloth or 'common' sails, of running constantly for forty-eight hours without shortening or in any way altering sail.

The mill shown on the 1695 map is evidently an earlier post mill which was replaced by the smock mill.

N

Walmer Road Mill. 1 furlong S. of Deal Castle. 1819-43.

The Walmer Road Mill was of smock type and was situated on the beach, quite near Deal Castle and exactly opposite the Clock on the Marine Barracks. It had a stage, three pairs of stones, two spring and two cloth sails.

John Mummery used it from 1844 to 1849. It occupied a good position at one time but, when the Barracks and some large houses were built in close proximity, the wind became so broken when blowing in certain directions that it became very inefficient and was demolished in the early fifties.

DENTON
(NEAR CANTERBURY)

3 furlongs NE. of Church. 1695, 1736, 1769, 1819-43.

I know nothing of this mill except that it is shown on the maps referred to above. The 1736 and 1769 maps mark it as Denton Mill.

DEPTFORD[1]

Black Horse Fields.* 5 furlongs NW. of Church, and 1 furlong N. of Railway. 1819-43.

The above position for this mill is that of the 1819-43 one-inch Ordnance Map but the site is more clearly shown on an undated map of London and Environs, by Wyld, of a larger scale. It was situated on the south bank of the Grand Surrey Canal, at the end of a lane called Black Horse Fields (known to-day as Black Horse Road), a turning off the left side of Evelyn Street, going towards London.

By the courtesy of Mr. Thankfull Sturdee, I am able to reproduce a picture entitled *The Grand Surrey Canal* which is one of the illustrations in Mr. Sturdee's splendid descriptive and pictorial record of Old Deptford. I am also indebted to Mr. Sturdee for the following reference to this mill :

> The windmill on the ground adjoining the Grand Surrey Canal, which ground was originally known as Black Horse Fields (now entirely covered with houses), was in the possession of a Mr. Martin until 1854, when it was burnt down while grinding corn for the use of the Government during the Crimean War. The railway also shown in the picture is that of the London and Greenwich line, which was at this time (1840) known as "The Three Hundred Arches."[2]

Windmill Lane. 7 furlongs NW. of Church. 1819-43.

This mill stood at a quarter of a mile north-west of the one previously noted. In addition to the Ordnance Map of 1819-43 it is clearly drawn on Cary's map of 1832 and also on Wyld's undated map. It was situated at the junction of Windmill Lane and Evelyn Street, both of which roads bear the same names to-day.

[1] See note on page 151.
[2] *Reminiscences of Old Deptford*, by Thankfull Sturdee, 1895.

I have traced nothing further of this mill, and Mr. Sturdee does not mention it in his Deptford records.

*Tanner's Hill.** ¼ mile NW. of St. John's Church. No map reference.*

I have not found this mill on any map, but am indebted to Mr. Sturdee for the following note :

> The old windmill on Tanner's Hill was occupied by Mr. Taylor, who also owned an old water mill at Deptford. It stood on ground which is now the gardens at the rear of houses in Lucas Street and which was also in a line with the present Board School. It was pulled down in consequence of its unsafe condition upon the opening of the North Kent Railway, in 1849, the constant running of the trains shaking its foundation.[1]

Tanner's Hill and Lucas Street still bear these names to-day and are turnings off the north side of Lewisham High Road, about three furlongs south-south-east of New Cross Station.

As can be seen from the picture reproduced by Mr. Sturdee's courtesy, it was an old post mill, with a round-house.

DODDINGTON
(NEAR SITTINGBOURNE)

*Elvey's Mill or Jarvis's Mill.** 3 furlongs W. of Church. Standing to-day, derelict. 1903-10.*

Elvey's Mill was built about 1820. It has not been worked by wind since about 1926 and the structure presents a derelict appearance to-day. A Blackstone oil engine was installed in 1909 and the base extended to accommodate it. At the same time another pair of stones was added, making three pairs in all. The mill is still worked by oil engine, occasionally.

It was a hard-worked mill at one time and it is said to have been run "in all winds, including *Sunday* winds." In fact during the 13 weeks that a certain man worked at the mill he had to work 12 Sundays. (Incidentally, he then thought it time to make a shift !)

The mill was evidently named Elvey's Mill after a former owner or occupier, but the miller for many years was John Jarvis who also had a small steam mill at Newnham. When there was no wind for the Doddington Mill, Mr. Jarvis's men put in a day's work grinding farmer's corn at the Newnham steam mill.

About 1854, during a strong gale, one of the sweeps was lifted right off the mill and carried a distance of nearly 200 yards towards the road leading up Chequer's Hill.

In 1876 sweeps were erected that came from a windmill at Newnham when that mill was demolished.

In 1886, in a high wind, the braking gear broke and the sails became unmanageable. It is said that the heat caused by the friction blackened the

[1] *Reminiscences of Old Deptford*, by Thankfull Sturdee, 1895, p. 65.

woodwork and that a fire would have resulted had not the speed been eased up by continually feeding corn to the stones.

Another incident related in connection with the mill is that during a snowstorm about 1902 the fan 'ran away' owing to the slipping of cogs and, in stopping it, a crowbar of about 3 in. diameter, used on the cogs, was bent out of shape.

DOVER

Dover Castle.

One of the towers of Dover Castle was once converted into a windmill, hence the following is of interest :

> Some time during the reign of the Norman kings, three, and probably more, towers were erected outside the original lines of defence. Those that were known to exist are marked 22, 23, 24. The tower numbered 22 was called Clinton, perhaps after Geoffrey de Clinton, Chamberlain and Treasurer to Henry I and Chief Justiciar of England. It was destroyed much earlier than the others, and its position was only discovered in 1794 by the workmen who were engaged in the construction of a new road. The tower marked 23, commonly called Valence, ascribed by Lyon to William de Valence, Earl of Pembroke, half-brother of Henry III, must have been built at a much earlier date. In all probability it was erected in the time of Henry I. The bill of works for converting it into a windmill in the days of Stephen de Pencestre may yet be found in the Record Office. It was destroyed during the war with America by the Ordnance Board under the plea of economy, but the "material never paid the expense of pulling it down."[1]

> It was better known latterly as the Mill Tower, from having been turned to the pacific use of a flour mill for the garrison.[2]

Buckland.* No map reference.

This mill stood on the right-hand corner of Union Road and the site is now occupied by the premises of Messrs. Palmers, the coachbuilders.

In the presentation copy of the official Illustrated Guide to the South Eastern, Northern of France Railways, 1863, a picture is given of the windmill (here reproduced) shown as standing in close proximity to Mr. Kingsford's Buckland Brewery. From a short reference to a visit to the Brewery, one is led to conclude that the mill was occupied in the services of the Brewery and not as a corn mill, for visitors to the Brewery were allowed to ascend to the stage, from which magnificent views of the surrounding country were obtained.

The mill evidently did not stand much later than 1863, for an elderly resident of Dover, aged 83, with a good memory, whose recollection would go back at least seventy years, does not remember the mill standing in his time. He always understood that the mill was never used for grinding corn but for pumping water—evidently for the brewery.

[1] *The History of the Castle, Town and Port of Dover*, by the Rev. S. P. H. Statham, 1899, p. 250.
[2] *The Church and Fortress of Dover Castle*, by the Rev. John Puckle, M.A., 1864.

W.C.F.   M. Rowland Packer

GUILTON, Near Ash

See page 214

W.C.F.   A. W. Tiffin

HEADCORN (White Mill)   HAWKINGE (The Old Mill)

See page 220   See page 219   Facing page 196

G. Mercer

HEADCORN (Black Mill)
As painted white in its early days

See page 219

A. W. Tiffin

HEADCORN (White Mill)
General view

See page 220

DOWNE
(NEAR FARNBOROUGH)

Gorringes Farm. ¼ *mile NNE. of Church.* 1819-43.

A fire, in June 1885, gutted the interior of the fine old brick tower mill at Downe. It had been working right up to the time of the fire and had been held since 1865 by Alfred Nicholls.

After the fire the Mill House was enlarged and joined up with the tower of the mill, as depicted in the photograph. Unfortunately another fire, in about 1902, destroyed both the house and mill tower, and nothing remains to-day but a little of the foundations of the old mill.

It had had five stories, a stage, and worked three pairs of stones. In its earlier history it had been enlarged by a Mr. Bannister.

DYMCHURCH

1 *mile SW. of Church.* 1829, 1903-10.

Originally the mill at Dymchurch stood about 200 yards from its later position near where the old Mill House stands to-day. The first site is now occupied by a private house named 'Redshire' in St. Mary's Road.

Early in its history the mill was for some time owned by the Rev. Brewer, who sold it to William Hill of Ashford, a relative of the millwrights. Later owners include the names of Kelton, Prior and Young.

It was a smock and stage mill. In its early days all four sweeps were covered with the old cloth sails but later two of them were replaced by shuttered sweeps.

About 1875 the fantail gear was out of order and, instead of automatically turning the cap and sweeps into the wind, the fan spun round loosely in the wind at a fast rate. This might have proved dangerous had the wind changed suddenly, so that it was necessary for the Ashford millwrights to come to the mill on a Sunday morning and make the fantail secure.

The mill was last worked about 1882 and later became a children's playground and a *rendezvous* for visitors. It was charted as a landmark on Government maps and when it became so dilapidated as to be a danger to the public, a Mr. Davis, who bought it and wished to pull it down, had to obtain special Government permission before doing so in 1905.

When demolished, the pair of Peak stones went to Woodchurch and were installed in the Lower Mill there ; the other pair, French burr, were transferred to the Union Mill, Cranbrook.

EASTCHURCH
(ISLE OF SHEPPEY)

SW. of Church. 1596, 1610.

A windmill is distinctly shown at Eastchurch on the Symonson map of 1596 and J. Speed's map of 1610. No doubt it was one of the earlier post mills. Either this or the Elmley Mill (later referred to) gave the name to Windmill Creek and Windmill Quay.

EASTLING

(NEAR FAVERSHAM)

¾ *mile SW. of Church.* 1858-72, 1903-10.

Eastling Mill stood on the west side of the road to Lenham. It was pulled down about 1912 with the aid of a wire rope and traction engine, having become dangerous by reason of its worn condition. It had not been worked for many years, although the sweeps remained until its demolition.

It was a tarred stageless smock mill of three stories, with four spring sweeps and two pairs of stones.

Successive millers and owners include the names of :

John Hill	(1823-35)
James Godden	(1835-68)
Rev. H. A. Barrett	(1868-70)
Thomas Court	(1870-79)
James Hawkins	(1879-99)
Thomas Read	(1899-1904)

It was then let to Thomas Elvy who used it last.

EASTRY

½ *mile SW. of Church.* 1 *mill*—1596, 1695, 1736 ; 2 *mills*—1769 ; 4 *mills*— 1819-43 ; 2 *mills*—1903-10* (*one remains, worked by engine*).

A windmill is clearly shown at Eastry on the maps of 1596 and 1695. On the 1769 map two are drawn but, when we come to the 1819-43 Ordnance Map, no less than four mills are indicated. Surely this is the order of prosperity ! Three mills only, however, can be remembered with any certainty. One of these, worked for many years (round about 1833) by John Mummery, was burnt down.

The remaining two mills were in good working order when I visited them in 1905 but, on my visit in 1930, I was disappointed to find one mill completely gone. I gleaned that the method of its destruction was somewhat ruthless, it having been hauled over by a traction engine in 1926. It was by no means a derelict when demolished ; the only reason for pulling it down was "to clear the ground !" The mill was quite an old structure. A beam in it bore the date 1743.

The last mill, the sweeps and fan of which were removed in 1913, is now worked by a suction gas engine. Corn is still ground and flour made by the roller process. The mill has been in the Clark family since 1826. The earliest deed in the possession of Mr. H. H. Clark, the present owner, refers to a sale in 1770, and he believes the mill to be quite 200 years old. There are four pairs of stones—two for wheat and two for barley.

N. of Church. 1736.

E. Bowen's map of 1736 distinctly shows a mill north of Eastry Church and marked as Eastry Mill.

EDENBRIDGE

¼ *mile S. of Church.* Standing to-day, derelict.* 1858-72, 1903-10.

The Sevenoaks Library has kindly supplied the following extract from a *History of Edenbridge :*

> The windmill which stands to the west of the main road, at the south end of the town, on high ground near Blossoms Farm, was built in 1812. It was used for grinding wheat until 1886. Its sails were then removed, and in 1911 it was sold for building materials for £30.

Although thus sold, the owner bought it back at the same price because, I understand, the tenant of the Mill House could not part with the quaint old derelict.

The brick tower is in good condition. It has an unusual 'bee-hive' cap.

EGERTON
(NEAR ASHFORD)

3 *furlongs S. of Church.* Brick base remains.* 1903-10.

A shed, used as a fruit store, is all that remains of a picturesque windmill that stood on Stone Hill, Egerton. It was an octagonal smock mill on a square brick base and worked two pairs of stones.

The mill formerly stood near the Church, on the north side of the street. A house there is known to this day as Mill House, which name has been a puzzle to many. Its second home, on a lofty prominence, was by far the better position for the wind. It is believed that the transfer took place about 1818, which might account for the mill not being shown on the Ordnance Map of 1819-43.

The mill was destroyed in a severe gale on December 2nd, 1919, while the owner was away at Ashford Market. The wind suddenly changed to the opposite direction, the mill was caught tail-winded and the sweeps, fantail and cap, also half the upper portion of the body of the mill, were blown off.

ELHAM
(NEAR CANTERBURY)

¼ *mile N. of Church.* 1769.

This is probably the post mill to which Sir Charles Igglesden refers as being "on the hills above the line." "The structure," Sir Charles says, "came to grief one stormy night, and the next morning its ruins were found lying in confusion in the meadow."

Bladbean. 1 *mile* 5 *furlongs N. of Church.* 1769.

The 1769 large-scale map is my only authority for a mill at this position.

*Cullen's Hill.** 1 *furlong NW. of Church.* 1903-10.

This was a well-built smock mill, with three floors above the stage. Two pairs of stones were driven, one for wheat and the other for cattle food. There was also a flour dressing machine.

It is believed to have been built about 1820. It was taken down in 1925, after standing idle for about seven years and sadly in need of repair.

ELMLEY
(ISLE OF SHEPPEY)

SE. of Elmley Chapel. 1695.

I have no reference to a mill here other than Robert Morden's map of 1695. (See also EASTCHURCH).

ELMSTED
(NEAR ASHFORD)

Itinge Mill, or Folly Town Mill. 1 *mile N. of Church.* 1736, 1769, 1819-43.

The situation adjoining Itinge Farm (Edings Farm on the 1769 map) gave this mill its first name. For its other name I am indebted to Mr. T. H. Gambrill of Petham.

The mill was moved here from Duckpit, Petham (see Petham, Mark's Folly Mill) about 1865. It was a post mill, of open trestle type, working two pairs of stones, and using four 'common' sails. It did not stand for many years at its new home, for it is believed to have tumbled down about 1875, having decayed with old age. Only a skeleton of the sweeps remained till the last.

The mill was associated in some way with Bodsham Green Mill, Elmsted, about five furlongs to the south-west.

The mill shown on the maps above quoted must have been an earlier one.

Stone Street Mills. 1¼ *miles E. of Church.* 1 *mill*—1769 ; 2 *mills*—1819-43.

The Stone Street Mills were also known as The George Seed Mills, being situated near The George Inn, and were used as seed mills. Their purpose was for separating and cleaning the seeds of clover, trifolium and trefoil. Both mills were of smock type, on brick bases, with stages.

The mills stood opposite each other, one each side of the Stone Street. One was situated on what was then Squire Drax's Estate. This was the older of the two and is the one shown on the 1769 map as on the east side of the street.

The other stood on Misling Farm. The land is to-day owned by Mr. Edgar Hammon but at one time it was in the possession of a Mr. Kelsey, who also acquired the land and mill on the east side of the street and worked both mills.

The mill on Misling Farm was pulled down about 1868; the one on Squire Drax's Estate about 1876. Both were demolished in much the same manner. Brickwork was knocked away from the base of the mill, ropes were placed round its body, and a number of men tugged it over. Mr. Stickells, a local carpenter, superintended the demolition of the mill that stood last.

*Bodsham Green Mill.** ¾ mile NW. of Church. Base alone remains. 1819-43.*

Probably built by Sweetlove's, the old firm of millwrights of Wingham, this was a fine specimen of a brick tower mill. It had no stage and its sails nearly swept the ground.

At one time the mill was owned by Sir John Honeywood and situated on his estate. John Wood (singular coincidence in the name), who worked it last, was miller here for twenty years. Prior to his occupation R. Newport worked it. At one time a bakery was run in conjunction with the mill. Two new 'patent' sweeps and a midling were fitted by T. R. Holman in 1886.

The mill was last worked in 1890; the windshaft and all the interior fittings were removed in June, 1891; and it was pulled down about 1895. There were no sweeps remaining at the time of its demolition; two had blown off and the other two had been removed.

There is a stone still to be seen in the brick base, bearing an inscription the meaning of which is not clear ·

Itinge M
the
Level . . . .
to
Top of S . . . . .

This stone was originally in Itinge Mill, Elmsted, and it is said that the letter S on the stone refers to Staple Lees Mill, Hastingleigh. My millwright friends assume that Itinge Mill was on the 400 feet level, while Staple Lees Mill was on the 600 feet level and that, when Itinge Mill was pulled down, the stone was put in Bodsham Green Mill, the top of which was level with Staple Lees Mill. This would now be in a correct position in accordance with Ordnance datum.

ELTHAM[1]

Mottingham. 1 mile 1 furlong SW. of Church. 1819-43.

A windmill is clearly drawn on the 1819-43 map as standing on Fairy Hill, Mottingham. The spot is marked "Mill House" on the map. I have not been able to trace any one who can give information about this old mill.

[1] See note on page 151.

ERITH

Northumberland Heath. 1 mile SW. of Parish Church. Base still remaining.
    1819-43.

This large black post mill was a landmark for craft on the river. It was purchased in 1858 by Samuel Strickland, who previously had held May Place Mill, Bexley Heath. Mr. Strickland is given in an 1878 directory as the miller at Northumberland Heath. I understand the mill was owned at one time by a Mr. Cooke.

The mill premises, known to-day as the Old Mill, 46 Mill Road, are in the hands of Messrs. House Bros., corn and seed merchants, who use as a store the two-storied round-house of the mill that still stands.

Several enquiries confirm that the mill was last used about 1880 and that the sails and body were blown down one first of January, about 1892. The round-house was then roofed in with a slate roof. I understand that the top floor of the existing base has still the old original flooring. The oak cross beams (12 in. square) on the ground floor, that take the weight of the upper storey, are supported by four brick piers and are in perfect condition.

UPPER EYTHORNE
(NEAR DOVER)

1¼ miles NE. of Sibertswold (Shepherdswell) Church. 1769.

Except that it appears on the 1769 map I have nothing to say about this mill.

EAST FARLEIGH
(NEAR MAIDSTONE)

1¼ miles SE. of Church. 1819-43.

Because of its proximity to Loose Church, from which it lies only three-quarters of a mile to the south-west, I had been led to give Loose the credit for once possessing a fine old windmill. When, however, I was able to search out the spot where this mill stood, I received evidence that the village of East Farleigh is the rightful claimant to the honour.

To reach the site of the mill to-day, one would turn down the little lane to the right of the road from Stocky Lane to Well Street (about one furlong from Stocky Lane).

Mr. F. Larking, who lives at Mill House, is the owner of the property which includes the three old Mill Cottages (now made into two). He has been there for twenty-three years. His predecessor, W. Lane, was there for about seven years, and before him, J. Martin and his father, who between them held the property for seventy years. The mill was not standing in the time of any of these owners, which means that it disappeared about a century ago.

I cannot trace the name of the last miller. The Rev. Percy Mason was the last owner of the property when the windmill was existent but he did not use the mill himself.

The mill, which was of smock type, with fantail and stage, was very similar in appearance to Mr. Ward's mill at Sutton Valence. It was destroyed by fire and when digging out the foundations of the mill recently Mr. Larking found a quantity of burned wheat. Some of the stones and bricks that formed the mill's foundations are lying about to-day and it looks as though Mr. Larking is about to make use of them for a pathway.

He pointed out the actual site of the mill—a strip of land enclosed by hedges—which he referred to as "the old Platt." To-day it is an orchard and fowl run.

FAVERSHAM

Forbes Road, Gravel Pit Mill. ¾ mile SW. of Church. 1819-43.

A near-by gravel pit gave this mill its name. It stood close to the railway line, in what is now a residential part of the town and was pulled down when the site was turned into a brickfield. It was a black smock mill, on a brick base of one floor and only used as a 'pug' or 'seed' mill. It was pulled down about 1910. In its derelict state—the condition in which it stood for many years—the mill is said to have leaned very much from the perpendicular, which made it a constant source of wonder that it did not topple over.

Hangman's Lane Mill. 5 furlongs S.W. of Church. 1819-43

The gibbet which once stood near this mill gave it its name. Its position was north of Watling Street (London Road), a little to the east of Upper St. Ann's Road. It was of smock type ; James Bennett was the miller ; it was pulled down about 1855.

Pumping Mill.* ½ mile S. of Watling Street. Standing to-day, disused. 1858-72, 1903-10.

The mill that stands here to-day without its sweeps, along the Faversham to Ashford road, has never been a corn mill. It was built by the Corporation for pumping water, as an auxiliary to the usual steam pumps. It was of 15 h.p. and raised, when necessary, as many as 10,000 gallons of water an hour.

FAWKHAM
(NEAR LONGFIELD)

Approx. ¾ mile E. of Church. 1719.

Except that it appears on the map in Dr. Harris' *History of Kent*, 1719, I have no record of this mill's history.

FOLKESTONE

*Cheriton, Ashley Mill.** ½ mile NW. of Shorncliffe Station. Brick base remains.* 1903-10.

Humphrey, the Cranbrook millwright, built this mill, said to have been a small replica of the large Union Mill at Cranbrook. There was exactly the same arrangement of the machinery, except that it worked two pairs of stones instead of three.

It was originally built at Hythe, where it was owned by the Horton family. It was purchased by Mr. Brissenden, a builder of Sandgate, who pulled it down and rebuilt it in Tile Kiln Lane, Cheriton, at a cost of £700. A millwright named Spray, of Folkestone, installed the machinery, and it was set to work by a Mr. Gilpin, of Dover, in 1877.

Between 1877 and 1889 the mill changed hands five times and was then taken over by Mr. W. Martin, who worked up a good business. By reason of the growth of Cheriton, more general trade was brought to the mill. It had previously been occupied mainly for cattle and poultry grist. Flour was last made at the mill in 1891, the flour dressing machinery then having become obsolete.

In 1902 one of the sweeps broke off close to the shaft, when running. The one opposite appeared to be weak, so it was decided to have two new sweeps. Unfortunately the old midling was thought good enough and the new sweeps were duly affixed but it collapsed and a sweep was broken away with it. Thus ended the use of wind power at the mill. A gas engine was then installed, which ran on until 1919, when, by reason of decay, the fine old tower was pulled down and the present brick building erected as a corn store. The square tarred brick base of the old windmill still stands, with the new red brickwork of the tower carried up to almost the height of the original mill. The photograph of this structure as it stands to-day takes in Mr. Geo. E. Ride, a genial Kentish windmiller, who has helped considerably with information about our old mills.

For some years prior to 1895 Ashley Mill was worked with two canvas sails and two spring shuttered sweeps but in 1895 all four sweeps were spring shuttered.

Cheriton. 5 furlongs ENE. of Cheriton Church. 1819-43.

My miller friend, Mr. W. Martin, assures me that there was another mill at Cheriton before the one referred to, for when he first went to Ashley Mill the old folks used to speak of it and how it was burnt down, the sweeps revolving in the flames.

This mill is evidently the one shown on the 1819-43 map, situated close to and north of the railway, just west of the road that crosses the line. Its position would have been about three furlongs south-west of Ashley Mill.

In October 1869 some repairs were carried out for Jesse Stockwell at 'Cheriton Mill' by the Canterbury millwrights. Perhaps this 'other' Cheriton

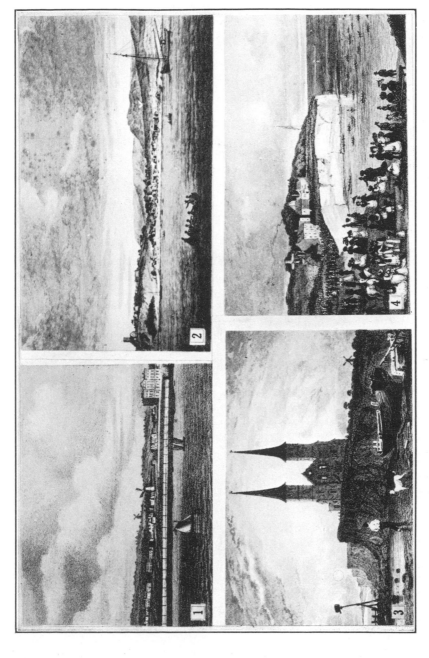

1. HERNE BAY and HERNE MILLS.   2. FOLKESTONE (Sweeps of Old Mill peeping above the hill).
3. RECULVER and the distant Chislet Mill (G. Shepherd).   4. PEGWELL BAY, 1828 (G. Shepherd)

See pages 187, 205, 221, 222, 254

Facing page 204

W.C.F.

HIGHAM (Rose's Mill)

See page 223

W.C.F.

HOO COMMON (Ballard's Mill)

See page 225

W.C.F.

N. Coles Finch

HILDENBOROUGH (Watts' Cross Mill)

See page 224

Facing page 205

Mill is the one. It could not have been the Ashley Mill as that was not erected at Cheriton until 1877.

Cheriton. No map reference.

As noted under Lympne, it is said that Lympne Mill originally stood at Cheriton, being moved to Lympne on farm wagons and rebuilt.

½ mile N. of Church, or ½ mile E. of Central Station. 1769, 1819-43.

The 1769 map refers to this as "Folkestone Mill." Its position according to the 1819-43 map is about three furlongs north-east of the mill (noted later) at Millfield, close to and south of the railway line, just east of the road from Uphill that crosses the line and leads south. I regret having been unable to trace any information regarding this old mill.

Along the coast.* 1769.

In an undated and beautiful old lithographic print of *Old Folkestone from the Sea*, reproduced in this volume, one notes the irregular scattered fisher dwellings along the foreshore, before modernization had set its seal upon the spot. Peeping above the near hill crest can be seen the two upper sweeps of a mill, behind which rises the higher and more distant range of hills. The mill shown near the coast on the 1769 map is evidently the same mill. Its position was half a mile south-east of "Folkestone Mill." Probably it was an old post mill. It does not appear on the early Ordnance Map and one presumes it was cleared away before the beginning of the nineteenth century.

Dawson's Mill, Millfield.* ¼ mile SE. of Central Station. See also Bethersden (Black Mill), and Penenden Heath. 1819-43.

The mill at Millfield was known to have been taken over by William Marsh from a Mr. Dawson in 1873. Prior to Mr. Dawson's occupation it was worked by a Mr. Gardner. In 1885 it was purchased by a George Jarvis who removed it to Bethersden where it was used for many years for timber sawing. It had always been used for corn grinding at Folkestone, however, and in Mr. Marsh's time a bakery was worked in conjunction with the mill.

The site is now occupied by the nurseries of Messrs. G. & A. Clark, Ltd., of Dover. Where, half a century ago, there were open fields, and a windmill had the free play of the winds, there is now a residential district.

In the growth of buildings the mill had to be removed and Mr. Marsh considered whether he would transfer it and the business elsewhere. He had seriously thought of re-erecting the mill on one of the Martello towers along the coast, if permission could be obtained. "You'd get enough wind *there*," some one remarked. "And perhaps *too much*," rejoined another.

(See also pages 64, 67, 161 and 255.)

FRINDSBURY
(NEAR ROCHESTER)

Quarry Mill. * 1 *furlong SE. of Church.* 1596, 1610, 1736, 1769.

The old Quarry Mill at Frindsbury is of special interest, for it was one of the earliest 'open trestle' or 'tripod' post mills in Kent.

It is the only post mill known to have existed in Frindsbury. It stood at the rear of Frindsbury Church, in the direction of the chalk quarries, east of the path leading to Upnor, at a spot known as Windmill Hill, overlooking Limehouse Reach of the Medway.

About 1850 it 'ran away' in a storm, caught fire, and was completely destroyed.

Prospect Hill. The Little Mill, or Manwaring's Mill. * ½ *mile NW. of Church* 1769, 1819-43.

This was the smaller of a pair of windmills that stood on Prospect Hill, built originally for a man named Baldock. Although small in comparison with its companion, it was really a large mill, working four pairs of stones. It was a black (tarred) smock mill with one floor under the stage—which was very narrow and had no railing.

No flour was made at the mill. The ground corn was conveyed in sack barrows along a concreted pathway connecting the mill with its larger neighbour, complete with its 'silks' and a high-class flour trade.

For eleven years, from 1843 to 1854, the mill was held by Thomas Manwaring from Preston Mill, Wingham, after whom it was named. Later it was owned by Mr. Kimmins who had all the three windmills remaining in Frindsbury—the Prospect Hill pair and one on Frindsbury Hill ; he also had held another that once stood on Frindsbury Hill, which completed the two pairs. In addition to these windmills he had two steam mills in the district and also one at Chatham. The three windmills and three steam mills were all in good working order in 1880.

The 20 h.p. engine and Cornish single-flue boiler from one of the steam mills (Chatham Intra Mill) were bought by Mr. Geo. E. Ride for £100 and installed in the Great Mill at Sheerness, being the last auxiliary power used in that mill. This very same steam engine came originally from a steam mill at Tonbridge, having been purchased and installed at Chatham by Mr. Kimmins.

The Little Mill was struck by lightning and given for the clearance of the site about 1886.

Prospect Hill. The Great Mill or Rose's Mill. * ½ *mile NW. of Church. Base used as cottages.* 1819-43.

The millwright, Warren, of Hawkhurst, used to say that this was the highest mill in Kent. It was certainly in every way a large mill. It had three floors under the stage and its sweeps were no less than 9 ft. 2 in. wide and 40 ft. long. It drove four pairs of 4 ft. 6 in. stones and was capable of turning out

250 sacks of flour a week. Together with its companion, the Little Mill, 400 sacks of flour could be produced in one week.

An unusual feature of the mill was that its interior was lathed and plastered and it had staircases as in a dwelling house.

A Mr. Yates worked the mill for some time and it was later acquired by W. Kimmins, who is said to have consulted the millwrights as to installing another two pairs of stones. Being such a powerful mill it was quite capable of driving six pairs of stones but unfortunately there was not sufficient room for the additional installation. The mill ran so regularly that one would almost think she was being driven by steam.

During Mr. Kimmins' occupation Mr. George Ride was stone dresser at the mill for three or four years—about 1859 to 1863. Mr. Ride's son, Mr. Geo. E. Ride, relates that once when his father was working at the mill a heavy gale sprung up and he asked Mr. Kimmins if it were wise to work the mill throughout the night. "Of course," replied Mr. Kimmins, who remarked that the mill had worked through other gales equally as severe and he felt sure she would be all right. It was indeed a rough night but all through the storm the mill toiled. Then daylight broke, the wind abated and the mill was brought to a standstill. She had accomplished yet another achievement but her neighbour a little way off, the House Mill, although a large and strong mill, was not such a warrior and had been obliged to shed a tear of mortification at not withstanding the fury of the elements. This tear took the form of a sweep wrenched off during the night's gale and found embedded vertically in the ground. It looked like a flagstaff placed ready to carry a flag in honour of the Great Mill's victory !

John Rose was the last occupier of the mill. It was pulled down about 1890 and its destruction was a matter of great regret. The reason for its demolition, known only to a few, is at least pathetic but not of special interest.

The base of the mill has been converted into a pair of substantial cottages.

Kimmins' Mill. 3 *furlongs NNW. of Church.* 1819-43.

This mill stood in a field near to and in a north-easterly direction from the lately destroyed ruined tower of the House Mill, near the foot of Prospect Hill. It was pulled down about 1865.

I learned from my friend, John J. Freeman, whose uncle was killed by the revolving sweeps of the mill, that it was a smock mill with no base. The sweeps reached very close to the ground and were the cause of the fatal accident.

I understand the mill was only used for grinding pollard. There were two pairs of stones and four 'common' sails.

The site is now that of a brickfield.

*House Mill.** 3 *furlongs NNW. of Church.* 1819-43, 1903-10.

This mill was most frequently known as the House Mill, because of its proximity to the house of the owner, Mr. Kimmins. It has also been known as Frindsbury Mill, or Kimmins' Mill. It stood on Frindsbury Hill, near Bill Street Road, opposite Prospect Hill, on the road to Higham.

It was a black smock mill, working four pairs of stones, which were all on one floor and were driven 'underdrift.' It did no flour dressing ; the whole of the meal ground was taken by conveyors into a steam mill adjoining, and dressed there.

The mill stood sadly derelict for about thirty years and was finally demolished in 1931, when the following letter appeared in a local paper :

Dear Mr. Gossiper,

You will learn with regret that I am leaving Frindsbury. I am the last of my family in this district. Years ago many of my brothers were settled near me. We all occupied exalted positions and led busy lives ; yet so exacting was our calling that the whole time was one continual 'grind.' I was never very robust and was affected by every change of the wind. For many generations I have occupied the same high situation, exposed to rain, hail, snow, thunderstorms and gales ; and whilst others were sleeping in their beds I have been working all night as well as all day. No! I did not belong to a trade union. It was hard and strenuous work, yet my path through life may be described as "floury." Though most peaceably inclined, my enemies had an uncomfortable time if they got caught in my embrace, for then they were crushed. My family on the paternal side were all landsmen, but we have some distant relatives who are amphibious ; that is, they were always half in and half out of water. This branch of the family were always called the Water Mills ; but I have no patience with their teetotal proclivities. Their position, too, was always low down, whilst ours was always up on the hills, and we were designated the Wind Mills.

A family of parvenues have sprung up styling themselves Steam Mills. They have taken all the wind out of our sails, and their competition has ruined us. For some years past I have stood unworked, unpainted and slowly going to decay, looking like a giant scarecrow : my limbs amputated, my ribs showing through my body, allowing the winds to whistle through my entire system. On Easter Monday men with ropes and iron windlass came and pulled part of my headgear down. No longer will men look up to me with respect. No longer shall I form a familiar figure in the landscape. No longer will the fishermen of the Medway look to me to see which way the wind blows ; and I am afraid I shall not even be able to vote at the next General Election! My ultimate fate is now a foregone conclusion. My body will be cremated piecemeal, and there will not be many of my older friends to shed a tear for me.

I remain, dear Mr. Gossiper,

Your sorrowful and shrinking friend,

The Frindsbury Mill.

P.S.—No flowers by request.

FRINSTED
(NEAR SITTINGBOURNE)

Frinsted Mill. N. of Church. 1736.

Apart from the fact that a windmill is shown just north of Frinsted Church, and east of Wormshill, on the 1736 Bowen Map, I cannot trace anything.

HOATH (Fuller's Mill) W.C.F.

HOATH A. W. Tiffin
Mill-stones in crazy garden path.

See page 225

See page 225

W.C.F.
WEST HOUGHAM

M. Rowland Packer

See page 226

Facing page 208

Messrs. Geerings (Ashford)   A. W. Tiffin

KENNINGTON
(Wind, Steam and Water Mill)

See page 228

Ridley's Studios, Tenterden   M. Rowland Packer

HIGH HALDEN   KESTON (Old Post Mill)

See page 223   *See page 229*   *Facing page 209*

FRITTENDEN
(NEAR STAPLEHURST)

7 furlongs NW. of Church.

Local inhabitants have heard that a windmill used to stand at this position, that it was situated on the right-hand side of the road from Maplehurst watermill to the Staplehurst road, about one furlong north of the watermill.

On a plan of the property dated 1836-7, the field directly opposite the watermill is known as Mill Field, and the field immediately adjoining that is called Windmill Field.

The following is an extract from a list of Martyrs of Kent. One wonders if the miller referred to worked a windmill or a watermill.

> Frittenden.—William Allin and Katharine, his wife. Allin was an intelligent and pious miller. It is recorded of him that in a year of dearth when the poor were like to starve, he fed them, selling his corn one half cheaper than others did. He fed them also with the bread of life, and read and expounded to them the Scriptures. This being known to the popish priests, he and his wife were committed to prison. They, with four other women and one man, were burnt at Maidstone, June 18th, 1557.[1]

Sinkhurst Green.* 7 furlongs N. of Church. Standing to-day, derelict. 1829, 1903-10.

This old Frittenden post mill is not shown on the early Ordnance Survey Maps but it appears on the 1829 Greenwood Map. Although of the older post type and doubtless between 200 and 300 years of age, it is not shown on the 1769 map. Local people think it was *moved* here, which would account for its absence from any earlier map than 1829.

It presents a sorry spectacle to-day, in its sweepless, broken-down condition. The owner, Mr. Thomas Durey, has been offered "a pound or two" for the mill for demolition but it is of more value to him as a store for tools, fruit and potatoes, and for chopping wood; so the weather-beaten derelict may stand for some years yet. Mr. Durey and his son-in-law have been patching up the mill and doing some rough repairs in order to hold it together.

Mr. Durey, who is now 70 years of age, worked the mill up till the Great War. Many difficulties then combined to make it impossible to carry on work at the mill, and as "no work, no pay, is the order of the day," it fell into disrepair as well as disuse. Latterly, owing to a broken breast beam, the four single-shuttered sweeps hung down loosely from the mill. The sweeps and windshaft were removed by Mr. Frank Pain in 1930.

No doubt the mill originally had flour cloth sails and later, probably, two cloths and two spring sweeps. It originally had a wooden windshaft which the millwright, Warren, replaced by an iron shaft, in about 1880. The mill was built on low ground but in its early days it stood fairly isolated and caught the main south-west and north-east winds unchecked by trees or houses.

[1] *The Martyrs of Kent*, J. H. Wood, 1885, p. 11.

O

A directory of 1878 has the entry :

Matthew Durey, miller, Sinksnorth Green.

The Green, as it is known locally, has, I understand, been called, variously, Frittenden Green, Sinksnorth Green and, as noted on recent maps, Sinkhurst Green. The mill is said to have been built originally by the farmer who lived at the adjoining farm of Appleton and that the succeeding owners were a family by the name of Sanders.

GILLINGHAM

Stedman's Mill.* *3 furlongs N. of St. Mark's Church.* 1819-43.

This mill originally stood at Snodland, near the site of the present Clock Tower. It was purchased there in 1839 by John Stedman and removed by barge from Paper Mill Wharf on the Medway to Gillingham Quay. The cost of dismantling, moving and re-erecting was about £100.

I know nothing of the mill's history at Gillingham, save that it was struck by lightning and burnt down in a violent storm which raged on the night of June 28th, 1892.

Stedman's Mill. *3 furlongs N. of St. Mark's Church.* 1819-43.

This mill also was known as Stedman's Mill. Like its companion, it drove three pairs of stones and was of smock type. It was used only for grinding pollards. About 1888 was the date of its demolition.

Charles Tutt was the miller about 1874—he worked the mill for the owner, Mr. Stedman. Mr. Tutt later worked for Mr. Bates at the Milton Regis Mill. He was found drowned in the water tank that supplied the auxiliary steam engine with water.

Charter Street, Huggins' Mill. *3 furlongs N. of St. Mark's Church.* *No map reference.*

Huggins' Mill was destroyed by fire. Its destruction must have afforded a spectacle worth witnessing, for I am told that its owner, Mr. Huggins, took a party of friends on the river to see it burn down.

Originally an oil-cake mill, it was converted into a corn mill. It drove three pairs of stones and was considered a large mill.

¼ mile E. of Hastings Arms Inn. 1819-43.

This mill stood in Mulberry Tree Place, at the junction of Grange Road with the roadway leading to the Quay. Of its history I can glean nothing.

Friday's Mill, Grange.* *7 furlongs ESE. of Gillingham Church.* 1858-72.

Isaac Friday, sen., was the builder of this mill, hence its name. He was the miller in 1839, according to an old directory. The mill stood on Mill Hill opposite Peckham Lodge, near the Twydell Redoubt.

I have no definite date of its destruction but I believe it was pulled down about 1896. It was, I understand, destroyed by Government orders, as it was in the line of fire from the fort built on the main road near by.

In 1878 the miller was Mr. J. Ride. The last miller was Mr. Frank Pain who, later, took Star Mill, Chatham.

By courtesy of Mr. Walter Stedman, of Grange, I am able to give a picture of this fine old mill, upon the stage of which may be seen a figure wearing a tall hat. This is James Boyer Stedman, Walter Stedman's father. James Boyer Stedman married Sophia Friday, daughter of the builder of the mill, Isaac Friday, who ran the mill for many years until his death in 1851, when it was carried on by his son, Isaac Friday, jun., later passing into other hands. The Fridays were noted millers in those times, being associated with three of the Hollingbourne watermills. A cousin of Isaac Friday ran the long-since vanished windmill at Hartlip Hill.

It was James Boyer Stedman who built the Brompton Steam Flour Mills, where he brought up a family of six boys and four girls. The name of Stedman in association with our windmills goes back farther than I can trace.

GOODNESTONE
(NEAR CANTERBURY)

SSW. of Church. 1736.

Reference to E. Bowen's map of 1736 proves the existence of a windmill, south-south-west of the Church and south-east of Ewell. It is probably another of the old post mills.

GOUDHURST

*Town Mill.** 1 *furlong NNE. of Church.* 1819-43.

Only the oldest inhabitants of Goudhurst can remember this picturesque smock and stage mill with its black cap, for it was taken down about 1890. It stood behind, and towered above, the row of houses facing the Church. A magnificent view can be obtained from the hill that was once crowned by both Church and mill. Looking down from the hill-top at Goudhurst into the plains below, one can echo the well-known saying (at least, it is well known in Goudhurst !) :

> If Kent is the Garden of England,
> Then Goudhurst is the Garden of Kent.

The mill was built by Humphrey, the millwright of Cranbrook, who also built mills at Hythe, Sheerness, and Cranbrook.

The mill had been in the Norrington family for a great many years, Mr. Joseph Norrington having worked it up till about 1875. A Mr. Thompson was the last miller, but he only worked the mill for about two years.

At one time the business was a combined one of milling and baking, but latterly there was very little of either. Mr. Norrington had once spoken of turning the mill into a sawmill, as trade was so poor, but this suggestion did not materialise.

After the mill was closed down the property was purchased by the late Mr. Haskett Smith. A letter from his son, Mr. W. P. Haskett Smith, states :

> My father had the 'swifts' taken off, and put on it a lead roof with railings, so as to preserve a most admirable viewpoint, superior in some respects to the church tower. The final demolition took-place before 1895 and probably not much before or after 1890. As a working mill it had probably been disused for ten or fifteen years before that.

After its demolition much of the mill tackle went to Mr. George Jarvis at Bethersden. The windshaft and other parts were installed in the Black Mill there and proved to be the best gearing Mr. Jarvis had ever worked in a mill.

The evidence of a windmill at Goudhurst is perpetuated in the name of Mill House (situated about forty yards to the south of the mill site) and Mill Cottages (which never had any connection with the mill!). There is no trace of the mill above ground, but Mr. L. J. Prickett, of Goudhurst, who has always taken a great interest in local history, states that there are remains existent of a cellar that had been built beneath the mill. Mill House has been altered considerably since the days of the mill, for at that time it consisted of two separate dwellings, in one of which the miller himself lived.

As mentioned under Appledore, a 'windmill token' issued by the Appledore miller in 1794 was also "payable at W. Friggles, Goudhurst."

(See also Addenda, page 314.)

ISLE OF GRAIN

Near Grain. 1596, 1610.

Symonson's map of 1596 clearly indicates this mill and it appears again on Speed's map of 1610.

1¼ miles ESE. of All Hallows Church. 1769.

The mill here referred to stood quite close to the Salt Pans on the eastern margin of the Creek, and it may reasonably be assumed that it pumped the water from the Creek to the evaporating pans.

The presence of windmills in connection with Salt Pans is noted in other places, for instance, at Stonar, near Richborough. The association of windmills in providing salt for our use gives an added interest to the vital services they have rendered in past years.

2 miles SW. of St. Peter's Church. 1769, 1819-43.

This mill is shown as standing near Red House and adjacent to a salt works of considerable extent. The site is near the railway terminus at Port Victoria.

KINGSDOWN, NEAR SEVENOAKS
The old Post Mill and the re-erected Smock Mill.

See page 230

KINGSDOWN, NEAR SEVENOAKS
See page 230

KINGSNORTH
See page 231

Facing page 212

1. KNOCKHOLT ("Invicta Mag.," Vol. I, p. 126).   2. MARGATE (Drapers' Mills, standing on either side of the tower of the Corporation pumping mill).   3. MARGATE (Gouger's Mills, Cliftonville).   *Inset*: MAIDSTONE WINDMILL INN TOKEN, obverse and reverse (enlarged three diameters).   Loaned by Mr. E. T. Clark.

See pages 233, 241, 242, 243

GRAVESEND

Windmill Hill. * 5 *furlongs S. of Church.* 1 *mill*—1596 ; 2 *mills*—1769, 1819-43.

Standing on the crest of Windmill Hill, near the Observatory, these two mills at one time were doubtless a prominent feature in the landscape. They were both post mills with round-houses. From the dates given above, it will be seen that Windmill Hill, known in far-off days as Rouge Hill and, later as Ruggen Hill, was occupied by a mill, or pair of mills, for two and a half centuries. The hill stands up prominently amid the otherwise flat part of Kent and it was an ideal wind ledge for adapting the ever noticeable breeze, and sometimes gale, that came off the Thames estuary.

Windmill Hill was formerly a Beacon Station. In Elizabethan times its light, part of the network of coastal beacons, passed the 'signal of danger' on to Erith, Shooter's Hill and to the London beacons. Reference to a map of Kentish beacons discloses the fact that many of these prominent sites were later occupied by windmills, which were used as landmarks for the navigation of vessels around the coast.

The 1769 large-scale map was evidently prepared from a survey made prior to 1763, for at this date one of the old Gravesend mills, probably that shown on the 1596 Symonson map, was destroyed by fire. This mill stood about 120 yards north-east of the other mill and a circular patch, apparently its old foundations, could be seen up to the time the Corporation took the hill over (in 1902) and laid all the top down to grass.

In 1787 the southernmost mill was pulled down, partly, some authorities say, because of a fire that had damaged it. It was soon rebuilt. At one time it was owned and worked by William Moss, one of a family of millers of that name who had the Stock Mills, Essex. It was last worked in 1856. It stood idle for some years and was then converted into a show building. Its upper stories were enlarged and 'ornamented' with protective railings, while two wooden effigies of soldiers guarded the entrance steps on the ground floor. On the very top, from which a magnificent view could be obtained, a sort of Victorian *camera obscura* was built.

Unfortunately, with the advance of time, and perhaps of ownership, the building, then hardly recognizable as a windmill, fell into disuse and decay and by degrees it was taken down. What was finally left of it, together with the old Mill House adjoining, went up in a glorious beacon in an excess of rejoicing on Mafeking night in May, 1900. The Mill House had for a number of years been used as licensed premises and called the Belle Vue.

The days of the old windmills are happily kept in memory by the names of two nearby licensed houses in Shrubbery Terrace that runs up steeply from Parrock Street near to the top of the hill. One of these houses—still quite a picturesque wayside tavern redolent of old-time peace and quietness—bears the charming name of The Miller's Cottage, whilst the other house—rather modernized—is called The Windmill Tavern.

Denton. 1 mile E. of Church. 1819-43.

The 1819-43 map shows this mill near Denton Wharf.
Mr. F. A. Mansfield, in his *History of Gravesend*, says :

Until about half a century ago a windmill stood at the rear of the 'Ship and Lobster.'[1]

He might have referred to a 'Sulphur Mill' that is believed to have stood behind the 'Ship and Lobster' about a century ago ; but a windmill is known definitely to have stood about 150 yards to the west of this inn.
Mr. Alex J. Philip, M.B.E., F.L.A., Librarian of the Gravesend Public Library, says :

I have no evidence as to whether the Sulphur Mill actually existed, or whether it was a windmill or not. It is said to have been only a blind for smuggling operations, as soundings from the surface show hollow workings beneath. The smuggled goods were landed at Folkestone, carried overland to Denton, transferred to boats in the Thames and carried up to Barking, where they were distributed.

The mill, according to the same authority,

was situated in the grounds of the first house on the right leading towards the canal at the corner of which is what used to be Wood's Powder Company's office. The remains of the mill were still to be seen some twenty-five years ago. I have a pencil drawing (in my own possession) of about 1840 showing the mill complete and standing. Mr. Mansfield's statement that a mill stood to the rear of the 'Ship and Lobster' should not be confused with the actual fact that the mill, as illustrated in my drawing, stood to the west of the 'Ship and Lobster' behind the river wall.

GREENWICH [2]

Greenwich Reach.* No map reference.

On the authority of Messrs. Holman Bros., the Canterbury millwrights, I can state that there used to be two windmills at Greenwich—a white tower mill with a bee-hive cap and a black post mill.
Unfortunately none of the local guide books in the Greenwich Library has any reference to the windmills.

GUILTON
(NEAR ASH)

3 furlongs N. of Ash Church.* Base remaining. 1903-10.

The following note appeared in a local paper dated October 20th, 1923 :

DEMOLITION OF OLD LANDMARK

After standing for several generations, the old windmill at Guilton, which has not been used for some years, has now been found to be unsafe owing to decay in the

[1] *History of Gravesend*, by F. A. Mansfield, Gravesend and Dartford Reporter, 1922, p. 3.
[2] See note on page 151.

woodwork. Accordingly it is being demolished. From its position on a hill, the mill could be seen for miles around. Some of the oldest inhabitants say it was formerly a landmark for ships passing near the coast.

The mill stood near The Volunteer Inn and was a smock mill, driving three pairs of stones. The sweeps had been taken down some years before the demolition of the mill itself and, latterly, during the ownership of Mr. Thos. Marshall, it was worked by a steam engine. The base of the mill remains and has been converted into a store.

Good Intent Mill. 3 furlongs W. of Ash Church. 1 *mill*—1769 ; 2 *mills*—1819-43 ; 3 *mills*—1854* ; 1 *mill*—1903-10.

William Carter was the miller at this mill for many years (he had it in the 1870's), hence it was known sometimes as 'Carter's Mill.' It was a smock mill, without a fan, the cap being turned by a wheel and rope. It was demolished about 1918.

According to the 1819-43 map, there were a pair of mills and, later still, in 1854, as evidenced by an illustration, here reproduced from *Inventorium Sepulchrale*, there were three. As shown, two of these mills were large smock and fantail mills and the other a post and round-house mill with a wheel at the end of the tailpole for facilitating the moving of the body of the mill into the wind. This old post mill and also one of the smock mills evidently disappeared over half a century ago, for I can ascertain no local news of them. The mill shown on the 1903-10 Ordnance Map is evidently the 'Good Intent' smock mill.

Inventorium Sepulchrale, a book edited by Charles Roach Smith, published in 1856, contains an account of some antiquities dug out of a sandpit at Guilton by the Rev. Bryan Faussett, between the years 1760 and 1763. In 1759, when the latter first visited Guilton, he wrote in his journal :

> At a place commonly called Gilton Town, in the parish of Ash, next Sandwich, in the county of Kent, on the right hand of the high road leading from Canterbury to Sandwich, and about a quarter of a mile short of Ash Street, is a large and deep sand-pit, in which from time to time for a great many years past, whenever sand has been dug within three or four feet of the surface, or whenever the surface has rushed down after frost or rain, as it usually does, many antiquities of different sorts have been discovered and picked up, either by the servants of the farmer who used the land, who have often been employed in carrying out the sand to manure the farm, or by the inhabitants of the village of Ash, or, perhaps, more particularly, by the servants of a miller, who has two large windmills on the west side of and close to this sand-pit. . . . The surface of the ground has been so entirely levelled by the plough, that not the least trace or appearance of a single tumulus is anywhere to be seen. The mills stand, as I observed before, at the west, or rather north-west, side of the pit, and upon rather higher ground than the surface near the other sides of it. And, I imagine, that on that spot, the most valuable antiquities might be discovered, as the highest part of the field was reckoned the most honourable. But the miller has put up a fence, beyond which he will on no account suffer any sand to be dug or removed ; and, indeed, he is much in the right, for otherwise his mills would soon be in the bottom of the pit, the sand being even now (notwithstanding his precaution) continually crumbling and running down after very wet or frosty weather.

GUSTON
(NEAR DOVER)

*Swingate Mill.** ¾ *mile ESE. of Church. Ceased working in* 1930. 1903-10.

Swingate Mill is with us to-day and is still a fine specimen of a Kent tower mill. It was built for Mr. John Mummery in 1849 and was in the Mummery family for seventy-three years.

It was an exceptionally well-built mill. I understand that the sweeps, cap, brake-wheel and many other parts were made specially for a windmill intended to be erected along the Rope Walk, by the Shakespeare Cliff, Dover, and in this exposed coastal position the mill would need to be exceptionally strong. It had been required by a large oil mill for crushing seeds but the proposition fell through because it was thought that the mill might not function properly, on account of the wind being broken by the background of the cliffs. The various parts were then purchased by Mr. John Mummery, the bricks ordered specially from a local brickfield (no less than 40,000 being required) and the mill erected at Guston, three miles north of Dover.

It was evidently a mill to be proud of and much business was done there at one time. Although now only grinding cattle food, the mill once made much flour which was dressed through silk. There are three pairs of stones.

The mill worked throughout the Great War but did not come under Government control, as it had ceased to make flour.

Mr. E. A. Mummery discontinued milling in 1918 and in December 1922 the mill was purchased by Mr. George Sheaff, who has since sold it, as he could not make a living there—which is, of course, typical of windmilling in these days.

The mill has been struck by lightning twice within the last twenty-five years, and on one occasion the links in the hoisting chain were welded together.

Behind an old spout in Swingate Mill there used to be (alas, most if not all of it is now obliterated) a chronicle of all the harvests since about 1850. The dates when the first new wheat was received each year and any interesting facts about exceptionally wet or dry summers and winters, causing loss to farmers, were recorded ; also the signatures, with dates of coming and going, of most of the apprentices and workmen at the mill. It might almost be called a 'Miller's Log.' At any rate, it shows that in times gone by the workmen had a love for their mill just as sailors have for their ship.

HARBLEDOWN
(NEAR CANTERBURY)

*The Old Black Mill.** ¼ *mile SE. of Church.* 1819-43, 1858-72, 1903-10.

Although this mill is not shown on the large-scale map of 1769, it appears on two prints in the Beany Institute, one of a west view of St. Nicholas Leper

Hospital, dated 1780, and the other dated 1857. It is noted on the 1819-43 and later Ordnance Maps, as on the south side of The Pilgrim's Way, near its junction with Watling Street.

I understand that it was one of the most picturesque of windmills and a favourite with the printers of Christmas cards, who pictured it as perpetually snow-bound and made it sparkle with crystal imitation of frost.

It was of smock type, working three pairs of stones. Mr. John Mummery had it from 1857 to 1859, after which the mill was worked by Mr. Charles Hancock until 1892. From that date there was a number of successive tenants but none seemed to prosper. At last the mill was doomed as unsafe. Two traction engines with wire ropes were sent to pull it down on July 9th, 1913. Pictures of this operation are in the possession of Mr. Holman, by whose courtesy they are reproduced here.

(See also page 96)

HARTLEY

(NEAR LONGFIELD)

1719.

The map accompanying Dr. Harris' *History of Kent*, 1719, shows this mill as situated about mid-way between Hartley and Ridley Churches.

HARTLIP

(NEAR SITTINGBOURNE)

Friday's Mill. ½ *mile NNE. of Church.* 1596, 1736, 1769, 1819-43, 1858-72.

Hartlip Mill was destroyed by fire in June, 1887. It stood on Hartlip Hill, about 200 yards to the south of old Watling Street. The owner was Miss A. Dawson.

It was at one time worked by Mr. J. Friday (who now lives at Bredhurst and is about ninety years of age) in partnership with his brother. Mr. Geo. E. Ride tells me that it was a large, white-painted smock mill, having steam power attached, with a high brick chimney. He also writes :

> She was considered to be a very ugly mill, having an extraordinarily large body and very narrow sweeps. On account of the large body there was a back lash with wider sweeps so that narrow ones were the only sweeps that could be satisfactorily worked.

Mr. Boorman succeeded Messrs. Friday Bros., and it was in his time that the mill was destroyed by fire. He was the last to work the mill.

I learn from a local resident, aged 60, that his father used to get all his meal for pigs, and his mother her flour for bread making, from Hartlip Mill. The whole family used to glean in the adjacent cornfields and the gleanings were taken to the mill to be ground into flour.

HASTINGLEIGH
(NEAR ASHFORD)

Staple Lees Mill or Brown Town Mill. ¾ *mile NW. of Church.* 1736.

This was an old post mill. The site is now occupied by a reservoir of the Mid-Kent Water Company.

The 'S' on the stone in the base of Bodsham Green Mill, Elmsted, refers to this mill.

HAWKHURST

Hawkhurst had six windmill sites, though not a trace of any windmill remains. Here is the list in order of date as they have been traced on the various maps :

1. 1719. South of Hawkhurst Church, near Old Conghurst, on the north bank of the river Rother. This mill is shown on the map accompanying Dr. Harris' *History of Kent*, 1719.
2. 1736 and 1769. ½ mile north-west of church, on the road from High Street to Hawkhurst Horn.
3. 1736 and 1819-43.* 1 mile 1½ furlongs N.E. of Church, at Pipsden, near the Tudor Hall School (now a hotel by that name). An oil painting, which shows this fine old post mill, entitled *Evening at Hawkhurst, Kent,* by the famous artist, M. Cazin, is in the possession of Mrs. Gunther, of Tongswood, Hawkhurst, by whose kind permission the picture is reproduced in this volume. The painting came from the Louis Huth Collection and was purchased at Christie's in May 1905, by the late Mr. C. E. Gunther. A label on the back of the framed picture gives the date 1874, and states that it was painted at Mr. Louis Huth's residence, Possingworth, Hawkhurst, where the artist was visiting.
4. 1819-43. 7 furlongs N.N.W. of Church, north of the main road at High Street. "A small post mill," says an elderly resident. It is believed to be the same mill as No. 2, moved here. The site to-day is occupied by fir trees on a bank. The mill is said to have been cleared away over half a century ago.
5. 1819-43. 1 mile 3 furlongs north-east of church. A post mill, at Gun Green, behind the 'Oak and Ivy' public house. (Gun Green took its name from the proving of the guns there.)
6. 1903-10. 1 mile 1 furlong east of church, at Four Throws.* This is the same mill as No. 5, moved here in about 1870, and it was then known as Nightingale's Mill.[1] (See also page 64.)

Of these mills No. 6 is the only mill of which any information can be given in addition to that above stated. The transfer of this mill from Gun Green to Four Throws was carried out by its being drawn along on rollers by a team of oxen. It worked at Four Throws for about thirty years ; the miller for the greater part of the time was a Mr. Corke, who hired it from Mrs. French, the proprietor until a few years ago. Otto Waghorn is also known to have worked the mill for many years and it was in his hands in 1878. Local people give the name of a Mr. Tobit as the miller here for some time.

[1] Later, I discovered that Four Throws is actually in the *Sandhurst* parish, just within its border.

During a high wind many years ago, the mill was tail-winded. She was badly damaged and stood for many years in the condition depicted in the photograph. In 1905 the cap and sweeps were removed and in 1926, the base.

HAWKINGE
(NEAR FOLKESTONE)

The Old Mill.* ¼ *mile NE. of Church. Standing to-day, derelict.* 1819-43, 1903-10.

The old smock mill at Hawkinge has been idle for thirty years or more and its present appearance leads one to agree that it must have been neglected for fully that period. Fan and stage have disappeared and only the midlings of two out of the four sweeps remain, with a fragment of one sweep attached. From an old inhabitant I learn that the mill was originally used for some years as a Seed Mill and that it first ground corn in about 1830.

Its early history is not known but from 1866 to 1878 it and about ninety-six acres of land were hired from the owner, Mr. Seath, at a rental of £140 per annum, by Henry Davison, father of Henry W. Davison who now owns Stelling Minnis Mill. At that time the mill was in splendid order, complete with its four sails. It worked two pairs of stones, and there was a flour dressing machine and a 'smutter.' There was no fan, the cap being pulled round into the wind by means of a chain attached to a 'Y' wheel. The fantail was fitted later, about 1890. When Mr. Davison's occupation ceased in 1878 the mill was taken over by Joseph Gardner. It was last used for corn grinding in 1902 by a Mr. Gibbons who, years before, had worked one of the Eastry mills.

It has been thought that the old shed still standing alongside the mill was at one time used as a bakehouse but Mr. Davison never knew it as such. It was used in his father's time for cutting hay and the loft for storing fruit.

Drellingore. 1½ *miles NE. of Church. No map reference.*

As noted later under Ringwold, Ripple Mill was originally built at Drellingore and worked there for some years before its transfer. The removal is believed to have taken place about 1810.

I cannot trace the mill at Drellingore on any old maps. It was evidently built after 1769, for the large-scale map of that period does not show it.

HEADCORN

Black Mill or Crow's Foot Mill.* 3 *furlongs NW. of Church.* 1769, 1819-43, 1903-10.

This was one of the earliest Kentish mills of smock type, as it is noted on the 1769 map, at which date, perhaps, it had not been built very long. It stood on the same bank as the White Mill, about one furlong to the west. Though a black mill latterly, it was painted white in its earlier days. The name of the mill survives, for at the entrance to the lane that led to the mill, a notice board points "To the Black Mill Poultry Farm."

The mill stood about ten years without its sweeps and was taken down in about 1910 by Mr. George Jarvis of Bethersden. It had become unsafe, so much so that Mr. Jarvis, instead of mounting the mill in order carefully to take out the midlings and anything of value (his usual procedure), was obliged to put up struts to support the mill, remove some of the bricks from its base, then take away the struts and allow the mill to topple over.

A great crowd watched the process of demolition and one would hardly have credited Headcorn with such a large population ! It took longer than was expected to pull the old mill over and the onlookers became impatient. One of the spectators was a visitor staying at a local inn. He watched from an upper window of the inn and waited about two hours for the pleasure of seeing the old derelict thrown down. He became tired of staring intently at the old mill. The monotony had also engendered thirst, so he decided to slip down to the bar for a few minutes and get a glass of ale. He would then feel sufficiently refreshed to continue his vigil, for he simply *must* see the mill go over after waiting so long. When he returned, however, he was thoroughly chagrined to find the mill had come down during his brief absence and was lying in ruins !

It is said that the millwright, Warren, of Hawkhurst, had been asked to dismantle the mill but had declined, for he said he never *would* pull down a mill.

To Mr. George Mercer of Tilden, Headcorn, I am indebted for the following particulars.

His father, Mr. George Mercer, was apprenticed at the Black Mill from 1820 onwards, and remained on at the mill after his apprenticeship, later purchasing the mill and working it himself until 1856. It was then let to David Goodman on a seven year lease for £100 a year—surely a remarkable rent. In 1863 it changed hands and there were many different tenants since, including Albert Love, Norton Cornes, Tom Burden (who had the White Mill at Headcorn) and a Mr. Large. When Mr. Mercer died, aged seventy-seven, in 1882, the mill was acquired by his son for whom, later, it was worked by a miller named Turner, who had previously worked for fourteen years in Mr. Goble's mill at Lydd.

Later the mill stood idle and went out of repair. It was then sold to a Mr. Richford who arranged its demolition and, with the 18,000 bricks from the mill base, built the house that stands on the mill site to-day.

Back in 1846 Mr. Mercer had a steam mill installed alongside the windmill, working two pairs of stones. The windmill worked three, so there were five pairs of stones in all, constantly in use. A large trade must have been carried on.

*White Mill.** ¼ *mile NNW. of Church. Standing to-day, active.* 1903-10.

Headcorn Mill, the survivor of the pair that once stood on this eminence, is perhaps the only windmill in Kent working to-day entirely by wind, there

A. W. Tiffin

A. W. Tiffin

KINGSTON (Reed Mill)

See page 232

W.C.F.

W.C.F.

KIPPINGS CROSS (Keys Green Mill)

See page 232

W.C.F.   W.C.F.

MARGATE (Drapers' Mills, 1905)

See page 242

W.C.F.   F. Pain

MARGATE (The sole survivor)   NEWCHURCH

See page 242   *See page 248*   *Facing page 221*

being no auxiliary power of any kind. It was erected in 1819 by the mill-wright, Ralph, of Sissinghurst, and is a wonderfully well-built smock and stage mill, on a stone base. Practically all the timber is of white pine. There are three pairs of stones, two Peak and one French. No flour is made at the mill now ; most of the grinding done is of cattle and pig corn, for the local farmers.

The mill is worked by Mr. Corke (who has been there for twenty years) for the owners, Messrs. Millen Bros., who purchased it in 1916 and also own the Maplehurst watermill at Frittenden.

For sixty years up till 1916 the mill was held by Tom Burden and his father before him. Local good-humoured gossip has it that when Mr. Borden, the Prime Minister of Canada, visited Headcorn about ten years ago and stated that he came from the same family as Mr. Burden, the latter soon had great difficulty in purchasing a hat—no shop stocked one big enough !

Two of the sweeps now on the mill came from Beacon Mill, Benenden, when that mill was de-sailed in 1926. Mr. Frank Pain re-erected these sweeps and also made and fitted an entirely new sweep. The mill had been struck by lightning on July 18th, 1926, when one of the midlings and a sweep were damaged.

The mill was last painted white (which has always been its colour, hence its name) in 1922. Various repairs were then carried out, including the fixing of new boards in the inside of the top of the cap. The mill now badly needs a further coat of paint and the staging needs repair. Otherwise it is in good condition.

On many of the battens on the first floor a great deal of information has been written up in pencil from time to time throughout the years. Much of the earlier writing is obliterated, but many interesting statements are to be seen, including notes of repairs to the mill, references to the weather (particularly about the winds), addresses of customers, records of transactions and items of local intelligence. Extracts of these records are given in an earlier chapter.

I understand that Donald Maxwell's painting of Headcorn, originally reproduced in the *Graphic* and later famous by being reproduced as a poster on the platforms of the Southern Railway, was painted from the window of the mill.

(See also page 71)

HERNE

½ *mile NNE. of Church.* Standing, active.* 1596, 1610, 1695, 1736, 1769, 1719-43, 1903-10.

This specimen of an early smock mill, situated on Beacon Hill, was built by John Holman in 1781—to replace an old post mill that had stood early in the sixteenth century. Dr. T. A. Bowes, M.A., F.R.S.A., as reported in the *Herne Bay Press* dated January 18th, 1930, stated in a lecture that the earliest reference he had traced of a windmill at Herne was in a will of 1511, a bequest being made of "three acres of land beneath the Mill Bank." The mill is shown on Symonson's map of 1596, it is one of the twenty mills drawn on J. Speed's map of 1610, and it appears on all later maps with regular persistence.

It is interesting to learn that John Holman built the smock mill thirty-four years before setting up the famous millwright business at Canterbury in 1815. He was working for Sweetlove's, the millwrights of Wingham, at that time.

In 1858 the whole wooden structure of the mill was bodily raised and two stories of brickwork built up underneath. This brickwork was intended to be exceptionally strong, for the walls are no less than 18 in. thick. In its early days the sweeps of the mill came almost to the ground and, by reason of trees close by, much wind power was lost. When the mill was heightened it was able to take greater advantage of the prevailing south-west winds.

My friend, Mr. Jack Holman, sends me the following notes :

> The mill has the earlier type of striking gear, the shutters being actuated by a rack and pinion to which a gear wheel is attached on the outside of the wheel. A similar arrangement is used at Cranbrook Mill while Sarre and Preston Old Mill were among others that used to employ it.
>
> In the Autumn of 1931 the cap stuck and refused to move. Upon examination by Messrs. Holman Bros. it was found that the mill required a new worm and new wooden cogs for the curb. The work was put in hand by the owner, Mr. Frank Wootton, whose father had the mill before him. Mr. Thomas Wootton took the mill over from Messrs. Lawrence & Sons in 1879. Before that Mr. T. Wootton was with his brother, Mr. John Wootton, at Chislet Mill. Mr. Wootton is a great believer in wind power and although there is an engine attached to Herne Mill, Mr. Wootton much prefers the wind as a source of power.
>
> A new iron worm was made to replace the old wooden one and new wooden cogs put in the curb. Various other improvements were made inside the mill at the same time, including strengthening the tower. Since the brakewheel was re-geared only about two years ago, the mill should work for many years to come in the capable hands of Mr. Wootton.
>
> Although only working on two sweeps it is a very hard worker and can nearly always be seen swinging round when there is sufficient wind.

HERNE BAY

*The Bay Mill.** 1½ *furlongs E. of Pier.* 1819-43.

The Bay Mill stood in a field near the Clock Tower. There is now a Windmill Café near the site, reminiscent of the mill.

The ground on which the mill stood was not five feet above high-water mark and the sea has often flooded the land around it during a gale.

The names of millers from 1839 to 1872 include : Henry Thorp, Richard Beard, Thomas Winder, Messrs. Lawrence (who also had Herne Mill at one time), Messrs. W. & H. Minter, Alfred Taylor, D. Kingsland, Messrs. R. Springate & Co., John Alexander, and a Mr. Hurst. This list of names in such a short period seems to indicate that windmilling at Herne Bay was not a very paying proposition. The owner of the mill was Mr. Gilderoy Brice.

It was more or less complete when it was sold, in 1878, to Mr. T. B. Gambrill, of Petham, for demolition, the land being required for building. This was a good stroke of business for Mr. Gambrill. He only paid £25 for the mill as it stood and, even allowing for cost of labour to pull the mill down, he made a handsome profit on the transaction. The four sweeps were sold to Breach Downs Mill, Barham, for £40; the windshaft for £15 to a new mill being built at Acrise; £12 was realized on the two pairs of stones, one pair to Throwley Mill and singles stones to Miles' Mill, Boughton-under-Blean, and Breach Downs Mill, Barham. The main part of the tower was left standing, for which the builders erecting houses near by paid £14—they split up the timbers on the spot for making laths for their plastering! Various machinery and gearing went to the Chequer's Mill, Petham, including the wallower wheel.

HIGHAM

(NEAR ROCHESTER)

*Rose's Mill.** 5 furlongs E. of Church. Base only standing.* 1819-43, 1903-10.

Sir Richard Head, of Great Hermitage Farm, Higham, had this mill built in 1760. It became known as Rose's Mill, taking its name from the miller with whom it was my pleasure to be intimately associated. It was a fine mill and a prominent landmark.

It was principally employed in providing flour for bread supplied to the navy at Chatham during the troublous times of the wars with France. That bread was made here is beyond doubt, for the owner of the mill remembered the capacious ovens especially constructed for this purpose, and he himself had made use of one of them for over fifteen years.

There were three pairs of stones, one for the flour and two others for farmers' corn.

Only the base of the mill now remains, which is roofed over and used as a store. The mill had been worked throughout the Great War and for some time afterwards. It was damaged in a storm in March, 1920. Later, the fan was blown off in a gale. As with many other windmills, costly repairs could not be afforded by reason of the diminished trade. The mill was therefore pulled down in April, 1921.

HIGH HALDEN

(NEAR ASHFORD)

*3 furlongs W. of Church.** Base only remaining.* 1736, 1769, 1819-43, 1903-10.

High Halden could once boast of one of the finest post mills in the county. It was indeed a splendid mill. Originally it was not so high, but was raised a storey in 1845. Sheather, the millwright of Rye, undertook the work.

Warren, the Hawkhurst millwright, used to say that the windshaft was the largest he had ever seen in a post mill. In 1865 he replaced the wooden windshaft with an iron one.

The sweeps last on the mill came from Aldington Mill when that was taken down. When High Halden suffered a similar fate, the sweeps went to a third home, being placed on the Lower Mill, Woodchurch, where they are still to be seen to-day.

The mill was last worked about 1918. It was idle for some years prior to demolition and, when taken down, the brick base was roofed over for use as a store. Mr. Jarvis says that after he had dismantled the mill he found that one of the four 'shores' had rotted. Had he known this he "would not have gone up on to the mill, shaking it about to get the midlings down."

It is known that the lads from the village school once so highly aroused the indignation of the miller that he made a vigorous complaint to the head-master of the school and that some chastisement followed ! The mischief perpetrated was that the mill steps were lifted clear of the ground and left like it. Such a simple thing, but the little rascals knew what they were doing. "Come a heavy wind," said the miller, "round she'd go ; might have done a hundred pounds' worth of damage."

Sir Charles Igglesden gives an interesting description of the mill :

> The mill, one of the kind known as "post mills," is the largest of the kind in Kent. The base is circular and, at a height of about fourteen feet from the ground, tapers upwards until a stone pillar rises. Upon the latter the mill revolves, not only the sails but the whole body of the building turning to meet the breeze. There is no mechanical contrivance for turning the structure in the proper direction of the wind, the whole being done by hand. Originally the mill stood by the side of the "Dragon," but it was bodily moved to its present position at the beginning of the century.[1]

HILDENBOROUGH

(NEAR TONBRIDGE)

Watts' Cross Mill. * ½ *mile NW. of Church. Standing to-day.* 1819-43, 1903-10.

The external appearance of this mill differs very little to-day from that of thirty years ago, for it is complete with its sweeps (although the shutters have been removed), is well looked after and stands in a private garden.

It is one of the oldest of smock mills. Every cog and wheel was made of wood. The only iron about it was the windshaft. There is a large 'Y' wheel *inside* the cap, to which a rope was attached for pulling the cap into the wind. It is one of the few Kentish windmills that were driven 'underdrift,' i.e. with the stones worked from beneath, like those of a watermill. It has four storeys and one of the floors of the brick base above the stage. It used to drive three pairs of stones and was last worked in 1910.

In a diary of Richard Children, then living at Oakhurst on Riverhill, occurs the following :

> 1812. Mr. John London built the Windmill at Wats Cross. Builder's name, Budgen (of) Speldhurst.

Richard Burfoot was the miller here in 1878.

[1] *Saunters Through Kent with Pen and Pencil*, 1900, Vol. I, p. 49.

W. H. Evernden

A. E. Harrison

SMARDEN
(A right-hand Mill)

LIMPSFIELD CHART, SURREY
(A left-hand Mill)

See page 58

See page 57

Ill. London News, 1858

Rev. W. A. Parker, 1932

JERUSALEM, PALESTINE (Jaffa Gate Mill)
Built by Holman, of Canterbury, Kent.

See page 50

Jack Holman

W.C.F.

EAST LANGDON (MARTIN MILL)

See page 234

W.C.F.

LEIGH, NEAR HILDENBOROUGH
(STOCKS GREEN MILL)

See page 235

Mr. Chapman

LENHAM HEATH

See page 237

Facing page 225

HOATH
(NEAR CANTERBURY)

Fuller's Mill.* ½ *mile NE. of Church.* 1819-43, 1903-10.

I made two recent attempts to visit this mill. On the first occasion it quite eluded my search, despite the fact that I had photographed it some thirty years earlier. On the second occasion I was only successful in finding that it had disappeared many years ago!

When I called at the old Mill House I was welcomed by two elderly ladies from whom I learned a little of the history of the mill. They produced from the recesses of an old bureau an auctioneers' sale catalogue, dated 1868, in which the mill was referred to as :

A stage windmill, fitted with four spring sweeps, fan, cast-iron windshaft, driving three pairs of stones, two of wheat, and one of barley, with flour machines, etc.

It was for many years in the Collard family. James Collard of Old Tree Farm was the miller in 1847. In 1878 Jonathan Packer was the miller.

The mill ceased work in 1912 and collapsed on July 18th, 1919, probably unable to withstand the rough winds, to which Sir Charles Igglesden refers :

Yes, it blows bleak up here at Hoath when a strong wind blows across the level lands of the Isle of Thanet.[1]

I was escorted round the garden and shown a number of old mill-stones which were embedded in and embellished a crazy pavement, which bordered a well-kept lawn and sunny flower beds richly garnished with old-world flowers.

Before leaving I gave to each of the ladies who had so graciously received me a photograph of the old mill as it appeared thirty years ago. They were delighted, never before having seen a picture of it in its prime.

This was not my last, though unintentional, visit to Hoath. In my Quixotic search for windmills, I was assured there was a mill at Chislet. This was news to me and so I sallied forth to find it. After many vain enquiries I met a boy who knew all about it—he told me it had been blown down. He directed me to the site, and I soon arrived at—the Mill House at Hoath ! This is by no means the only time I have been led 'a merry dance' in hunting for our old windmills.

HOO COMMON
(NEAR ROCHESTER)

Ballard's Mill.* 1 *mile NW. of Church.* 1769, 1819-43, 1903-10.

The mill shown on the 1769 map was evidently a post mill, for the smock mill was not built on the site until about 1799.

I found the mill derelict in 1905 and it had been out of use for a quarter of

---

[1] *Saunters Through Kent with Pen and Pencil*, Vol. VIII, p. 25.

P

a century. The sweepless tower, with fan only, was still standing but in a state of ruin.

Mrs. R. L. Gardener, who was living at the Mill House at the time of my visit, told me she was the grand-daughter of Mr. R. Ballard, the builder and first occupier of the mill, and the only survivor of the Ballard family that had, for three generations, carried on milling operations here.

WEST HOUGHAM
(NEAR DOVER)

¾ *mile W. of Hougham Church.* * *Standing to-day, working. 1903-10.*

The smock mill at West Hougham has been in the Tanton family since 1827. Previously it had been in the Morris family. In those early days there was a bake-house alongside the mill but this was moved further away in about 1830 although still worked in conjunction with the mill.

The mill was built in 1801-2, apparently just too late to be included in the first Ordnance Survey Map of Kent which was then being prepared. The initials of the master bricklayer, Matthew Woodcock, are cut in a brick at the entrance. A carpenter named Cricket also co-operated in the building. It was well built, of pitch pine and fumed oak, and has been well saturated with tar during its history and is, therefore, still in fair condition.

The sweeps at first almost swept the ground but in about 1825 they were shortened, a stage built around the mill and the base below the stage extended in order to allow more storage room.

Mr. E. H. Tanton, the present owner, says that his grandfather did a big trade both in the mill and in the bake-house. There were two pairs of stones, one for wheat and one for the cattle corn, wire dressing machines, wheat smutter and cleaner, and the usual implements.

In 1926, owing to one of the midlings slipping slightly in the canister, one of the sweeps struck the side of the mill and flew off into an adjoining field. The midling was broken and had to be removed. Since then the mill has worked with only two sweeps but they have given sufficient power, with the aid of an oil engine installed in 1905 as auxiliary power, to carry out the work required. Mr. Tanton, however, believes that a far greater strain is put upon the mill in working two sweeps only. He says one can distinctly *feel* the tower twisting from side to side as the single pair of sweeps revolve. This sensation was not felt when the complete four sweeps were in action.

HYTHE

½ *mile E. of St. Leonard's Church. 1819-43.*

This mill is not shown on any later map than that of 1819-43 and it was not standing in the 1840's, at which period Mr. Frank Pain's father attended school at Hythe. It is, therefore, presumed that it must be the old post mill that was removed almost entire a distance of nine miles by barge along the Military Canal and re-erected at Ruckinge, close by the canal.

I cannot trace any information about the mill's history at its original home at Hythe, except its position as indicated by the 1819-43 map. By comparing this with recent maps it seems that the mill was situated to the east of Cannongate Road, between it and the railway line (which, of course, came much later), about ¼ mile south-south-east of Hythe Station.

Stade Street. Approx. 3 furlongs SW. of St. Leonard's Church. 1829.
This mill of smock type is one of three shown on Greenwood's map of 1829. Mr. Frank Pain remembers it as it stood in 1877 and writes:

It stood on the right-hand side going down Stade Street and a little above what is now known as Windmill Street. The mill was then used by a Mr. Cadman and a few years later on by a Mr. Burch who also carried on the water mill at the top of Bell Lane.

An 1878 Kent Directory confirms Mr. Pain's remarks in the following entry:

James S. Cadman, baker and miller, Park Road.

Park Road is close to Windmill Street and parallel with it. I learn that Mr. Cadman's father used to have the windmill at Whitfield, near Dover.

In 1878, according to a Kent Directory, George Burch had a baking and milling business in the High Street. He is known to have had the windmill at least as late as 1889. I have been unable to trace any information as to date and circumstances of its disappearance.

Stade Street. Approx. 3 furlongs SW. of St. Leonard's Church. 1829.
In 1877 all that remained of this mill was a square brick base of one floor. The structure of the mill itself had then only recently been removed to Cheriton, near Folkestone, where it later became known as Ashley Mill.

Stade Street. Approx. 3 furlongs SW. of St. Leonard's Church. 1829.
Like the mill last mentioned, only a brick base remained of this one when Mr. Frank Pain was at Hythe in 1877. It must, however, have been a larger and more powerful mill. The base was octagonal and of two stories. It is not known what became of it.

? position. No map reference.
Mr. Frank Pain tells of another mill at Hythe. He says:

Another smock mill stood near the town, but closer to the hill than the Stade Street mills—too close to the hill for effectual working, except when the wind blew *along* the coast. This mill was demolished at least seventy years ago, as the iron windshaft that was taken out of it was put in a new mill that was being erected at Hereson, Ramsgate, in the early '60's.

IDE HILL
(NEAR SEVENOAKS)

Near W. side of Church. 1819-43.
An elderly miller friend tells me that this mill was worked last by Mr. Aynscomb (now deceased) and that it was burnt down about 1860.

100 yards E. of Church. No map reference.

A large four-storied black post mill stood here. It was owned by a Mr. Ashby, by whom it is said to have been erected in 1858. The millers from time to time include the names of Rose, Homewood, Burton, Sage, Kingsland, and Bassett.

I understand that, except for the missing sweeps which had blown off prior to demolition, it was in good condition when pulled down in 1882. It had not worked since 1875, the growth of trees hindering its doing so effectually.

¼ mile E. of Church. No map reference.

A third windmill at Ide Hill is believed to have stood above Hanging Bank, or Windmill Bank, known locally as Windmill Point. The remains of the foundations were exposed when digging for gravel. The postmistress at Ide Hill, who has been to great trouble in seeking information about the Ide Hill Mills from old local residents, cannot trace any one at Ide Hill who could throw any light on its history. It is even doubted whether a mill was erected at Windmill Point. A local supposition is that the building of a mill was begun but, perhaps through lack of funds, it proceeded no further than the foundations.

KENNINGTON
(NEAR ASHFORD)

Kennington Lees. ¼ mile NW. of Church. 1769.

The old post mill at Kennington Lees stood about half a mile from the smock mill next described. It was a fine, large mill, worked latterly by a miller named Stephen Sharp and pulled down about 1878. A pair of French stones were then transferred to the Lower Mill, Woodchurch.

My friend, Mr. E. T. Clark, of Maidstone, tells me that in early boyhood he often watched the revolving sweeps of the old Kennington Lees post mill in the lenses of his grandmother's spectacles as he sat opposite to her near the window of a house close by ! After the mill was closed to corn grinding, the wind power was used for some time to operate a sawmill.

"Wind, Steam and Water Mill."* ½ mile E. of Church. Standing to-day, derelict.
      1819-43, 1858-72, 1903-10.

As the name of this mill implies, all three motive powers were used here. The water, which came from Eastwell Lake, is now no longer to be seen and the steam shaft is not now standing. The sweepless body of the tall, smock windmill, however, still remains. The weather-boarding has recently been repaired to some extent and re-tarred, a Canterbury builder having under-taken this work. The life of the structure has, therefore, been prolonged. It is, however, just an empty shell, all machinery having been cleared out and floorings removed.

Miss Goble

LYDD (Old Post Mill)

See page 237

E. H. Greening, M.P.S.

LYDD (New Mill)

See page 237

E. H. Greening, M.P.S.

LYDD
New Mill in flames, 1927.

See page 237

A. W. Tiffin

CHATHAM (Ordnance Street)
Bacon's Mill. Base now a shop.

See page 183

Facing page 228

Mrs. Rolfe

LYMINGE (White Mill and Old Black Mill)

See page 238

W.C.F.

J. Russell

LYMINGE (White Mill)

See page 238

Facing page 229

It was erected in 1813. This is confirmed by a dated stone over the door.

Y D
H
1813

The initial 'H' evidently refers to Hill, the Ashford millwrights, who were the builders. It is said to have been built for Daniel Young, one of a long line of millers. The present owner is Mr. W. J. Jennings, of Kennington Hall.

In 1886 all three mills, wind, steam, and water, were in full swing under Messrs. H. S. Pledge & Son, who later transferred the trade to the Steam Mill at Ashford, where a large business has since been developed.

It is many years now since Kennington Mill was worked; the last miller was Charles Stanley from Blean Mills. He took over the business from Messrs. Pledge in 1892. The sweeps were removed soon after it finished working and were transferred to Pluckley Mill; fragments of them are keeping company with that sad derelict to this day.

During the Great War the mill was used as a signalling station.

A miller friend writes :

> I wonder if you know of that wonderful combination of the Kennington Mills, near Ashford. I believe it to be unique. The house and watermill are on one side of the lane, a steam mill opposite with a windmill built upon the top of the steam mill, and a footbridge over the road from the top floors of the water and steam mills. Of course, it is all gone to decay now, but it just *did* make a joyful noise once upon a time.

Of the footbridge no trace remains to-day, except that the ends of the beams that formed the bridge can still be seen in the brickwork.

KESTON
(NEAR FARNBOROUGH)

Old Post Mill. *5 furlongs N. of Church. Standing to-day, derelict.* 1736, 1769, 1819-43, 1903-10.

This, the last of three windmills that originally stood in the Keston parish, is one of the few old Kentish post mills now remaining.

It was built in 1716 and, being in a corn producing area, evidently had a busy life up till 1900, when it is believed to have been last worked.

? position. 2 mills. No map reference.[1]

I understand from Mr. J. Fells, who lives at the Mill House connected with the old Keston Mill previously noted, that there were two other mills in the Keston parish at one time. One of these, known as the Olive's Mill, was destroyed by fire some time prior to 1885. The other stood near Holwood Park.

An 1878 Kent Directory states that Luther Olive was miller at Keston in that year.

[1] See later note in Addenda, page 315.

KINGSDOWN
(NEAR SEVENOAKS)

Old Post Mill. * ¾ *mile SSE. of Church.* 1819-43.

Although of the older post type, this mill does not appear on any earlier map than 1819-43.

It was in the Norton family for many years and in their possession when it was destroyed by fire in May 1909. Permission was given for a road roller to draw in near the mill, and it is supposed that a spark from the engine set light to some straw close by and that this in turn set fire to the mill which, being all timber, was very soon demolished.

One of the Norton family who now has Meopham Mill, says that this post mill at Kingsdown originally stood at the Vine, Sevenoaks, and that an eighteenth century date was carved in the main post. It is said that the sweeps of the old mill, coming so close to the ground, once hurried pork to the table sooner than had been anticipated !

From 1880 onwards the mill had a companion, a smock mill from Farningham (the one next described) having been moved there and placed about fifty yards away. I am able to give an interesting picture of both mills, in their working days, side by side.

Nothing remains of the old post mill, save the foundations which can be clearly traced in the meadow.

¾ mile NW. of Church, 1819-43. *¾ mile SSE. of Church since* 1880.* *Standing to-day, disused.* 1819-43, 1903-10.

The original home of this mill was on Chimham's Farm, in the Farningham parish. David Norton, grandfather of William Norton, the present owner of Meopham Mill, came to Farningham Mill from Tovil Watermill, near Maidstone, and hired it together with cottages and land from the then owner, Walter Whiting. Tanner Norton, a son of William Norton, purchased the mill outright and removed it in 1880 to Kingsdown where it now stands. The re-erection cost £800 ; George Paine carried out the work. A foundation stone in the mill base bears an inscription to Minnie Louisa Norton, April 21st, 1880.

The mill was run at Kingsdown in conjunction with the old post mill there. On the death of Tanner Norton, his son, Frank, carried on the mill. Later it was sold to a Mr. Cork, who held it until purchased in 1929 by Mr. Hankin, its present owner.

The mill was last worked in 1928. The end of one of the sweeps, beyond the midling, was broken off in a gale on Christmas Day, 1929, and its absence rather spoils the mill's appearance. Otherwise, the structure, except for the missing fan (which was blown down in November, 1930) looks very much as it did in its working days. The interior apparatus is still practically complete.

KINGSDOWN
(NEAR SITTINGBOURNE)

¾ mile NNE. of Church. No map reference.

I can find no reference to a mill at Kingsdown, near Sittingbourne, on any map I have searched. A personal assurance of reliable source is all I can offer. I understand the mill disappeared about 1890.

I called at a somewhat pretentious house, said to be the Mill House, and was disappointed that I could gain no information concerning the mill. An elderly farmer and his wife occupied the house. The wife only was able to see me ; the husband, I believe, was unwell and could not be consulted. I was treated with politeness, and assured there were no remains of a windmill on the estate. Instinctively I felt that at their age and with infirmities, they could not be bothered with one who had windmills on the brain. I must add that this was one of the rare occasions when the idea of being dubiously received suggested itself to me. Even in this instance it may not have been so, but I had not found a derelict mill and was disappointed. In any case one cannot expect everybody to be interested in long-vanished windmills.

Later I paid a further visit to Kingsdown but renewed enquiries only resulted in a supposition that the mill disappeared at least eighty years ago! No local reminiscences exist regarding this old grinder.

KINGSNORTH
(NEAR ASHFORD)

Millbank Place. ¾ mile NNW. of Church.

The words 'Millbank Place' appear on the 1858-72 and 1903-10 Ordnance Maps, but the windmill is not shown. One wonders whether this is the mill to which Sir Charles Igglesden refers, or whether it is the one next described. Writing in 1930, he says :

> On the main road that runs through Kingsnorth from Ashford to Ham Street, the original one being that which passes the church, on the top of the hill stood a windmill, but that has disappeared.[1]

3 furlongs W. of Church.* Base heightened and converted into a dwelling. 1903-10.

I cannot trace this mill on any earlier map than 1903-10. It stood on the left side of the main road from Ashford to Ham Street, about a quarter of a mile beyond the public house at Kingsnorth Pound. To-day the site is occupied by a labourer's cottage, the square brick base of which formed part of the windmill. Mr. George Jarvis superintended the work of demolition and was given all the metal work from the mill in payment.

I understand from the Canterbury millwrights that a new corner post was fitted in 1892 and, therefore, it may be presumed that the mill was in working order for some years after this date.

[1] *Saunters Through Kent with Pen and Pencil*, Vol. XIV, p. 73.

A Mr. Cheeseman was once the miller. Edwin Pepper had the mill in 1878. There were three pairs of stones.

KINGSTON
(NEAR CANTERBURY)

*Reed Mill.** 1¾ *miles SW. of Church. Capless tower standing.* 1858-72, 1903-10.

To-day the brick tower alone remains of this old mill that stood on Westwood Farm, Kingston. The cap, sweeps and fantail are all gone. The tower is now a refuge for owls, and I learn from the occupier of the quaint, thatched Mill House that their nocturnal hootings almost make sleep impossible at times.

Mr. F. J. Fagg, who worked the mill for many years, writes :

> The mill was working up till 1914. It was then put under thorough repair and was in good working order in the spring of 1915, with the exception of the fan gear, of which a new cog wheel was being cast. Whilst waiting for this wheel, the mill head was turned round by hand. On March 28th, 1915, we were working the mill all day, with the wind due south. We left it right about six o'clock that evening. About eight o'clock a terrific snowstorm arose from the north.   The fan gear being out of order, and no one on the spot to turn the mill head, the eighty-mile-an-hour wind lifted the whole of the head with the sails right off the mill. As the cost of replacing would be at least £300, we decided to close down the mill.

There is some fine old oak timber in the tower and most of the machinery is still intact. Three pairs of stones were driven and up to about 1880 there was a bakery attached to the mill.

In searching out this derelict, the good folks of Barham, evidently thinking it was the nearest way, directed me through a desolate, winding valley, along a single track overhung by trees and soft with recent rains. It turned abruptly into a rough woodland path, then up a steep incline. When the crest was reached, the old brick tower of Reed Mill loomed up clear in the distance. Had I taken another course, a good road would have led me to the mill, for by this road I made a quick return to Barham.

KIPPINGS CROSS
(NEAR PEMBURY)

*Keys Green Mill.** 7 *furlongs SSW. of Matfield Church. Capless tower standing.*
     1819-43, 1858-72, 1903-10.

Keys Green Mill was in good working order when I first visited it about 1900. It now stands, as I found it in 1930, a complete derelict, the cap with its sweeps and fans having disappeared entirely. I learn that it was decapitated in a high wind about 1916. Warren, the Hawkhurst millwright, had predicted that this would happen. He had been asked to inspect the mill a little while previously and report on the repairs needed, and presumably these repairs had not been carried out.

This was the second time the mill-cap had been blown off. On the previous occasion, during the great gale of 1861, the miller, who was in the cap at the time, was killed in falling down the steep steps in the mill.

I have climbed these same dangerous steps in the dark, dusty interior and I wonder that many others had not broken their necks in descending from floor to floor. It is a very small mill, and on the floor where the two sets of stones were installed there was hardly room to move. Warren used to say that it was the worst mill he had been in, with not a single window in it, which made it necessary to go about almost on one's hands and knees with "hardly room to breathe."

According to an old directory, George Clarke was the miller here in 1878.

*   *   *   *   *

I understand from a local resident that a story has been handed down that there were once three mills at Kippings Cross, near the Blue Boys Inn, and that two of them were pulled down because there was not enough wind to drive all three at once! I do not include them in the total of Kentish mills because of the insufficient evidence.

KNOCKHOLT
(NEAR SEVENOAKS)

About 1 mile E. of Church.* No map reference.

I understand from a miller friend that this mill stood near the Horse Shoe Inn and the Police Station. The Mill House is standing to-day and the Mill Lane can still be traced as leading from Chevening Park.

It was a six-storied brick tower mill, working three pairs of stones. An 1878 Kent Directory gives the names of Alfred Brame, Stoneham & Co. as the millers at Knockholt Mill. It was known to be working in 1882 but is believed to have been taken down about 1886. It is said that the miller was killed by falling from a sweep when it was being demolished. My informant has seen his tombstone in the churchyard.

LAMBERHURST
(NEAR TUNBRIDGE WELLS)

Windmill Farm. 1 mile NW. of Church.

Although the words "Windmill Farm" are given on the 1769 and all later maps, no windmill is drawn at this site on any of them, neither can any information regarding the existence of a windmill be ascertained on the spot.

Maybe, an old post mill stood on the farm a great many years ago and was cleared away before the 1769 Survey was made, but this is only supposition.

EAST LANGDON
(NEAR DOVER)

Martin Mill.* 5 furlongs NE. of Church. Standing to-day, derelict. 1769. 1819-43, 1903-10.

The earliest milling business at Martin Mill was transferred from an old post mill at Mill Close, near St. Margaret's, Dover. The owner had Martin Mill built and apparently forsook the older mill. This must have taken place about the middle of the eighteenth century, for Martin Mill is shown on the 1769 map. It is an old type of smock mill and has a cap of unusual shape.

It was in the Stanger family for half a century and then came into the possession of William Ellson, who worked it for ten years. His son, T. W. Ellson, then ran the mill for no less than sixty years. When the railway came through the district in 1881, trade at the mill was expected to increase by leaps and bounds and a man named Wiles purchased the mill by way of speculation. The increased business did not come up to expectations, however, and T. W. Ellson bought it back for £80.

At one time the mill had so much work that the whole of the staging was often covered with sacks of corn waiting for grinding ; the two bins up in the mill, one holding thirty quarters and the other twenty quarters of wheat— that is, one hundred sacks in all—were always kept full. There were three pairs of stones—two 4 ft. 2 in. French burr and one 4 ft. Peak. No machinery is left in the mill now ; it was sold for 'a mere song.'

An unusual happening at Martin Mill occurred about forty years ago. All four sweeps came to grief during a high wind. At first one broke off and embedded itself in the ground. The other three sweeps, following one after the other, crashed and broke off in turn ! New sweeps had to be fitted (by T. R. Holman) and the mill was soon hard at work again.

Somebody has likened the sweeps of Martin Mill to the clipped wings of an old hen ! They were cut back a few years ago for the sake of safety, to decrease the wind pressure on the structure.

As will be guessed by the flue pipe protruding from the side of the mill, as shown in the photograph, the base of the mill has been used as a dwelling. It is hardly suitable, however, for living accommodation and I am afraid the cost of making it a comfortable dwelling is somewhat out of proportion to the rent that could reasonably be charged.

LEE[1]

½ mile SE. of Church. 1819-43.

The position of this mill was at the south-east corner of Lee Park, between Eagle Terrace and Williams Place, on the north side of the road to Eltham, near the Tiger's Head Inn. It probably disappeared somewhere about 1850, for at this date the land was beginning to be built over. The district to-day has entirely lost its rural character.

[1] See note on page 151.

LEEDS
(NEAR MAIDSTONE)

Brogden Mill. ½ *mile WSW. of Church.* 1819-43.

Brogden Mill was of smock type, on a brick base, having a stage and working three pairs of stones.

Mr. Walter Blinkhorn, who was born in 1851, tells me that when he was a boy the tenant was Tuddenham ; later it was held by Hooker and finally by Else.

It was sold to Mr. Thomas Goodwin, of Maidstone, about 1877 and at once pulled down by him. The owner was a Mr. Parks, a baker, of Maidstone. Some years ago it was struck by lightning, one Sunday morning.

The mill site is now an orchard, part of Arnold Hill Farm, a stone's throw from the farm house. Mr. L. Brown, the present owner, pointed it out in the corner of the orchard, reached by a track opposite the entrance to the farm-yard. A house known as Windmill Cottage close by is reminiscent of the mill, although I cannot say whether it is old enough to have been the miller's home.

There is a Brogden Farm not far away, from which the mill doubtless took its name.

LEIGH
(NEAR HILDENBOROUGH)

Stocks Green Mill.* 1 *mile NE. of Church. Standing to-day, active.*

Sidley, near Bexhill, was the original home of this mill. It was taken to Leigh in 1928 and stands close to the Old Barn, which, at some considerable expense, has been converted into a tea house and dance hall and attracts a large number of visitors the whole year through.

On the main road stand the Village Stocks which tempt visitors to try them, when they soon discover that by a simple device they are really 'in the Stocks' and cannot extricate their feet. They also discover that the fee for regaining freedom is sixpence or more, which I believe goes into the coffers of certain well-known charitable institutions.

A notice board states that the mill was

> Erected 1723
> Burnt 1797
> Rebuilt 1798
> Restored 1928

The first three of these dates relate to Sidley and were given to the present owner by the miller who used to work the mill. On the notice board is also quoted the text from Ecclesiastes, chapter xi, verse 4 :

He that observeth the wind shall not sow; and he that regardeth the clouds shall not reap.

This mill is a typical example of the vicissitudes through which many of these old structures have passed, for, though a stranger imported into Kent, to renew its activity there in the closing days of windmill utility, the sweeps and two sets of stones came from the now derelict mill at Sissinghurst, near Cranbrook, the princely sum of £5 and £2 respectively having been paid for them !

(See also page 85.)

LENHAM

(NEAR MAIDSTONE)

Town Mill. ¼ *mile SW. of Church.* 1819-43, 1858-72, 1903-10.

This mill stood opposite the Railway Station and is said to have been badly placed for the wind. It was a white smock and stage mill of four stories, on a brick base of one storey under the stage. There were two spring sweeps and two 'common' sails. Latterly a portable steam engine was installed to run the mill in calm weather. There were three pairs of stones—two wheat stones 3 ft. 10 in. diameter and one barley 3 ft. 8 in. A new pair of spring sweeps were fitted in 1886 by T. R. Holman. The mill was last worked in the 1890's, and unfortunately fell to the flames in 1904. It is reported that as the mill was being consumed the sweeps revolved rapidly and had the appearance of a giant Catherine-wheel—a wonderful sight.

Nothing remains of the mill to-day ; its site is occupied by a corn store owned by Messrs. L. J. Clark & Co.

The mill shown on the 1819-43 Ordnance Map was an earlier mill on the same site, the one above described not having been built until later in the nineteenth century—shortly after the opening of the S.E. & C.R. line from Ashford to Tonbridge. The brick foundations of the old mill were utilised for the new one, which in its early days was in the occupation of the Tanton family. I learn with interest that Mr. Frank Pain, who has since become so well-known among the miller folk of East Kent, worked the Town Mill as a journeyman in 1885-87.

Downs Court, Hill Mill. 1 *mile* 1 *furlong ENE. of Church.* 1819-43.

The situation of this long-lost mill was near The Pilgrim's Way, some little distance to the north-west of the site of the present sanatorium. The actual spot was in a field on the hill top, just beyond a disused chalk quarry and behind the Mill House, which still stands.

Mr. Frank Pain says :

> I have been told that the mill got out of hand in a gale and caught fire ; anyway, it had disappeared when I first visited Lenham in 1881.

I understand the mill was held by a miller named Hunt at the time of its destruction.

Mrs. Geo. Smith   W.C.F.

LYNSTED (CHAMPION'S MILL)

See page 240

E. Hopper   A. W. Tiffin

RODMERSHAM GREEN

See page 265   *Facing page 236*

J. Russell   W.C.F.

MEOPHAM GREEN

See page 243

W.C.F.   Rex Wailes

MILTON REGIS (Meade Mill)

See page 245

Facing page 237

LENHAM HEATH
(NEAR MAIDSTONE)

1½ miles SE. of Lenham Church.* Base only remaining. 1769, 1819-43, 1903-10.

The stage and a two-storied base are all that remain of this mill, which had been in the Tanton family for ninety years. The present owner, Mr. E. Tanton, is a cousin of both Mr. A. Tanton of Woodchurch Mills and Mr. E. H. Tanton of West Hougham Mill. Frederick Tanton was the miller at Lenham Heath in 1878. It is one instance amongst many of how our old windmills have run in families.

A beam in the mill was dated 1760, presumably the date of erection, and bore the initials W.N., probably those of the builder. In 1848 the body of the mill was raised in order to increase the storage room and to take better advantage of the wind. It drove three pairs of stones, and much flour was made in days gone by. It was last worked in 1910 and dismantled in 1925. A gale first started the dismemberment of the structure by depositing the fantail a quarter of a mile away!

LUDDESDOWN
(NEAR GRAVESEND)

Henley Downs Mill. ¼ mile N. of Church. 1829.

I learned from the Misses Wigan, daughters of the late rector, that this mill was blown down in a storm in 1856 and that, as children, they clambered over the wreckage and played there. The mill-stones remained upon the site for many years and are now probably covered by brambles and other wild growth in the copse on the crest of the Downs to which I was directed. It was a smock mill and was last worked by a miller named Waterman, who went from Henley Downs to Five Ash Mill, Perry Street, near Gravesend.

LYDD

¼ mile NW. of Church. 1596, 1610, 1769.

The above maps are my authorities for a windmill at this position.

The Old Mill.* 3 furlongs SW. of Church. 1596, 1610, 1769, 1819-43, 1858-72.

This old post mill fell to the flames on February 26th, 1900, according to the records of the local Fire Brigade. It was owned by Messrs. Goble Bros., who also held 'The New Mill' next described. It was evidently a successor of an earlier mill that is shown on the old maps of 1596 and 1610.

The New Mill.* 3 furlongs NE. of Church. 1858-72, 1903-10.

The smock and stage mill that stood at this position until burnt down on September 22nd, 1927, was built in 1805. It was a landmark from the sea and had the distinction of being marked on ships' charts. Sailors out at sea missed it when it disappeared.

In the later days of its milling career it had been worked by a steam engine, but not for grinding. Since 1920, stripped of its sweeps, it was in use as a store.

I am told by a man who witnessed the fire that a heavy gale was blowing at the time and the whole body of the mill was soon glowing red hot. Owing to the high wind the structure seemed to take a very long time to burn out and bystanders questioned whether the mill was of *iron* construction that she should be so red hot and not collapse ! Evidently the substantial oak corner posts helped to keep the mill erect until they themselves were burnt through.

At the time of the fire it was noticed that a pigeon sat on the fan stage and remained there until within two minutes of the collapse of the structure.

I understand that Messrs. Goble Bros., the owners of the mill, did not shed any tears over its destruction ! It had latterly become a useless structure, rates had to be paid on it and there was difficulty in getting the authorities to allow it to be pulled down in view of its utility as a landmark. The fire was apparently an accidental but, nevertheless, practical solution to the problem !

LYMINGE

3 *furlongs NW. of Church.* 1736, 1769, 1819-43.

This was one of the three windmills that can be traced at Lyminge. It was an early post mill and is evidently the one to which Sir Charles Igglesden refers when he states :

> A post mill stood in the corner of the Sibton Park Estate, close to the bungalow residence on the road from the street towards Stowting . . . like that at Elham, it fell a victim to a heavy storm.[1]

3 *furlongs N. of Church.*   *Black Mill,** 1819-43.   *White Mill,** 1903-10.

Two smock mills stood at this position, about a quarter of a mile east of the mill previously mentioned. One was known as the Black Mill, which fell to the flames in September, 1891. The other, the White Mill, a slender smock with a stage, was built alongside in 1860 and survived until 1920. I am fortunately able to give a photograph taken in about 1878 showing both mills.

In 1852 the Black Mill was purchased from a Mr. Gibbs by Leonard Francis, who had the white one built by Messrs. Hill, the Ashford mill-wrights, to increase the output. In 1877 both were sold to Henry Rolfe, of Stone Bridge Farm, Ottinge, in whose possession they were when the Black Mill was burnt down. It is said that the tarred timbers were consumed long before the fire engine could arrive from Hythe.

During Mr. Rolfe's occupation the mill was valued for the purpose of insurance by T. R. Holman of Canterbury at £625, and the stock in trade £65. It was noted that :—

[1] *Saunters Through Kent with Pen and Pencil*, Vol. III, p. 57.

the mill comprised one octagonal timber built framework about 35 feet in height, 22 feet diameter at base, 9 feet at top, standing on oak sills and built on brickwork foundation, fitted with four floors. The tower is covered with weather-boarding and tarred. Wooden curb, fantail and timber framed cap, iron windshaft, four sweeps, two pairs of stones (one Peak, one French) and flour machine.

After the fire, the White Mill carried out the work for the business until 1920, when, by reason of it having fallen into disrepair and being thought dangerous, it was taken down. Mr. D. E. Fisher, the last owner, replaced it in 1921 by an engine-driven brick structure, in which the milling business has since been carried on. The only remains of the windmill to-day are several old mill-stones that form steps to the terrace lawn of the Mill House.

LYMPNE
(NEAR HYTHE)

3 furlongs WNW. of Church. 1829.

Lympne Mill was a small smock and fantail mill on a brick base working four cloth sails. The sweeps were only about 20 ft. in length and whirled round at a high rate, the inside gearing giving but little increase of speed.

The mill was blown down in a high wind during November, 1891. It had been worked by T. Maylam since 1883, and was complete with its sweeps right up to the time of its destruction. John Brenchley, who owned and worked it from 1850 to 1883, had improved the property and built up a good business as miller and baker. The bake-house remains to-day, and also a few fragments of the brick base of the mill, which form part of the garden of the Mill House.

Mr. V. Laker, who worked at the mill for Mr. Brenchley, says that he understands the mill originally stood at Cheriton, near Folkestone, and was brought to Lympne on farm wagons and rebuilt.

LYNSTED
(NEAR SITTINGBOURNE)

7 furlongs N. of Church. 1819-43.

This was a Seed Mill, at Claxfield. It must have disappeared over eighty years ago.

Union Mill. 7 furlongs SE. of Church. 1736, 1819-43.

A Union of farmers built this mill to grind their corn, hence its name. It was a little, tarred smock mill without a stage, having an old-fashioned wooden windshaft and working two pairs of stones.

A miller who once had this mill was standing by his open door during a terrific thunderstorm when lightning ran down the doorway and killed him.

In about 1870, during the ownership of a Mr. Thomas, a gale wrenched the head of the windshaft off and the sweeps crashed to the ground. This ended the milling career of the Union Mill. Mr. Thomas had the ragged end of the wooden windshaft sawn off flush with the front of the cap to make it look more tidy and it remained like that for a few years until pulled down.

No mill is shown here on the 1769 map, so that the mill noted on the 1736 map must have disappeared before 1769 and that the mill on the 1819-43 map was built after 1769.

On visiting the site recently (April, 1933) the tenant of Windmill Cottage kindly showed me where, in an orchard near by, he had lately dug up stones and debris that were evidently remains of the old mill.

Champion's Mill.* ¼ *mile NNE. of Church. Standing to-day.* 1819-43, 1903-10.

This was a fine smock mill in its time and a large trade was done. It was named after W. H. Champion who worked it for many years. I am able to give two photographs : one shows the mill without its sweeps and fan, as it appeared in about 1895 ; the other is a recent photograph, showing the remains of the old mill. The cap and a little of the body were removed and a summer house perched on top, the whole draped with wistaria.

I have since learned that the mill originally stood on the London Road, near Teynham, and that when Mr. Champion bought it he had it moved almost entire by means of a specially constructed low trolley, and re-erected in a field just behind his Steam Mill at Lynsted. Mr. Littlewood, the mill-wright of Milton, then had the task of heightening it. Mr. Geo. E. Ride writes :

> My cousin, who was serving his apprenticeship with Mr. Littlewood, was on this job. They lifted it with jacks and kept building up with bricks at the rate of a foot a day until they had got about 20 feet of base under her. When finished she rolled so much with a high wind that tie rods had to be fixed from the top right down through the mill to the brickwork to help keep her steady.

(See also page 95)

MAIDSTONE

½ *mile N. of All Saints' Church.* 1819-43.

According to the position given to this mill on the one-inch scale 1819-43 Ordnance Survey Map, it was situated almost opposite the present County Offices, close to and on the north side of the site of Maidstone East Station.

Mr. Wm. Day tells me that he has an original Ordnance Map that shows a row of cottages then called Windmill Row.

It is to be regretted that there is nothing on record in the Maidstone Libraries to throw light on the history of this old mill; and the Southern Railway, with whom I have been in correspondence (in the hope that the deeds of the property might have made mention of it), have been unable to help in the matter. This is not surprising, for I believe Maidstone East Station was opened in 1886 and the windmill was probably cleared away half a century or more before that.

In my further searches, I found that a Street Plan accompanying an 1834 Guide to Maidstone (kindly lent by the County Library) does not show the

E. Gasston   W.C.F.

NONINGTON

See page 250

F. Pain   W.C.F.

NONINGTON (Seed Mill)   NEWINGTON, Near Ramsgate

See page 250   *See page 249*   *Facing page 240*

NORTHBOURNE (Old Mill)

See page 251

NORTHBOURNE (New Mill)

See page 251

mill ; and Pigot's Directory of 1839 does not give the name of a windmiller. One is, therefore, led to presume that the mill disappeared a century or more ago.

Mr. F. J. Blinkhorn, of East Farleigh, whose family have had a long connection with watermills of the Maidstone area, writes :

> I have heard that my grandfather, John Blinkhorn, as a young man, worked in a smock windmill in the Sandling Road. It was probably owned or rented by his father, Robert Blinkhorn. My grandfather, John Blinkhorn, was born in 1800 and died in 1873. His father, Robert, had Sandling watermill, the mill in the gaol (this was a treadmill, worked by the prisoners—W.C.F.), and the windmill on Penenden Heath.

The following is an interesting note from the columns of the *South Eastern Gazette*, following an enquiry made by Mr. A. W. Tiffin :

> With reference to the letter from Mr. Alfred W. Tiffin, of Woodside, Staplehurst, in the *South Eastern Gazette* last week, inquiring for information as to the existence of a windmill at Maidstone a century ago, as indicated by a map, dated 1819, Mr. Walter French, of 13 Waterloo Street, Maidstone, says there can be no doubt that the site was part of the area now occupied by the Maidstone East railway station and sheds.
> Mr. French was born in a house in Bones Alley, opening out of Week Street on the south side of the West Kent Hotel and continuing by the wall of what was then an orchard, belonging to a Mr. Southwell (the present Brenchley Gardens), and is now the line of Station Road. He has a clear recollection of this part of Maidstone and knew not only Oyster Path Row, which stood at right angles with Bones Alley about where the Station Road entrance to the Brenchley Gardens now stands, this being at the back of St. Faith's Green, now occupied in part by St. Faith's Church, but also Windmill Row, to which Bones Alley led and which was on the line of the present footpath at the back of Brenchley Gardens.
> The house in which Mr. French was born was at the junction of Bones Alley and Oyster Path Row. He says that before the Maidstone East Station came, with the opening first of the railway line from Swanley to Maidstone, an area of the land taken for it was occupied by Mr. Stephen Aldridge, father of Maidstone's present tent proprietor of that name, and within that area he is confident was the site of the windmill marked on the map of 1819.
> Adjoining Mr. Aldridge's premises, Mr. French says, were those originally occupied by Mr. Stevens, timber merchant, later of St. Peter Street, which were approached by Wharf Lane, on the Sandling Road side of Maidstone East Station.

*   *   *   *   *

In connection with a windmill at Maidstone, it may be noted that Mr. E. T. Clark, of Maidstone, an enthusiastic collector of coins and tokens, possesses a seventeenth century token, the centre design of which is an old trestle windmill. Mr. Clark has kindly consented to a copy-photograph of this token being reproduced in this volume. The wording on the token is :

IOHN. HOAD. IN
MEADSTONE 1657.

The inference would be that an old post mill stood in Maidstone as far back as 1657, and that the miller's name was John Hoad. I have, however, received a letter from Mr. J. W. Bridge, the Honorary Secretary of the Kent Numismatic Society, from which the following is an extract :

Q

I thought it might interest you to know that in a Precept dated April 12th, **1699,** summoning all the Innkeepers of the Town to renew their licences, "William Baker at the Wind-Mill" is mentioned. This Inn is supposed to have been somewhere in King St., and as the greater number of the seventeenth century tokens were issued by Inn-keepers, grocers, etc., who required a quantity of small change, I am inclined to think that the John Hoad token is more likely to refer to the Inn than to the actual mill. The difference in the names could be easily accounted for by a change of ownership or tenancy during the period of forty-two years between the above mentioned dates.

MARGATE

Lydden.   Humber's Mill or Chamber's Mill.   Approx. 2 miles NW. of St. Lawrence Church, Ramsgate. 1695, 1719, 1736.

Dr. Harris' map of 1719 notes this mill as Humber's Mill. E. Bowen's map of 1736 describes it as Chamber's Mill. Its situation was a little to the north-east of the village of Fleete.

Drapers' Mills.   7 furlongs SE. of Church. 1 mill—1695, 1719, 1819-43 ; 3 mills—1858-72 ; 2 mills—1903-10 (one remains standing ; the other a base only).*

One mill only stood at this position until about 1869, when a second smock mill was brought from Barham and re-built. The third was a large tower mill, erected about 1874 for the Corporation for pumping water, and it is thought that Hill of Ashford was the builder. This made a group of three mills (as shown on the 1858-72 map) of which I give a photograph. The two corn mills are shown complete, but the pumping mill cap-less with its tower embattled.

1. *The Old Mill.*—This mill was built on its present site by John Holman of Canterbury. It has not worked by wind since about 1916. The sweeps were thought to be unsafe and were removed, with the fan, in 1927. To-day it is worked by a 20 h.p. gas engine. It stands on a brick base with its weather-boarded body kept well tarred. The mill shown on the 1819-43 Ordnance Map was evidently a predecessor at the same position, believed to have been brought from along the coast, near Nayland Rock, about half a mile west of Margate Church. A mill is shown at that position on the 1801 First Ordnance Survey Map, and is probably the one that was transferred.

2. *Little Drapers' Mill.*—This windmill was moved from Barham about 1869. Mr. Frank Pain knows the actual site near Barham Railway Station, and he tells me that the mill mound is still there. I cannot trace in what way the mill was conveyed such a long distance but I understand that each portion was numbered to facilitate the re-erection, which was executed by T. R. Holman, for Messrs. Darby. The brick base alone remains to-day and has been used as a garage.

3. *The 'Pumper.'*—The pumping mill was a large and powerful mill built originally with five sweeps but, after a severe gale in January, 1878, repairs and alterations to the tune of £280 resulted in a four-sweep mill. In August,

1894, when the mill was tail-winded in a high wind, the windshaft, midlings and sweeps were wrecked and damage done to the value of £275—at least that was the estimated cost of re-instating the mill ; but it was not again repaired and the tower stood for many years as depicted in the photograph. Nothing remains to-day.

Town Mill. 3 furlongs NW. of Drapers' Mills. 1719, 1858-72.

The Town Mill stood near St. John's Church and was known to be working in 1889, when it was held by a Mr. Fright who probably last worked it. Previously it had been held for about fifty years by E. A. Banks.

Cliftonville. Gouger's Mills.* ¼ mile S. of Coastguard Station. 1819-43.

Although the 1819-43 map shows only two mills at Cliftonville, named thereon as Margate Mills, there were at one time three mills, as depicted in the old engraving here reproduced. They were all large smock mills and were known as Gouger's Mills after their owner, Daniel Gouger, who had them as far back as 1839.

An old miller friend remembers his father saying that when one of the three mills was burnt or pulled down, one pair of its stones was added to each of the remaining two mills, which worked for many years more until pulled down about 1875. Nothing remains of them to-day and the ground has been built on.

Mr. Jack Holman sends me the following interesting note regarding the two mills that stood latterly :

> These mills were bought by Mr. T. R. Holman of Canterbury. The timber was sold on the spot while the machinery went to the Canterbury works. The mills were usually known as the East and West Mills. Before they were pulled down Mr. T. R. Holman had to make estimates for the rebuilding of each mill. The cost for rebuilding the East Mill is quoted as £700, while that of the West Mill £395. A Mr. May of Sutton Court, near Deal, considered having the West Mill erected at his farm but it never matured. The mills were pulled down in November 1875.

MEOPHAM
(NEAR GRAVESEND)

Meopham Green.* ¾ mile SSW. of Church. Working to-day, two sweeps. 1903-10.

This mill at Meopham Green was erected in 1801 by three brothers named Killick, who walked daily a distance of eight miles from Strood, to build the mill. They were millers, carrying on business there, as well as millwrights ; and built it as a model mill. It was visited by millers from near and far, many of whom were thinking of having a mill built and this one proved a good example to aid them in their decision.

The mill was taken over from Thomas Killick by John Norton in 1889, and his nephew, William (the present owner), joined him in partnership. Hence the present name of the firm, J. & W. Norton.

It was a thoroughly well-built mill. Substantial oak is to be seen everywhere, timbers are strutted and supported to prevent buckling and there is a feeling of solidity about the whole structure. I understand the brickwork in the base has never required pointing during its life of 132 years and the original weather-boarding is still there, each length of board being numbered with the Roman numerals, which are still visible.

There were only two pairs of stones originally. Now there are four although only three are in actual use, the insurance policy allowing only this number. Mr. Norton once bought a pair of Peak stones (as well as an oil engine) from Richardson's Mill, Boughton. Flour was last made at the mill about 1914. Mr. Norton says it was often delivered locally by a donkey !

Two of the sweeps are missing. These came to grief many years ago and for long could not be renewed owing to the difficulty in obtaining well-seasoned timber. Eventually some considered suitable was obtained and new sweeps were erected but the timber could only have been artificially seasoned, for the sweeps crashed after a year and did considerable damage to the mill, which had to be repaired.

With the exception of the missing sweeps, the mill is in splendid condition. A 15 h.p. oil engine, equal to the power of the remaining sweeps in a fair wind, has been installed, and there is also a roller plant for making flour. The present trade is chiefly that of grinding pig and poultry food for the neighbouring farmers, and there seems to be plenty of work always in hand.

There is every facility in the mill for carrying on a good trade, but the main difficulty, Mr. Norton says, is in buying corn at the right price. It is impossible adequately to compete with the large Steam Mills ; the extra two or three shillings paid by a windmiller for the smaller quantities is a serious handicap in these days of cut prices and mass production.

Every inch of space in the mill is utilised. In fact it is astonishing what a large amount of useful machinery and appliances is stored in such a small space. There is, however, ample room to move about and to work the mill in comfort. It makes its own electric light, which is rather unusual.

Priestwood Mill. 1 mile SSE. of Church. 1769, 1819-43.

An account of my search for this mill is given in an earlier chapter. As there stated, nothing remains to-day.

(See page 87)

MILTON
(NEAR SITTINGBOURNE)

Chalkwell Mill. ¾ mile W. of Sittingbourne Church. 1819-43.

The Ordnance Map of 1819-43 shows this mill as standing on the south side of Watling Street, at its junction with the road to Bredgar. It was a black smock mill having one floor under the stage. Four 'patent' sweeps worked the three pairs of stones.

M. R. Packer

W. Whiting

OSPRINGE (Water Lane Mill)

See page 254

W.C.F.

A. W. Tiffin

NORTHWOOD (Thanet Mill)

See page 253

Facing page 244

A. W. Tiffin

OARE

See page 253

W.C.F.

OARE (WINDMILL PUMP)

See page 315

Basil Schon

AT HARVEST TIME

I look down over the farms ;
In the fields of grain I see
The harvest that is to be.
And I fling to the air my arms,
For I know it is all for me !

Longfellow.

See page 103

The miller in 1878 and for many years about that date was Richard Thomas Snoard. He was a farmer as well as a miller and it is said that often while the mill was running the old gentleman, wearing his white smock and tall hat, would be seen out in the field, ploughing with his horses.

The mill was sold for demolition on account of the laying out of an estate. As it was in such a good state of repair the purchaser thought he had secured a bargain when he paid £40 for the structure as she stood. He had it carefully taken to pieces and the items laid out in lots and then sold by auction. The total proceeds of the sale amounted to £42 and, as labour in pulling it down had cost £27, he was considerably out of pocket !

Mr. F. Littlewood, the millwright of Milton, purchased the steam tackle (installed in the mill but never used) and later on fitted it for John Bates in Meade Mill, Milton Regis.

MILTON REGIS
(NEAR SITTINGBOURNE)

*Meade Mill.** ¼ *mile NW. of Church. Standing to-day, derelict.* 1819-43, 1903-10.

This derelict windmill stands near the branch railway line from Sittingbourne to Sheerness. I am able to give a picture of it in its working days and one as it appears to-day—left to the elements to bring about its gradual dismemberment. It was abandoned as an active mill about 1914. The end of one of the sweeps looks as though it might drop off at any moment but I understand it has been hanging like this for some years. It is held in position by the iron rod that regulated the shutters.

John Bates owned the mill at one time and in 1878 J. Barnard was the miller. In 1889 a steam engine was added as auxiliary power and three pairs of stones were worked.

Flour was never made at this mill. It was not intended for the flour trade, which was carried out at a near-by watermill that ran in conjunction with it.

The mill suffered badly in a gale one night about 1868, when the sweeps, cap and stage were carried away. Substantial repair and replacement had to be carried out. Mr. J. Ride, who was working in the mill when the gale arose, was injured.

In 1879 the whole of the body of the mill was rebuilt. Every corner post, all quartering and weather-boards were renewed by Mr. F. Littlewood, millwright of Milton.

* * * *

Since collecting the material for these notes, Mr. Geo. E. Ride has stated in a letter :

This mill, when my uncle had it, had two pairs of stones on the stone floor and one pair very small, about 32 in. diameter, on the bin floor, used only for bean splitting and was driven by underdrift gear. Soon after Mr. Bates added the steam power he put another pair of Peaks down on the stone floor, so the mill had actually four pairs.

In a further letter dated April 5th, 1933, Mr. Ride says :

I see they have made the poor old windmill down on the Meads at Milton Regis look a little more decent ; those two dangling portions of the two top sweeps have been removed ; in fact the whole of the sweeps have been cut away, with the exception of the main pole. The cross bars have all been sawn off level, so that she now stands with two long poles and two halves ; they have given them a coat of white paint, also the cap. The timbers that carried the fantail have been cut off flush with the back of the cap, and the windows appear to be all boarded up and the body has had a fresh coat of tar. The engine house has also been cleared away. They have turned the sweeps round so that the two long ones stand at the top instead of the bottom, as you saw it last.

MINSTER
(ISLE OF SHEPPEY)

Pigtail Corner. ½ mile E. of Church. 1596, 1610, 1695, 1769, 1819-43.

Here there was a smock mill of the early type without a stage, believed to have been over 200 years of age. Evidently it was the successor of a post mill that stood here in 1596 and 1610 as noted on the early maps.

The mill is known to have been working in 1878, when the miller was G. L. Franks. It could not, however, have been in use for long after this, for she was derelict for some years following a gale that caught her tail-winded and blew off practically the whole of the sweeps. In 1889, I am told, "some one had the credit of setting her alight and, being coated with several layers of felt and tar, she made a pretty good blaze."

Mr. Geo. E. Ride writes :

This mill did very little work after Mr. Franks left it. One or two had a try at it but only for a few months. I remember it standing so long idle that the Rural District Council complained of it standing in a dangerous condition with the sweeps across the road, and I was the last one to help the caretaker to pull her round in the opposite direction. There she stood until the sweeps and head of the windshaft were blown off, and she was later burnt down.

1 mile SE. of Church. 1819-43.

This mill is noted on the 1819-43 Ordnance Map, but I have no record of its history or of its disappearance.

MINSTER
(THANET)

Minster Mills. 1½ miles NE. of Church. 1 *mill*—1596, 1610, 1695, 1719, 1769 ; 2 *mills*—1819-43.

There was evidently an old post mill at this spot centuries ago, replaced by a smock mill in more recent years, and then another smock mill added to make a pair. They stood one on each side of the Monkton-Ramsgate road.

Sir Charles Igglesden, writing in 1903, in reference to this pair of mills, says :

The high road running from Ramsgate to Canterbury was formerly dotted by two windmills, which were conspicuous landmarks. One fell a prey to fire, the other to the elements. At the present time the village cannot boast of a single windmill.[1]

In 1870 T. R. Holman fitted four new spring sweeps to one of them. Both were known to be working in 1875, under a Mr. Harnett. The earlier of the two, which disappeared some years before its companion, originally had a wooden windshaft. It was replaced by an iron shaft by T. R. Holman. Richard Fright is given in a Directory of 1878 as the miller at Minster.

The mill last standing had an underground floor, which can still be seen. Mr. Holman tells me he was asked to quote for various replacements in 1882, such as new curb, windshaft and fantail, but the owner of the mill evidently could not afford the expense and the work was not carried out.

MOLASH
(NEAR CANTERBURY)

¼ *mile SW. of Church.* 1819-43.

The last date appearing in Messrs. Holman's ledgers in connection with repairs to this mill is 1877. It was of smock type, with fan and shuttered sweeps. It has been gone a great many years and I can trace no information as to when or how it ceased to exist.

GREAT MONGEHAM
(NEAR DEAL)

Mongeham Mill. SW. of Church. 1596, 1695, 1736.

A mill is shown on the above maps, and the 1736 Bowen map refers to it as Mongeham Mill.

MONKTON
(THANET)

Monkton Mill. 1½ *miles NE. of Church.* 1596, 1610, 1695, 1719, 1736, 1769.

The following is an interesting extract in connection with Monkton, from the pen of Sir Charles Igglesden, culled from one of his fascinating series of articles in the *Kentish Express* :

Here is the history of the obelisk at Monkton. Many years ago a windmill stood in the cornfields on the high ground on the west side of the road leading from Brooksend, near Birchington, to Monkton, and near the junction of the road leading towards Acol. It was used as a landmark from the sea, but it was removed to Sarre, where we see it to-day, and then the sailormen, while cruising up and down the Channel,

[1] *Saunters Through Kent with Pen and Pencil*, Vol. V, p. 29.

found that they had lost their beacon. An obelisk of brick, similar in shape to Cleopatra's Needle, was subsequently erected, but in October 1922 it was pulled down and the bricks scattered. It had become unsafe with cavities in the brickwork, and the Brethren of Trinity House decided upon its demolition. Here in the rock garden of Monkton Court is the cone which was perched at the summit of the obelisk.

It has been doubted whether the Monkton mill was really moved to Sarre, but in any case Sir Charles Igglesden's statement evidently explains the absence of a mill at Monkton from any later map than 1769.

MURSTON

(NEAR SITTINGBOURNE)

7 furlongs NE. of Church. 1819-43.

The 1819-43 map clearly shows a mill at this position, near Ferry House, but it does not appear on later maps.

NEWCHURCH

(NEAR NEW ROMNEY)

3 furlongs E. of Church.* Two-storied base remains. 1903-10.

A rector of Newchurch, the Rev. Nares, is said to have built this mill in 1810 and to have carried it on at first. A story has been handed down that the farmers when they came to church often brought samples of corn in their pockets for the rector to examine. The Mill House was built from the materials pulled down from the old rectory.

It was a small though substantial brick tower mill. Mr. G. Prebble, who worked it last, from 1893 to 1901, remembers his father saying that he had never seen a better bit of brickwork than the tower. Right up to its closing days there was not a crack in it. Prior to Mr. Prebble's occupation the miller was William Carlton, and references to others who worked the mill at one time or another include the names of Green, Collingham, Godden and Harris.

It was pulled down because of the expense of repairs required to the woodwork, and given to Mr. George Jarvis for his work of clearing the site. All four sweeps were on at the time of its demolition—in about 1906. Two brick floors still remain and are used as a store for corn and meal.

Flour was not made at the mill after about 1890, since when the trade was in grinding farmers' corn.

Mill Bank. 1¼ miles WSW. of Church.

The words "Mill Bank" at the above position are noted on all the Ordnance Maps since 1800 but I cannot trace a windmill there on any map.

NEWINGTON
(NEAR RAMSGATE)

½ *mile N. of St. Lawrence Church, Ramsgate.* Standing to-day, worked by engine.* 1819-43, 1903-10.

In connection with this mill I cannot do better than quote from an interesting letter received in 1931 from Mr. Peter Mack, the owner :

> The mill is about 100 years old. The sails, which are in fairly good condition, were last used twenty-seven years ago (1904). I think considerable repair would have to be done for them to be used again. The shutters, of course, have been dismantled. We used up to quite recently two pairs of stones, one Derbyshire Peak and the other a French Burr. We now only use one pair (for grinding barley and farmers' corn). The other pair have been removed for an oat crushing, maize kibbler and grinder combined.
>
> We make our own gas (from anthracite coal) to drive the gas engine, which drives a small flour plant, the stones and crusher all together. We also have a bakery adjoining the mill in which we bake bread. So you see we make our own gas, make our own flour and produce bread from same. Our trade is a mixed one, of course, as is the case with similar businesses, consisting of corn, fodder, flour, bread, which is retailed at our two shops.

Mr. Mack added that he had heard that the mill originally stood on the old S.E. & C. R. Station site in the town and was moved by the railway company to make room for the line. This is a misunderstanding, I think, for the Canterbury millwrights tell me that the mill was erected on its present site by John Holman.

Prior to Mr. Mack's ownership, the mill was in the Mascall family—for whom it was probably first built.

NEWINGTON
(NEAR SITTINGBOURNE)

3 *furlongs SW. of Church.* 1819-43.

This mill stood on the north side of Watling Street, at the entrance to the village. It was pulled down many years ago but was known to be standing in 1884. It was at one time used by a family named Foster, and one of the sons worked in the old Tide Mill at Strood, next Rochester.

In 1878 the miller was George Maxted and in 1884 the mill was in the possession of Miss Dawson. It had also been held for some time by the Franks family from Staple and later by a Mr. Else who had some extensive repairs carried out—although it did not stand many years afterwards.

It was a smock and stage mill with two floors under the stage, fantail, two 'patent' sweeps and two canvas sails. An unusual feature was a pair of stones that were exceptionally large, having a diameter of five feet.

NEWNHAM
(NEAR SITTINGBOURNE)

1½ furlongs N. of Church. 1819-43.

A very old mill of the early smock type once stood at Newnham. It had no base or stage. Although worked almost to the last, it had become very shaky. The sweeps were on the mill to the end and were then purchased and transferred to Doddington Mill.

The mill was dismantled by Mr. T. B. Gambrill, of Petham, who bought the gearing. He was asked to leave half of the tower standing. This was filled with tar barrels and faggots and the whole set alight on Guy Fawkes' Day, November 5th, 1876.

NONINGTON
(NEAR DOVER)

1 mile 1 furlong ESE. of Church.* *Standing to-day, worked by engine.* 1596, 1695, 1736, 1819-43, 1903-10.

As far back as 1596 a windmill had stood at Nonington. This early mill was, of course, of post type. It evidently disappeared before 1769, for the large-scale map of that date fails to show it.

The next map reference is 1819-43, doubtless of the smock mill that stands derelict to-day. It had no base or stage and the sweeps came very close to the ground. There were three pairs of stones.

About 1890, the mill was covered in with heavy gauge iron sheeting. The sweeps, considered unsafe, were removed about 1905 and an oil engine installed. A little business is still done at the mill—mostly provender and family trade.

For many years the mill has been held by Mr. E. Gasston. Previous occupiers were T. Clark and, in 1878, James Dilnot.

Seed Mill or 'Pug.'* *1 mile 1 furlong ESE. of Church.* 1903-10.

This mill was situated about 200 yards south-east of the mill previously noted and, although built much later, nothing now remains of it. But the thistle-clad bump on which it stood can still be seen.

It was of exceptional interest, being what was known as a Seed Mill or 'Pug,' built by a member of the Pain family and originally run by them for some years. Latterly it was owned by John Harvey, seedsman of Nonington.

It was taken down about 1905 after the cap and sweeps had been blown off.

NORTHBOURNE
(NEAR DEAL)

¾ mile SW. of Church. 1596, 1736.

It is difficult to place this mill precisely by reason of the small scale of the old maps but it would appear to have stood about 3 furlongs north-north-west of Little Mongeham and ¾ mile south-west of Northbourne Church.

Northbourne Old Mill.* ½ mile WNW. of Church. Working to-day, two sweeps. 1769, 1819-43, 1903-10.

A mill stood at this position in 1769 and is probably the old smock mill standing to-day. It is owned by the Rt. Hon. Lord Northbourne and the miller is J. Court. Marsh Gilbert was the miller half a century ago. In years gone by a large trade was done. It was considered a powerful mill and sometimes known as the 'Big Mill.' I understand that at one time in its history two millers and a boy were employed there regularly, besides loaders.

In 1868 T. R. Holman carried out renovations at a cost of £150.

The mill is worked entirely by wind and there are three pairs of stones in use. Flour is not milled, although the old flour dresser is still there.

Two of the four sails came to grief in 1925. In 1928 the late Lord Northbourne decided to recondition the mill. At first the two remaining sweeps were to be used but, upon inspection by Messrs. Holman Bros., they were found to be in too bad a condition. Consequently two new sweeps were made and inside repairs carried out. It must be the only case recently of a mill starting to work after being derelict.

New Mill.* 1 furlong SW. of Church. Working to-day, two sweeps. 1903-10.

Messrs. J. J. & T. R. Holman of Canterbury built this mill in 1848 for Richard Fuller, in whose family it has always been held. The successive generations are as follows :

1848-1881, Richard Fuller.
1881-1902, Thomas M. Fuller.
1902 to date, Ernest M. Fuller (the mill is now in charge of his son, R. J. Fuller).

It stands on a tall brick base and has a stage. The two missing sweeps were taken off by a high wind in July, 1915. Since then the mill has been worked with the remaining two sweeps. There are three pairs of stones but the wind power from two sweeps only drives two at one time. An Austin tractor is the auxiliary power in calm weather.

Northbourne is the only village in Kent and Sussex to possess two working windmills each worked with two sweeps only.

NORTHFLEET
(NEAR GRAVESEND)

Three windmills. 1819-43.

The 1819-43 map shows three mills at the following positions : 1 mill—¼ mile west-north-west of Northfleet Church, near "The Hive." 2 mills—a pair together, ¾ mile north-west of the Church, near "Stone Bridge." One of the pair is remembered by Mr. F. W. Boorman, who says he thinks it was worked by a Mr. Gorham for some years—and he has "a distinct recollection of playing cricket for Gravesend (about fifty years ago) against the St. Botolph's Cricket Club at Northfleet, on a ground very near to this mill."

Perry Street. Fiveash Mill. 1½ *furlongs N. of Perry Street Church.* 1819-43.

Fiveash Mill was situated about a quarter of a mile north-north-east of the Six Bells Inn, on the north side of the Dover Road, where the footpath from Style's Lane crossed on its way to Springhead.

Mr. F. A. Mansfield gives the following interesting reference :

> The Fiveash Mill at Perry Street was for very many years an object of considerable local interest. This old windmill, however, ceased working over thirty years ago, and was pulled down some ten years later. It was originally built by Mr. John Fiveash, whose body lies in a grave near the entrance of Northfleet Churchyard. It then passed into the hands of Mr. Waterman,[1] at whose demise the business was carried on by his son.[2]

Fiveash Road at Perry Street to-day is reminiscent of the mill. The house attached to the mill, formerly occupied by the Waterman family, is now used as a dairy.

Rosherville. 5 *furlongs ESE. of Church.* 1819-43.

This mill stood at a *cul-de-sac* near Belmont Cottages, at the end of Rural Vale, a branch road leading south from the New London Road.

Mr. F. W. Boorman, a solicitor of Gravesend, tells me that his grandfather, Thomas Boorman, purchased the lease of the mill about 1832 and worked it for some years ; after his death in 1874 it was used by two sons, William and Thomas A. Boorman.

It was a five-storied, cemented tower mill, with a stage about 30 ft. from the ground. It worked three pairs of stones, two for wheat and one for barley, and flour was made. Latterly steam was used as an auxiliary power. In fact, the mill was known as the Northfleet Wind and Steam Flour Mill. It was last worked about 1894.

The cap and sweeps were on the mill until the last, but the whole fabric was in need of repair. It was pulled down gradually about 1916 and nothing remains to-day. A few small sheds occupy the site.

[1] Stephen Waterman was miller at Fiveash Mill in 1878.

[2] *History of Gravesend,* by F. A. Mansfield, Gravesend and Dartford Reporter, 1922, p. 38.

1. PLUMSTEAD COMMON. 2. WOOLWICH (THE CO-OPERATIVE MILL).
From Records of Woolwich District, by W. T. Vincent, 1845.
3 and 4. BEXLEY HEATH (MAY PLACE MILL), A. H. T. Boswell.

See pages 162, 257, 307

Facing page 252

A. W. Tiffin   W.C.F.

PLUCKLEY

See page 257

T. H. Gambrill   W.C.F.

PETHAM (Chequers' Mill)   PRESTON, Near Wingham
                                           (Solly's Mill)

See page 256   See page 260   Facing page 253

Mr. F. A. Mansfield informs me that the mill was situated on the edge of a cliff created by the excavation of chalk for use in the neighbouring cement works. Mr. F. W. Boorman states that in 1887 some warehouses adjoining the mill collapsed and fell down the chalk quarry owing to a landslide at the rear of the mill. This incident gave rise to an action for damages against the owner of the quarry for excavating too near the mill premises, depriving them of the support of the adjoining land.

NORTHWOOD
(NEAR RAMSGATE)

Thanet Mill.* ½ *mile N. of St. Lawrence Church, Ramsgate. Standing to-day, derelict.* 1819-43, 1903-10.

This mill, for many years in the Hudson family, was worked by Mr. Hudson about 1877 in conjunction with the Ramsgate Mill in Grange Road.

It is of curious shape. In 1848 the railway company made a cutting for the Ramsgate to Margate railway close to the mill and the owner successfully claimed damages, maintaining that the excavated earth obstructed the wind for the mill, necessitating its being raised a storey higher. The cost of the necessary work and the litigation was estimated at £400, apart from the loss of business during the alterations. If, in heightening the mill, the extra portion had been built on at the same angle as the existing lower part of the mill, it would have proved too narrow at the top and a new cap would have had to be made to fit, so the addition was built vertically. Hence its unusual shape.

OARE
(NEAR FAVERSHAM)

½ *mile S. of Church.** *Standing to-day, derelict.* 1819-43, 1903-10.

This five-storied brick tower mill has been a fine specimen in its day, well built, splendidly equipped and the motive power of a large business. It worked four pairs of stones.

Originally it was built for a Mr. Elliott and later sold to Thomas K. Hope, who had it up to about 1878. Afterwards it came into the possession of the Gunpowder Company. For four years, from 1882 to 1886, the mill was hired and worked by Mr. Herbert Filmer, of Preston, Faversham, who tells me that the mill was at that time in splendid order. Mr. Filmer had a subsequent experience with the mill, for he worked it under Government orders during the Great War, from September 1917 to June 1919. Very few windmills worked under Government orders ; most of those in Kent had given up making flour before the war.

It is a great pity that the mill is such a derelict to-day. The fan and one of the sweeps are missing and the remaining three sweeps are in a bad state of repair. The present owner has recently refused a fairly high offer for its demolition. There must be many thousands of bricks in the tower.

An explosion of the boiler used in connection with the steam engine in this mill many years ago did much damage to the adjoining cottages and to the Windmill Inn.

(See also Addenda, page 315.)

OSPRINGE
(NEXT FAVERSHAM)

Water Lane Mill.* ¼ *mile N. of Church.* 1903-10.

Edward Packer was the miller here in 1878 according to an old directory. Not long after this the mill did not pay its way and ceased working. It stood in Water Lane, on the south side of Watling Street, somewhat remarkable for the height of the stage. It was pulled down about 1915.

¾ *mile N. of Church.* 1819-43.

The early Ordnance Map shows a pair of mills at this position, on the north side of both Watling Street and the railway, near Ospringe Union House.

Mr. Herbert Filmer, of Preston, Faversham, who knows the district well, has only known of one windmill at this position. This was a smock mill, without a stage, and the miller was a Mr. Ralph. It was burnt down about 1910.

I have since learnt that, before Mr. Ralph's occupation, a Mr. Carr owned it and his miller for a time was Thomas Manwaring, then quite a young man, who later had Luton Mill, Chatham. At that time it had all cloth sweeps.

PEGWELL BAY*
(NEAR RAMSGATE)

I do not remember ever hearing of a windmill at Pegwell Bay and must rely on a picture by George Shepherd, dated 1828, which clearly shows one.

A miller friend assures me there has been no windmill at Pegwell Bay for the last hundred years. He can vouch for sixty years of his own lifetime, and had his father, who also knew the district well, heard of the supposed mill, he would have mentioned it at some time or another.

I can only assume that the mill shown in George Shepherd's picture was cleared away about 1830. One can surely dismiss as unworthy the suggestion that this famous artist should have let his imagination run riot in connection with a picture that purported to be a *view* of a certain spot. A landscape picture, not localised, would be a different matter.

PENENDEN HEATH
(NEAR MAIDSTONE)

1¼ *miles S. of Boxley Church.* 1819-43.

This is believed to have been a weather-boarded smock mill. Mr. F. J. Blinkhorn, of East Farleigh, tells me that his great grandfather, Robert Blinkhorn, who died in 1840, worked the mill and was probably the last to use it. Mr. F. J. Blinkhorn later writes :

I heard this mill was dismantled and erected, or the important parts put into a windmill for a relative, Robert Dawson, at a seaside town, Margate, I think.

After I received this letter I had a chat with a relative of Mr. F. J. Blinkhorn—Mr. Walter Blinkhorn, of Maidstone—who told me he believed the mill was moved to *Folkestone*. This is of particular interest, for there definitely was a miller named Dawson at the windmill at Millfield, Folkestone (which mill was later moved to Bethersden). And Mr. George Jarvis, who dismantled the mill at Millfield, is sure the mill was not originally built there, as the four corner posts had at some time in the mill's history been renewed—indicating that this was carried out when it was re-erected at Millfield.

There is to-day not the slightest trace of the windmill ever having stood at Penenden Heath.

In view of the low lying position of the heath, I can only think that the mill did not stand actually on the heath itself but on higher ground a little to the south. From a study of the vicinity, and failing definite information, I hazard a guess that the mill stood on or about the site of 132 Boxley Road, an oast-house that has been converted into a dwelling. The occupier, who has been there only for about four years, could tell me nothing.

PETHAM
(NEAR CANTERBURY)

Mill Downs Mill. Near Church. 1829.

This was known also as the Workhouse Mill, or Parish Mill, for such it was during the period of its early history. Its original purpose was to grind corn for the inmates of the Petham and Waltham Workhouse situated at Waltham. This workhouse has been remodelled and, standing to-day, is known as Waltham Court, the residence of Capt. Gilbert G. P. Hewett, R.N.

In about 1850 the mill was moved to Stelling Minnis (see Stelling Minnis, Brambleton Mill).

The body of the mill was not dismantled but moved entire, being put on a huge six-wheel trolley, called locally a 'tug,' and hauled by men and horses. One of the roads along which the structure was carried proved to be too narrow and the bank had to be cut away to allow the trolley to pass through !

The removal was carried out under the anxious and strict supervision of the miller, Mr. Bartlett, by whom it was re-erected and whose son, later, succeeded him at the mill at its new home at Stelling Minnis.

(See also page 63.)

Duckpit. Mark's Folly Mill. 1 mile SW. of Church.

A mill certainly stood at Petham during the last century, for an old post mill was moved from there to Elmsted (see Elmsted, Itinge Mill) but I do not find it noted on any map.

At Petham it was known as Mark's Folly Mill, or the Duckpit Mill. It was moved to Elmsted probably about 1865, drawn along by horses on a trolley specially made for the purpose.

Chequers' Mill.* 3 furlongs E. of Church. 1858-72.

Sweetlove's of Wingham erected this mill in 1821. It stood on the left-hand side of Stone Street, a little nearer Canterbury than the Chequers' Inn.

By the courtesy of Mr. T. H. Gambrill I am able to give a picture of the mill as it appeared in 1900. The Gambrill family held it for the whole period of its history. The first owner was Harry Gambrill, for whom it was built. He was followed by his son, Thomas Gambrill (1844-1871), then his grandson, Thomas Boys Gambrill (1871-1889), and finally his great-grandson, Thomas Henry Gambrill (1889-1900) who still lives, aged 74, at the Mill House at Petham.

The mill originally cost about £600 to build but, in 1870, £500 was spent in renovating it, including the alteration to 'patent' sweeps, the fitting of an additional pair of stones (there had been only two originally), an iron wind-shaft to replace an old wooden one and the making of a cellar.

It is said to have been one of the finest smock mills in Kent, 'running like a clock.' Its sweeps had a span of nearly eighty feet and were seven feet broad, and it had no trouble to work its three pairs of stones in an ordinary wind. It was situated on very high ground and caught the slightest breeze. Often when other mills in the district were becalmed, there was sufficient wind to work the Chequers' Mill gently with one pair of stones.

A record was created at this mill in 1870. Wheat was cut in an adjoining field in the morning, threshed, taken to the mill, made into flour, passed over to the bakehouse belonging to the mill, baked into bread, drawn out of the ovens and completed by ten o'clock the same night.

The mill was in perfect order when burnt down on April 1st, 1900. It had been making flour only a day or two previously. There had been no wind all that day, but at 10 p.m. a breeze sprang up and the mill was put to work. At midnight it was closed down and, between twelve and one o'clock, was in flames. The outbreak was probably caused by the neck-brasses running dry, for marks of 'scoring' were found after the fire, and the sparks, thrown out as the sweeps revolved, had evidently set fire to accumulated grease, etc., near.

An estimate to build a new mill for £1,300 was sent in by T. R. Holman of Canterbury but the transaction did not mature. Although the mill was insured, a quibble arose in connection with an 8 h.p. steam engine which drove the mill during calm periods. Hence only £75 was realised from the insurance company and no new mill replaced the old.

No trace remains of this fine mill except a slight depression in the ground, now used as a dump for rubbish.

Having been built in 1821, the mill just escaped inclusion on the 1819 map and, being demolished in 1900, it does not appear on the 1903 map.

(See also page 74.)

W.C.F.

A. W. Tiffin

PRESTON, Near Wingham
(Dunn's Mill)

See page 259

Herbert Filmer

A. W. Tiffin

PRESTON, Next Faversham

See page 258

RAMSGATE (Grange Road)

See page 260

F. A. Humphrey

RINGWOULD (Ripple Mill)

See page 262

Facing page 257

PLUCKLEY
(NEAR ASHFORD)

¼ mile NW. of Church.* Standing to-day, very dilapidated. 1903-10.

Should the reader be tempted to search out this gaunt wreckage of a once fine smock mill, he will be well repaid by the view from the site on which the battered and weather-worn grinder stands.

The mill is a deserted, hopeless derelict, tumbling to pieces bit by bit. It was last used for corn grinding in 1916. It had been worked for forty-five years by Richard Buss, who rented it from Sir Henry Dering. Mr. Buss found he could not carry on the business alone after his son joined up in the Great War, and was obliged to close down the mill. He used it for a little while for sawing up firewood for the villagers but the structure, in its exposed position, receiving the full force of the elements, soon became a derelict. Children made it their playground ; local people pulled up the floorings and other timbers and broke them up for firing ; visitors took away fragments as souvenirs and gradually the ill-used old grinder became an empty shell.

Two of the sails were taken down about 1912 and the mill worked afterwards with only two sweeps. The four sweeps last on the mill came from Kennington Mill and were re-erected on Pluckley Mill by Mr. George Jarvis.

At one time, about 1872, the fantail was painted red, white, and blue. A Mr. Pearson was the miller for the then occupant, James Steer, from whom Richard Buss took over about 1874. In preparation for Mr. Buss' tenancy the mill had been put in thorough repair by Messrs. Hill of Ashford, including the fitting of new yellow deal corner posts from timber chosen from Sir Henry Dering's estate and sawn up on the spot.

There was a cellar, used as a store, underneath the ground floor of the mill, with steps leading down to it from outside.

One pair of stones, a set of French burr, was of exceptional size, having a diameter of five feet.

There was at one time a bakery attached to the mill, which was as good a business as the milling. The bakehouse, however, is now situated farther down the street.

The present owner of the mill, Mr. G. K. Benton, to whom the property was sold about 1928, had thought of turning the mill into cottages but he could get no tenants for the proposed dwellings.

Mr. George Jarvis was once asked, during Sir Henry's ownership, to pull down the mill but his relatives persuaded him not to undertake this dangerous work.

PLUMSTEAD COMMON[1]

¾ mile SW. of Church.* Brick tower remains to-day. 1819-43.

Here I am indebted to the late Mr. W. T. Vincent, whose monumental

[1] See note on page 151.

R

Records of the Woolwich District gives a delightful picture of the mill (here reproduced), in addition to the following interesting reference :

The old mill on Plumstead Common, of which Mr. Ranwell has left us such a pleasing picture, was the scene of a startling occurrence in 1827, the recollection of which is in the minds of old inhabitants. The mill was at that period in full work, and the housewives regularly carried their little store of wheat to the miller, Mr. Longmore (who also kept the "Prince of Orange" in the village), to be ground into flour. A grand sham fight was arranged for the instruction of the neighbouring garrison, and the battle raged from Bostall Heath to Woolwich. A number of Mr. Longmore's customers, friends, and neighbours swarmed upon the staging round the mill, heedless of warning, until it gave way and injured several of them, the worst sufferer being Mr. Flick, a tailor, of New Road, Woolwich. Mr. Clements afterwards owned the mill, but its presence in modern Plumstead grew anachronistic, its sails and superstructure decayed for want of use, and at last, somewhere about 1848, it was diverted from the making of bread to the selling of beer, and, being eventually granted a full licence, was tacked on to the public house which bears its name.[1]

The following extract also has slight reference to the old mill :

Richmond Place in its diagonal course is a relic of an ancient footpath leading from the Manorway through the Warren to Plumstead Common at the Old Mill.[2]

Two of a number of convicts who, in November, 1832, endeavoured to escape from Woolwich Arsenal where they were employed, were found "concealed in a quickset hedge in a secluded spot behind the mill on Plumstead Common."[3]

Part of the brick tower of the mill still remains to-day and is incorporated with the Old Mill Inn in Old Mill Road, Plumstead Common.

Mr. Rex Wailes, on seeing a photograph of the mill, described its external structure as follows :

A tower mill with a hemispherical cap, which is turned by means of a hand chain and wheel. The "batter" or taper of the tower is unusually large.

POSTLING
(NEAR HYTHE)

NW. of Church. 1596, 1719.

I can only assume that this was a post mill, another of the vanished mills of Kent.

PRESTON
(NEXT FAVERSHAM)

¼ *mile S. of Church.** *Standing to-day, derelict.* 1819-43, 1903-10.

This derelict smock mill, standing on the south side of Watling Street, was owned for a great many years (since 1850) by Mr. Benjamin Filmer, whose executors still own the mill.

[1] *Records of the Woolwich District*, by W. T. Vincent, 1890, p. 533.
[2] ibid. p. 555.　　　[3] ibid. p. 362.

One of the sweeps broke off on August 6th, 1914, two days after war was declared. The other three sweeps were then removed. During one of the earlier air raids of the war, a bomb was dropped within fifty yards of the mill. It seemed as though the hostile aircraft had aimed at the mill.

It is of interest to note that a boiler and steam engine were introduced in 1859 and a very tall chimney erected, about a hundred feet high, which completely dwarfed the mill. The height of this shaft was later reduced to eighty feet, as it swayed dangerously in a gale. It was finally taken down in 1924.

Three pairs of stones were used—two Peak and one French. Later, an extra two pairs of French stones were erected on the ground floor and driven by steam up to 1919, when the mill was closed.

On February 8th, 1906, the mill was struck by lightning, during a thunderstorm accompanied by the biggest flakes of snow ever seen. The lightning ran down and up the steel chain and came out of the cap, from which the blue smoke could be seen. Workmen on the ground floor heard the 'click' of the lightning from the chain and smelt the dust burning. Fortunately, the mill was not set on fire.

The mill once had a very busy life. Often, in a strong wind, it worked all night for many nights in succession.

A magnificent view can be obtained from Preston Mill, embracing almost the whole of the Isle of Sheppey and a large stretch of the River Thames, with its liners and ships of every kind from all parts of the world.

PRESTON
(NEAR WINGHAM)

*Old Mill or Dunn's Mill.** 5 *furlongs NW. of Elmstone Church. Standing to-day, worked by engine.* 1819-43, 1903-10.

This mill was built in 1778. I am able to give two photographs, one as it appeared in 1905 and the other in 1930 when it stood without sweeps and fantail.

In March, 1916, the Mill was tail-winged during a heavy gale, and Mr. H. J. Dunn, the owner, recalls that for two hours he tried to bring it to a standstill. But not even by standing on the brake lever could the revolving sweeps be brought under control. During his efforts the shutters were flying off from the sweeps in every direction, and afterwards some of them were found a quarter of a mile away. The mill was very badly damaged and did not work again by wind. The sweeps were beyond repair and were removed some years later. The oil engine, installed a few years previously as an auxiliary, became the sole driving power, and works the mill to-day. Three pairs of stones were worked at one time.

Mr. H. J. Dunn was born in the Mill House and the mill has been in the Dunn family for fifty-five years. Previously George Manwaring had it for some years. He was the father of Thomas Manwaring who was born there in 1814. William Manwaring, now of Willesborough Mill, has in his possession a receipt for fourteen and a half quarters of wheat sold to George Manwaring of Preston Mill at 90s. per quarter, November 13th, 1816. George Manwaring died at Stone Cross Farm, Luton, Chatham, in 1840, aged 72 years.

The sails of Preston Mill caught the slightest breeze. A miller here was once standing on the stage when the mill was idle, talking to a friend on the ground below, when without any warning, the sweeps began to revolve. It is said that the miller began a sentence while on the stage and finished it standing by his friend on the ground beneath !

(See also page 77)

New Mill or Solly's Mill. 1 mile NW. of Elmstone Church. 1819-43, 1903-10.

T. R. Holman built this mill in 1852. A workman who once helped Mr. Dunn, remembered assisting in its erection when he was quite a lad.

It was known also as Solly's Mill, having been built for, and first worked by, Stephen Solly. It drove two pairs of wheat stones, one pair of barley stones and a small pair of bean stones.

About 1912 it was pulled down because, I understand, there was insufficient work for two mills at Preston.

QUEENBOROUGH
(ISLE OF SHEPPEY)

Near E. side of Church. 1819-43.

The Queenborough Mill was burnt down some time before 1860, and the only trace left of it is a house built in the main street in front of the site and known to-day as Mill House.

RAMSGATE

½ mile E. of St. Lawrence Church. 1596, 1719, 1769.

The above map dates are my only references for this mill.

Grange Road. ½ mile SSE. of St. Lawrence Church. Base alone remains. 1 mill—1719 ; 2 mills—1819-43 ; 1 mill—1858-72, 1903-10.

An early mill stood at Ramsgate in 1719. Then, in 1819-43, as evidenced by the early Ordnance Map, there were two standing. One of them must have disappeared many years ago, for the 1858-72 map does not show it and there was no sign of it in 1905 when I photographed the remaining mill, of which I also give a picture as it appeared in 1930, when the body of the mill was completely gone and the wreckage of the base alone remained. This base is now used as a motor garage. Its "black-timbered walls are smothered with advertisement posters. Grimy mechanics grapple with cars in its bowels."[1]

The mill stood on the West Cliff, at the junction of Queen Street and

[1] *Pearson's Weekly.*

A. W. Tiffin   Miss Thomas

STAPLEHURST

Burnt down Coronation Day, June 22nd, 1911

See page 283

Basil Schon

RINGWOULD (Ripple Mill)

See page 262   *Facing page 260*

Facing page 261

DELCE MILL

ROCHESTER

See page 263

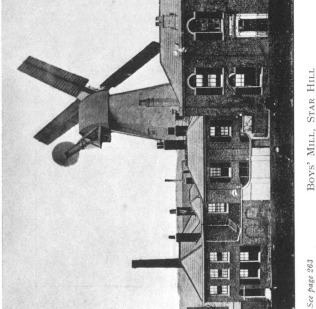

BOYS' MILL, STAR HILL

See page 263

DELCE MILL

(Towering above a sea of slates.)

See page 99

Grange Road. It was a large mill, working four pairs of stones and was considered to be one of the best mills in its day. It was built by Mr. Knott, grandfather-in-law of the famous Baptist minister, Charles Haddon Spurgeon. Unfortunately, owing to a heavy fall in the price of wheat during the Napoleonic wars, Mr. Knott was declared bankrupt. He had bought heavily when wheat was as much as £10 a quarter but the price suddenly dropped to 30s. After giving up the Ramsgate Mill, Mr. Knott started some bakeries in the East End of London and bought wheat at Canterbury market. He would have it sent to the Kent windmills to be ground, have the flour put on the barges at Sandwich (this was before the railways were started) and sent by water to his bakeries in London.

Later, the mill was worked by Mr. Thornton, who had one of the Sturry watermills. It is said that he paid the men overtime in summer, when water was short in the river, to be on duty all night, in readiness for the wind when it 'came up.' Being dependent on the only then known motive powers, wind and water, when one ran low he was obliged to utilise the other to the utmost.

For many years after Mr. Thornton's occupation, the mill was worked in conjunction with Thanet Mill, Northwood, by William Hudson. An 1878 Kent Directory has the entry :

Hudson & Parkin, millers, Grange Road, Ramsgate.

Hereson Mill. ¼ *mile E. of coastline.* 1858-72.

Hereson Mill, a smock, with 'patent' sweeps, stood on the East Cliff, near the synagogue. It was working in 1885 and used by Peter Mack, father of the present proprietor of Newington Mill. Previously it was held by Joseph Evenden, during whose occupation a new steam engine was installed by the Canterbury millwrights at a cost of £310.

In 1888 it was in use by a Mr. Chiswick, and was burnt down about 1890.

RICHBOROUGH

1 *mile NE. of Castle.* 1769.

According to the 1769 map a pair of mills stood close to the Stonar Cut Salt Pans, presumably serving a useful purpose in this ancient salt industry. It is not the only instance where mills are shown beside salt pans and suggests that they pumped the sea water to the evaporating pans.

Plate 3 of *The Kentish Traveller's Companion,* 1787, shows the two mills distinctly, standing by the side of the New Cut, the waterway which connects Ebs Fleet with Hope Bay. In the same volume, page 195, I find the following reference to Stonar :

Among other improvements some salt works have been erected here, which are curious and worthy of observation. The sea brine is drawn, during the hottest of the summer months, into open, broad, shallow pans, of great extent ; having continued till the more watery particles have been exhaled by the sun, it is conveyed into large boilers, and made in the usual method.

The salt having thus undergone a double process, both by the sun, and by common fire, is found to partake so far of the qualities of bay-salt, as to answer all its purposes. It is perfectly white and clear, and supposed, from a variety of experiments, to be at least equal in strength to any made in the kingdom.

The windmills had not survived when the 1819-43 Ordnance Map was prepared but it shows the word 'Salterns' at the position above noted.

RINGWOULD
(NEAR DOVER)

*Ripple Mill.** ½ *mile N. of Ringwould Church. Standing to-day, active.* 1695, 1819-43, 1903-10.

There was a mill here as early as 1695, probably a post mill that disappeared before the erection of the mill that stands to-day.

This present mill was originally built at Drellingore, in the Hawkinge parish, and was used there for some years before being brought to Ripple early in the nineteenth century. It was the custom when taking a mill down for transfer, to cut the eight corner posts down the middle and, when re-erecting, to bolt them together again. One of the original posts with the bolt in it is still to be seen in the mill.

The stones in this mill are driven like a watermill, from underneath instead of from above, known as 'underdrift.'

John Mummery came from Eastry to this mill in 1833 and it was worked by his family for twenty-eight years. In those days, with the aid of a telescope, nearly forty windmills could be picked out !

In one feature I think this mill is unique, having a mound of earth thrown up to take the place of a stage. About 1834 a little girl of four or five years climbed up this bank to see her daddy at the mill and was struck fatally by the sweeps. Some years later a customer to the mill was struck by the knotted end of a rope used to tie the sails down on the sweeps. Happily this did not prove fatal, and she escaped with a broken jaw.

In 1878 the miller was Edwin Pope. To-day the mill is owned by Captain J. E. Monins. It has been in his possession and that of his father before him since 1880. He tells me that in 1895 the Trinity House made a grant to repair the mill, for it is a landmark for shipping up and down the Channel.

Two of the sweeps fell down in 1927 but, as the mill is situated in an exposed position with sufficient wind for all the work required, they are not likely to be replaced.

There are three pairs of stones, two of which are in constant use. An oil engine is the auxiliary power but it is rarely used.

ROCHESTER

Star Hill. The Old Mill. 1 *furlong SE. of St. Peter's Church.*

Built in 1787 and pulled down about 1865, the Old Mill at the top of Star Hill had a useful life. It was only a small mill, yet, in the troublous times of the wars with France, it earned sufficient money to pay for the erection of the large mill next described.

Star Hill. Friday's Mill. 1 furlong SE. of St. Peter's Church. 1819-43.

Friday's Mill stood near St. Peter's vicarage. The present residence of Mr. Apsley Kennette, former Town Clerk of the city, is I believe the original Mill House. On a map of the city, dated 1882 and issued during the mayoralty of Edward Manclark, the mill is shown standing on this spot.

It was of splendid but curious construction, one of the handsomest in Kent, with two fantails, an outside staircase, and was surmounted by a carved figure of Mercury. It was built by Nathaniel Stedman, the grandfather of the late James Stedman, who died at Brompton Mills in 1908, aged 94 years. The tomb of Nathaniel Stedman is to be seen, I believe, in St. Margaret's churchyard, Rochester, between the gate and the church.

The mill had canvas sails until 1846, when Friday introduced adjustable slat sails. Unfortunately, the mill broke away in a gale in 1852, firing the sweeps, which revolved wildly, enveloped in flames.

Star Hill. Boys' Mill or Belsey's Mill.* ½ furlong E. of St. Peter's Church.

This white smock mill was originally known as Boys' Mill, having been built for a Major Boys, who lived in the house now occupied by the Rev. John Bailey. Later it was known as Belsey's Mill after F. F. Belsey who ran it for many years. Later still Messrs. Stedman and Wingent had the mill, with steam power added, until they built the Town Steam Flour Mills (of roller type) in Medway Street, Chatham, in 1877.

Boys' Mill was an active windmill within the memory of many now living and I am able to give a picture of it. It stood on the top of Star Hill, on the site now occupied by the works of Messrs. Rootes, Ltd. It was pulled down by Messrs. Payne and Seymour about 1890-5, who paid £50 for it.

It was a splendid mill, with three floors under the stage, driving four pairs of stones. My friend, the late John Rose, of Higham Mill, had reason to remember it, for he spent £100 on its renovation shortly before its destruction, and the mill never had an opportunity of earning for him one penny of that amount.

Delce Mill.* 3 furlongs SSW. of St. Peter's Church. Standing to-day, active.
1903-10.

Delce Mill, known also as Glover's Mill, is the only active mill of which Rochester can now boast. It was built about 1853 by Henry Payne & Sons, millwrights, who lived in the present Mill House, the mill being built for one of the sons, Thomas.

It was worked for a short time by a Mr. Chapman, and in 1859 was bought by Glover & Callaway, during whose occupation it was burnt down (in 1872) and for whom it was re-built by Messrs. Payne. When Mr. Callaway died it was carried on by John Glover and, at his death, by his son, Walter James Glover, the present owner.

In October 1909 the mill lost one of its sweeps, which fell to the ground with a terrible crash, doing considerable damage to the surrounding buildings. It was soon repaired and put to work again.

The mill was actuated by both wind and steam and, later, a roller plant (by Henry Simon of Manchester) of one sack an hour was installed.

Before the Great War the present owner fitted up an admirable little jam factory alongside the mill, doing a considerable business, particularly under the Government during the War, and to-day delicious preserves may be obtained there.

Messrs. Payne later transferred their business to Strood, where they became known as millwrights of repute, carrying on a successful business until the death of the proprietor.

(See also page 99.)

Borstal Mill. 1 furlong SSW. of Borstal Church. 1858-72.

This mill stood near the Mount. It was built by a Mr. Nightingale in about 1870 and had an unusually short life, being pulled down about 1885. Henry Perris was the miller in 1878.

As a boy I frequently spent many happy hours in this mill. Well do I remember one of the sweeps breaking off and piercing the miller's dwelling from roof to basement, and in its passage grazing the arm of the miller's wife, tearing her sleeve—truly a miraculous escape.

The only remnant of anything connected with the mill is the recess formed in the brick retaining wall at the bottom of the steep incline leading up to the mill. Here the farmers would deposit half their load of corn, for the horses could not carry the full load up so steep a climb, the remainder to be hauled up on a second journey.

St. Margaret's. Church Mill or Horsnaill's Mill. 1 furlong S. of St. Margaret's Church. 1769, 1819-43.*

I remember the post mill that stood just beyond the Church, opposite St. Nicholas Old Cemetery. It was known to me as Horsnaill's Mill, and is shown on the picture by Stockdale reproduced facing p. 268.

A companion of the miller's son, I was frequently to be found at this mill, a congenial place for boys to play in during inclement weather. It possessed a capacious brick round-house, and its last owner, Mr. Alfred E. Horsnaill (who had been preceded by Messrs. Horsnaill & Reynolds) has reminded me that the huge oak centre-post upon which the mill revolved bore the date 1700. His memory goes back to the year 1860, and he recalls but this one post mill at St. Margaret's. Owing to the lack of wind, due to the obstruction of houses built in St. George's Terrace, it was sold by auction and pulled down about 1880.

The picture of the *smock* mill reproduced facing p. 268 is taken from a painting by the late Stephen Aveling, of Restoration House, Rochester, and was presumed to be of Horsnaill's Mill ; this, of course, is not so as Horsnaill's Mill was of *post* type. Maybe, a smock mill for a time replaced one of the earlier post mills that stood there. One cannot doubt the sincerity of Mr. Aveling, for he was not only an artist but an antiquarian ; hence his picture is reproduced here, despite the fact that no particulars of the mill are obtainable as to its actual position or date.

St. Margaret's. Zenith Mill.* 1 furlong S. of St. Margaret's Church. 1769, 1819-43.

Having spent my boyhood days in the neighbourhood of St. Margaret's, I certainly heard tell of a second post mill there, that it stood a little distance from the Church Mill. I cannot trace any record of its destruction but an old resident, Mr. John J. Freeman, remembers seeing the centre post standing, gaunt and lonely, where Zenith House now stands. Mr. Alfred E. Horsnaill assures me, however, that the mill had absolutely disappeared in 1860.

*   *   *   *   *

Since writing the above, a Mr. Clogg, of Fair Row, Chatham, sends an interesting note *re* the St. Margaret's mills. It was copied from the scrap-book of Humphrey Wickham, the Strood Antiquarian, and appeared in the *Rochester Journal* of August 27th, 1881, in reply to an article on "Vanished Mills," in *Notes and Queries*.

> I think your correspondent of June 4th is wrong in attributing to William Huggins the initials which appeared upon the post of the old mill lately removed and known as Horsnaill's Mill. The Mill called Huggins' Mill was burnt down 50 or 60 years ago, and occupied the site upon which now stands the house of Mr. C. Willis, some little distance beyond the other mill. It was in my early days the property of a Mr. Hulkes, and it is a curious coincidence that "H" should be the initial letter of the three families for two centuries associated with these mills. The matter is of special interest to me, as my great grand-father carried on business at the lower mill 145 years ago. F. M. W.

St. Margaret's. 1 furlong S. of St. Margaret's Church. 1769.

As to a third mill having stood near St. Margaret's, I doubt if a single citizen of Rochester, be he ever so old, "ever heard of such a thing." Truly I had the surprise of my life when searching the 1769 map, for I found three marked as standing at that date, close beside the street, all in line and very near to one another, the third apparently standing between the Church Mill and the Zenith Mill or, at the most, a little beyond the latter. Hence St. Margaret's could at one time have boasted of three post mills—an imposing trio, as viewed from the old stone bridge, or from the distant Strood or Frindsbury Hills.

In Eastgate House Museum, Guildhall Offices, and in many homes, can be found fine pictures of two of the three mills. Maybe, in these general views the mill nearest the Church would not be seen, due to its low-lying position behind the Church, but the other two, being perched high on the rising ground to the south, were plainly visible.

RODMERSHAM GREEN
(NEAR SITTINGBOURNE)

5 furlongs WSW. of Church.* Standing to-day, derelict. 1819-43, 1903-10.

This derelict tower mill presents a sorry appearance to-day. The fan is absent, the stocks only of the sweeps remain, while patches of the cement facing which covers the brickwork are falling away, to complete the disfigurement. The ground floor is now used as a garage.

The mill was built in 1835. In 1878 T. Witham was the miller. It was taken over in 1898 by E. Hopper, who did a fair flour trade, as well as one of farmers' hog corn grist. There were three pairs of stones—two pairs of French burr for flour and one pair of Derbyshire Peak for hog corn. There was also a flour dressing machine.

Mr. Hopper continued to work the mill until 1917 at which date, he says, "the Government conscripted my man named Carter, and the trade all fell off ; then I sold all out ; took off the sweeps and dismantled it altogether."

I am able to give two pictures of the mill—one as it looked in its working days, with Mr. Hopper's horse and the van being loaded up ; the other is a recent picture of the derelict.

ROLVENDEN
(NEAR CRANBROOK)

½ mile WNW. of Church.* Standing to-day, derelict. 1596, 1610, 1769, 1819-43, 1903-10.

The gaunt, quaint old veteran post mill at Rolvenden is my favourite. Its antiquity appeals to me, for it is probably the mill that stood here in 1596. It should not be allowed to join the long list of vanished corn mills, although I would not see it other than a picturesque derelict.

Gazing at this specimen of the ancient millwright's art, one cannot but conjure up a story of its witness to the vagaries played by time and man with the agricultural and domestic life of our country, the enforced idleness, the abandonment and decay. As one old countryman remarked, as I stood near the mill, "The state of the country generally is wusser than the state of the old mill."

When I saw the mill in 1906 it had lost two sweeps and was evidently idle, for there was no canvas on the sweeps ; but the round-house was intact and, except for the missing sweeps, it looked a fine specimen of our old post mills.

I have recently renewed my acquaintance with it and regret to find that the indiscriminate elements and the mischief of man (who burnt what could be removed for firewood during the Great War) have played sad havoc with it. The round-house is now gone and there can be seen bare and exposed the massive timber trestles which carried the centre post.

Sir Charles Igglesden's reference to this mill is valuable here :

> Along the Cranbrook Road, and overlooking Hole Park, is the old windmill that has stood there many years—since the days when almost every village had its parish mill for grinding corn. An obsolete post-windmill, it has not been in use for some time, but it is a unique specimen, and has a pair of regulators and a spindle of wood ; they are usually made of iron.[1]

The mill was held by John Greenhill about 1878, but the last miller was

[1] *Saunters Through Kent With Pen and Pencil*, Vol. V, p. 89.

Horace Dunk who gave up the business in 1883. I understand that it was then hired by Mr. Collins, who owned the Sandhurst five-sweep mill and closed the Rolvenden Mill in order to keep the trade for his own mill. He may have done a little grinding at Rolvenden Mill, however, for some say the mill was working as late as 1885. It is known that the two sweeps were removed in that year.

OLD ROMNEY

¾ *mile W. of Church.* 1596, 1610, 1769.

The early maps show a mill at Old Romney, which was evidently of post type and disappeared before the earliest Ordnance Map of about 1800 was prepared.

1 *mile NW. of Church.* 1596, 1769.

Doubtless this was another of the old post mills. It is noted on the 1596 map and, although absent from J. Speed's map of 1610, it appears again on the large-scale map of 1769.

NEW ROMNEY

3 *furlongs NNE. of Church.** 1596, 1769, 1903-10.

I have a note that in the *Kent Archæological Society's Magazine* it is recorded that a mill at New Romney was falling to pieces about 1500.

A mill is shown north-east of Romney Church on the 1596 map, perhaps a predecessor of the smock mill that stood until recent times at the above position.

This smock mill worked three pairs of stones and was at one time used by a miller named Ashby and later by Carey who last used it. In 1878 Stonham & Son were the millers here. It was working in 1894, when repairs were executed by T. R. Holman.

5 *furlongs NE. of Church.* 1769.

The 1769 map is my only authority for a mill at this position.

RUCKINGE
(NEAR ASHFORD)

¼ *mile E. of Church.** 1903-10.

Although I cannot trace a windmill at Ruckinge on any map, one certainly stood there. It was of post type and originally stood at Hythe. It was moved to Ruckinge by barge, a distance of nine miles, along the Royal Military Canal, probably about a century ago. Its site at Ruckinge was on the canal bank, not far from the Blue Anchor Inn.

A miller friend tells me that he remembers in 1883, when at Aldington, seeing Ruckinge Mill working away in the distance, with four sweeps complete. It was geared very low and the sweeps spun round like a peg-top.

It was in the Russell family for many years—father, son and another son (who worked it last) succeeding each other. In 1878 John Russell, jun., was the miller.

The main structure of the mill was pulled down about 1912 by F. Couchman, a builder of Ham Street. The brick base alone remained and this was used as a store until about 1924 when it was cleared away. To-day nothing save a small mound in the meadow marks where it stood, and three old mill-stones are used as door steps at the Mill House.

Mrs. Russell still has its keys, on which is stamped the following lettering :

G. S.
F.25.
1 8 0 9

ST. MARGARET'S

(DOVER)

Mill Close. NW. of Church. 1596, 1695, 1736.

This old post mill, noted on the above maps, was known as St. Margaret's Mill—it is named thus on the 1736 Bowen map. Its owner built the Martin Mill (see East Langdon) and transferred the business there, and it is inferred that the post mill then fell into disuse and was pulled down. It is not noted on any later map than 1736.

ST. MARGARET'S BAY

(DOVER)

Near the Old South Foreland Lighthouse.*

This very fine mill is the latest effort of that well-known firm of millwrights, Messrs. Holman Bros., of Canterbury. It was built for Sir William Beardswell. Perhaps it ought not to be included in this long list of vanishing windmills, for it only started its life of activity in June 1929. Also, it is not a corn mill—its task is to generate electricity. It is, however, so fine a specimen that this brief reference must be made to it.

ST. NICHOLAS-AT-WADE

(NEAR MARGATE)

Approx. ¾ mile W. of Church. 1719.

The 1719 Thanet Map is my only authority for this old mill.

ROCHESTER

1. VIEW FROM STROOD HILL. 2. The ST. MARGARET'S POST MILLS (by J. Farington, R.A., 1795). 3. ST. MARGARET'S CHURCH AND MILL (by F. W. Stockdale). 4. MILL AND DISTANT CHURCH (by Stephen Aveling).

See pages 264-65

Facing page 268

W.C.F.   N. Coles Finch

ROLVENDEN

See page 266

A. W. Tiffin

NEW ROMNEY

See page 267

A. W. Tiffin

NORTHWOOD (Thanet Mill)
Flour Bag.

See page 253   Facing page 269

SANDGATE
(NEAR FOLKESTONE)

As noted under Bethersden, the Little Mill originally stood at Sandgate, where it was owned by Mr. Brissenden, a builder. It was transferred to Bethersden by its purchaser, Mr. George Jarvis, by whom it was subsequently used. It did no corn grinding, either at Sandgate or Bethersden, being a timber sawmill.

SANDHURST

1 mile 1 furlong NE. of Church. 1769.

The 1769 large-scale map clearly shows a mill on the north side of the main road from Sandhurst to Newenden, which is said to have been moved to Boxhurst Farm, and to be the same mill as that next described.

Boxhurst Farm. 1¼ *miles ENE. of Church.* 1819-43.

An old coloured parchment plan, dated 1793, now in the possession of Mrs. Malton (whose family had Boxhurst Farm for over a century), clearly shows this mill, a survey of the farm having been made by the then owner, Mr. Joseph Fowle.

Strangely enough, the large-scale map of 1769 does not show a windmill on Boxhurst Farm, but shows one on the north side of the main road, about the site of the present five-sweep mill (which was not built until 1844). One wonders if the 1793 mill on Boxhurst Farm was the 1769 mill moved there. The 1819-43 Ordnance Map shows the one on Boxhurst Farm.

The mill was owned by James Collins, of Ringle Crouch Green, but the surrounding land was owned by a Mr. Ellis and tenanted by a Mr. Pinyon. When a field near the mill, known as the Watchhouse Field, was planted with hops, Mr. Collins insisted that the poles obstructed the wind ; on account of this he gave up the mill and arranged with the millwright Warren to build one in another position, north of the main road, on his farm at Ringle Crouch Green. This is how the five-sweep mill, standing derelict to-day, came to be built.

The old post mill came to grief during a high wind in about 1842. An elderly resident of Sandhurst remembers his father saying that the field by the mill was so covered with flour that it looked as if there had been a fall of snow.

Ringle Crouch Green.* 1 mile 1 furlong NE. of Church. Standing to-day, derelict. 1858-72, 1903-10.

This fine octagonal smock mill, the only five-sweep corn mill known to have been erected in Kent, was built for James Collins in 1844 by the millwright Warren of Hawkhurst, and was known as Warren's masterpiece. It was built on the north side of the main road to replace an old post mill that stood on Boxhurst Farm, to the south of the road.

It was apparently a new venture for Mr. Warren to build a five-sweep mill, for he made a special journey to examine such a mill in the north of England and take a pattern.

A local story has it that James Collins insisted on going one better than anybody else in having a mill with five sweeps instead of the customary four and, had another five-sailer been erected in Kent, he would have rebuilt his to have six sweeps. Some years later a six-sweep mill was built at Great Chart. Mr. Collins, however, had died soon after the completion of his five-sweep mill and may therefore be said to have been prevented from building one with seven sweeps !

Some of the material from the old post mill on Boxhurst Farm, I am told, was used in the making of the new mill, but this is open to question. It is known that, on completion of the mill, a member of the Warren family, to celebrate the event, stood on his head on top of the cap !

It was certainly a well-built mill, of six stories, with a stage, single-shuttered sweeps and a fantail. There were four pairs of stones, which could all be run at once in a strong wind—two for wheat, one for corn cracking and another for oat grinding. It is estimated that the total weight of the cap, windshaft and sweeps was twenty-five tons ! The brick base was always painted red and the body of the mill white.

There was one obvious disadvantage, however, with this five-sailer. If one of the sweeps was blown off, or had to be renewed, the mill had to stand idle until it was replaced. With the usual four-sweep mill, if one sweep had to be removed, its fellow opposite was removed also and the mill worked with only two sweeps—not so much power, of course, but work was not held up.

James Collins evidently did a large business at the mill as well as at a watermill at Bodiam (about two miles away). He worked both mills together or alternately, as the wind and circumstances permitted. A baker's shop was also acquired in Sandhurst village, as an outlet for the flour, the baker renting the shop from the Collins family.

On the death of James Collins, his son, Edward, took over the mill, and his other son, Tom, went to Benenden windmill. The two sons were the youngest of the family, there being seven elder sisters.

Edward Collins carried on the mill up to his death in about 1911. His sons, Edward and Harry, worked it for a few months and then it was hired for about a year by C. J. Bannister, of Northiam, who was the last to work it. Later, he bought the stones, chain and tackle, and transferred them to Northiam.

One of the sweeps was blown off in a high wind and is now used for keeping cattle out of a pond ! The fantail and shutters were removed some time later. The staging, which had been getting in a bad condition, was taken down in about 1926. The mill had become a delightful playground for the lads of the village who clambered about it in a manner fit to alarm any parent, but the removal of the staging put an end to their pranks for there was then no easy means of ascent !

The ground floor of the mill is now used as a store for farm produce. On the second floor are three large water tanks (with a capacity of 500 gallons each) which supply the neighbouring cottages and cowsheds, a well forty feet deep having been dug and a wind pump erected alongside the mill.

Charles Burt, who was loader at the mill for eighteen years up till it last worked in 1912, still works on the farm at Ringle Crouch Green, where the mill is situated. Much of the information given here has been supplied by him.

In connection with five-sweep mills it is interesting to note that the only working specimen of this type of mill to be found in England is Tuttle Mill at Nuneaton.

SANDWICH

1695—1 *mill NW. of Town.* 1736—2 *mills NW. of Town.* 1769—1 *mill NW. of Town ; 2 mills SE. of Town.* 1819-43—4 *mills NW. of Town (3 E. of railway and 1 W. of railway) ; 2 mills SE. of Town.* 1903-10— 1 *mill NW. of Town (W. of railway) stands derelict to-day*. 1 mill SE. of Town.*

Sandwich has possessed a number of windmills from time to time throughout the years, as the above map references show. The first trace of a mill is the 1695 map, no mill being shown on the early maps of 1596 and 1610.

There have evidently been six mills here at one time or another—four north-west of the town (three east of the level crossing of the railway, and one west of the crossing) as noted on the 1819-43 map ; and two south-east of the town, as shown on the 1769 map. Of these six mills, four can be remembered by at least one old miller friend. They are as follows :

Three mills north-west of town.—Two of these stood to the east of the level crossing, one of which was the large Black Mill and the other a little old post mill that stood near by and worked in conjunction. The second of the two is probably that shown on the 1695 map, which disappeared some time before 1880, although definitely known to be working in 1842. The third mill, which stood to the west of the level crossing, is the White Mill that still stands.

The remaining mill of the four in living memory is the mill that stood south-east of the town. This was a smock mill on a low brick base known as the Millwall Mill, or Town Mill. It was situated near St. Clement's Church, not far from the railway station, and was worked by a miller by the name of Alfred George Larkin, who was known to be here in 1878. Steam power was added later. This mill was burnt down.

The large Black Mill was known to be constantly at work on a Sunday, and when it fell to the flames about 1910 that was thought to be a just punishment for the profanation of the Sabbath ! The miller in the 1870's was Stephen West. In 1883 a Mr. Billing took over the mill from Mr. West. (See also page 79.)

The other two of the six mills must have disappeared about 1850 or before. One of these made up the group of three, east of the level crossing, north-west of the town, as noted on the 1819-43 map ; and the other was at one time a companion mill to the Millwall Mill above mentioned.

The White Mill, the sole survivor, is owned by Messrs. Stanley Bros. and is now worked by a 28 h.p. oil engine. One of the brothers says that at one time no less than fourteen windmills could be counted from this spot. Thomas Stanley was the miller in 1878.

SARRE
(NEAR BIRCHINGTON)

¼ *mile E. of Church, or 1 mile 1 furlong W. of Monkton Church.* Standing to-day, disused.* 1819-43, 1903-10.

Sir Charles Igglesden states that this mill was brought from Monkton but the records of Messrs. Holmans of Canterbury show that the mill was built at Sarre by John Holman in 1820. Perhaps some of the timber and machinery were used from a mill that used to stand at Monkton. As noted under Monkton, there was a mill as late as 1769 at one and a half miles north-east of Monkton Church, and one wonders if there is any connection between the two mills. Here, however, I must leave the matter.

Sarre Mill was said to have been built "eight miles from anywhere"— eight miles from Margate, Ramsgate, Canterbury and Sandwich.

Like its neighbour at Herne, it was heightened about 1856, making the base two stories instead of one. The work was carried out by Thomas Holman. The whole mill was raised by hand-jacks, a short distance at a time, and underpinned, until some fourteen feet was accomplished.

It was a very busy mill during the Great War. It is said that no less than thirty tons of flour (240 sacks) were sent every week to Chatham Barracks from Grove Ferry Station. At this time the mill was mainly worked by steam. It is interesting to note that it was the first windmill in Kent to have a steam engine installed. When it ceased working by wind power in about 1920, the sweeps were removed on a four-ton lorry to Cranbrook and erected on the Union Mill there.

Until recently a little grinding was done at the mill by means of a gas engine, but it is now disused. Some repairs were carried out late in 1931— new quartering and weather-boarding—and it is therefore likely to remain standing for some years yet.

An 1878 Kent Directory has the following entry :

George Thomas Steddy, miller, Sarre.

SELLING
(NEAR FAVERSHAM)

Shottenden Mill or Perry Wood Mill.* 7 furlongs S. of Church. 1596, 1736, 1769, 1819-43, 1903-10.

A description of my visit to the site of this mill is given on page 89.

It was of the early type of post mill and was situated in what is to-day a favourite spot for picnics and a *rendezvous* for school outings, char-a-banc excursions, and the like.

W.C.F.   A. W. Tiffin

SANDWICH (White Mill)

See page 272

W.C.F.   N. Coles Finch

SANDHURST (Ringle Crouch Green)

See page 269

A. W. Tiffin

SELLINGE (STONE HILL MILL)
See page 273

W.C.F.

SHORNE (SHORNE HILL MILL)
See page 277

W.C.F.

SHEPHERDSWELL
(or *Sibertswold*)

See page 277

G. E. Ride

SHEERNESS (GREAT MILL)

See page 275   *Facing page 273*

The mill was last worked in 1910. A year or two later two of the sweeps were removed and the structure gradually decayed until it became a danger to visitors and was pulled down in 1920.

George Atkins was the miller at Selling in 1878. Other millers were : John Sutton (1866), George Harris (1873), Frederick Neame and a Mr. Pearson (1881). Lord Sondes was the owner.

Two pairs of stones were worked—one pair 3 ft. 8 in. French wheat stones and one pair 4 ft. 2 in. barley stones. In 1881 T. R. Holman fitted a new iron windshaft to replace the wooden one, at a cost of £58 10s.

SELLINGE
(NEAR ASHFORD)

*Stone Hill Mill.** 3 *furlongs N. of Church.* 1819-43, 1903-10.

Stone Hill Mill was a small, black smock mill that was pulled down about 1898, not having worked for some years previously. It was known to be working in 1884. Nothing remains to-day but the words "Mill House, Stone Hill" on the gate of the dwelling. A Mr. Cheeseman used this mill for many years. He also worked the windmill at Kingsnorth.

SEVENOAKS

Tubs Hill. ½ *mile NW. of Church.* 1819-43, 1858-72.

As stated in the note on Kingsdown, an old post mill that was once there is believed to have been brought from Sevenoaks, and one wonders if this is the mill.

An old miller friend gives the following position for the mill :

> It stood on Tubs Hill, between the church and the railway station, on the right-hand side of the road, proceeding up the hill, near the 'Rock and Fountain' public house.

The lane which led up to the old mill can still be traced, but the mill must have disappeared over sixty years ago.

Mr. Geo. C. W. Bennett, librarian and curator of the Sevenoaks Library, has kindly sent me the following information :

> There is a water-colour sketch of this mill in the local collections at Sevenoaks Library.
>
> In 1792 William Knott, miller, of Sevenoaks, leased the house adjoining the site of the mill—formerly known as The Middle Messuage—which was late in the occupation of Thos. Pattenden. The lease is "with liberty to set up a windmill" and also "to pull down and carry away the same."
>
> In 1814 the same William Knott buys the property "with a windmill erected by the said Wm. Knott." He pays £1000 for house, mill and three acres.
>
> In 1864 Charles Knott, of Sevenoaks, miller, sells the land and mill to J. F. Austen of Horsmonden, Esq. (related to local family of lawyers—but not apparently a mortgage).
>
> In 1864 J. F. Austen leased the mill, etc., to William Eames, of Sevenoaks, miller, at £13 15s. 0d. quarterly.

s

Hubbard Hill. 1 *mile* 1 *furlong SSW. of Church.* 1819-43, 1858-72.

This mill stood on Sevenoaks Common. No trace of it remains to-day and the site is now surrounded by trees.

I am indebted to the Sevenoaks Library for the following note :

> At a Court Baron for the manor of Sevenoaks in the year 1669 it was evidenced that William Floyd was seised of a mill at "Hubbert Hill" at a rent of 10s. This rent is clearly not an ancient one and it may be that the mill was then newly built. But the record is much damaged.

Whitley Woods. 1¼ *miles SW. of Church.*

A report on the windmills of the Sevenoaks district, kindly supplied by the Sevenoaks Librarian, includes the following :

> There is a spot in Whitley Woods known as Millbank, and it is so placed that only a windmill could be in question. It gives name to Millbank Wood, part of Whitley Forest. Near it is Milridge. On the supposition that these names are equally evidence of a windmill (although the latter is equally near Dibden water mill) we have here evidence of a windmill as early as 1388, when "Melregge" is a wood in which one Ralph Dene has wrongly cut faggots of the Lord's wood.
>
> The name Milbanck appears in 1719 but no mill is mentioned, but only "two tenements at Whitley, alias Milbanck, with eight acres of land." In 1737 certain premises are "On Millbank in Whitley" and in a very illiterate deed of 1743 endorsed on last, we read, "The Cow Houses one Mill Banck In Whetly ockepyed by thomas Lingham and Henerie Parsons." One gathers that there was no mill there in the eighteenth century, but there probably was one at an earlier date. The position now wooded is similar to that of the undoubted mill on Hubbard Hill.

SEVENOAKS WEALD

½ *mile SW. of Church.*

Although I have no map reference for this mill, I learned from the Sevenoaks Library that a mill stood there and subsequently received a letter from an elderly lady who used to live near by. She told me the mill was working in 1880 and was then in good condition. It was situated in the centre of The Green.

I have since received an interesting letter from the Rev. R. C. Taylor, of the Weald. He says :

> From two of the oldest inhabitants I gathered that the windmill originally stood on the top of Bayley's Hill overlooking the Weald. About seventy years ago my two informants tell me they saw it drawn by five horses down the hill, which is a mile long and even now one in eight gradient, and because the hill past the church was too steep and the bridge probably too narrow, they took it round the church and through the village, and then for fear lest the body of the mill should fall on the houses while the horses pulled it up on to the village green, they built up a gradual slope with brushwood.
>
> It was put up very near the spot where the Wesleyan Chapel now stands.
>
> One of my informants described Squire Lambarde riding past the mill and the hunter being frightened by the noise of the sweeps, and ordering his groom to bring it down the next day and break it in.

A family named Burfoot seemed to have owned it at one time, but they could not tell me when it was taken down.

The Windmill Inn and Windmill Cottages are reminiscent of the mill, although nothing actually remains of it to-day.

SHEERNESS
(ISLE OF SHEPPEY)

The Great Mill, or Ride's Mill.* 1 mile SE. of Church. Base still remains. 1829.

The millwright, Humphrey, of Cranbrook, built this white smock mill in 1813. It was almost a replica of the splendid Union Mill at Cranbrook, erected by the same millwright, although perhaps not as tall, being sixty-six feet to the top of the cap against Cranbrook's seventy feet. This difference is very little really, for the Cranbrook Mill has a very tall brick base. Both mills had almost identical machinery.

The words "Humphrey, Builder, 1813" are still to be seen on the foundation stone of the brick base which is all that is left of the mill, standing in High Street, Sheerness, and used as a corn store for Messrs. Henry Filmer, Ltd., of Sittingbourne. This brick base, by the way, is no less than twenty-one inches thick !

There was a very unusual occurrence in connection with the building of this mill. The work was begun for George and Elizabeth Jackson but, owing to the swampy nature of the ground, the foundations had to be laid very deep down. The expense of this undertaking proved too much for the Jacksons, so that when the structure had only reached as high as where the stage had to be fixed, about twenty-two feet above ground level, the work was stopped through lack of funds.

For two years the structure stood thus, until it was bought by Thomas Webb (the owner also of the Little Mill at Sheerness), who financed its completion, and by whom, and later his son, the mill was owned for a great many years. The son lived to a great age. He was known to be 95 years old in 1887 (at which date he granted a lease to the miller at the Great Mill) and he lived for a year or two after that.

From February 1864 to its demolition in the autumn of 1924 the mill was held by Messrs. G. Ride & Son, first as tenants and later as lease-holders. This long association with the mill accounts for its being known locally as Ride's Mill.

It was one of the few later smock mills in Kent that never had a fantail. It worked three pairs of stones, a dressing machine, a smutter and bolter. In 1889, there were added steam power, two extra pairs of stones on the second or loading floor of the mill (driven by 'underdrift'), as well as steel rolling mills.

Flour was not made here after 1890. The sweeps and stage were removed in 1905 and the mill worked entirely by steam power until the autumn of 1918. It did not stand idle for many years, for, having become very weak, to avoid its collapse, it was pulled down, as stated, in 1924, the brick base alone being left.

From the stage of this mill, in 1880, with the aid of a pair of glasses, no less than twenty-five other windmills could be counted (see page 74). Only two of these now remain—Rodmersham and Milton Regis—and they are derelicts.

Mr. Geo. E. Ride tells me that in 1887, at the time of Queen Victoria's Jubilee, the mill was gaily decorated in honour of the occasion. A rope was stretched round the sweeps from tip to tip and flags attached. To each of the two top sweeps a flagstaff was affixed, with a Union Jack.

Another of Mr. Ride's reminiscences is that in 1881 one of the sweeps broke off. As it fell it carried away a large portion of the stage. Having retained a portion of the midling bolted to it, the sweep was top heavy and up-ended as it reached the ground, narrowly missing the engine room beneath and a stable alongside. It embedded itself in the ground. A young mare was in the stable at the time and the tremendous crash so frightened the poor creature that she stood shivering in a nervous state for some days afterwards.

Mile Town. *The Little Mill.* 1 mile SE. of Church. 1819-43.

No trace remains of this mill to-day and houses occupy its site. Its position was to the rear of the Masonic Hall in the High Street, not far from the Football Ground (Sheppey United).

The mill was at one time in the possession of Thomas Webb, who also owned the Great Mill. He worked it himself for the greater part of its life, but latterly the miller was James Clarke, during whose occupation it was burnt down, on February 7th, 1862. It was then in good working order.

It was a tarred smock mill, working two pairs of stones. Its name was an appropriate one—so small at the top that there were no steps up to the bin floor and cap. The only way to get to the top was by placing a ladder through the trap-hatches where the sacks went through.

Marine Town. *The 100-acre Windmill.** Base alone remains.

It is known that this mill was built for a Mr. Venable but I cannot trace why it was called 'The 100-acre Windmill.'

It was a small tower mill, the body of which was cement washed. It had a low stage, about seven feet from the ground. There were four stories and two pairs of stones were used. No auxiliary power was installed. It was last worked about 1872, the miller then being a Mr. Adams ; previously it had been held for a few years by Henry Ride ; both millers hired it from the owner, George McKee (who also, by the way, owned the Sea View Hotel close by).

I understand that Mr. Ride paid a rental of £30 a year for the mill and, after painting it up, about 1860, Mr. Ride was asked by Mr. McKee for an increase in rent of £10 a year ! Mr. Ride's reply was to hand the key to Mr. McKee and ask him to find another tenant !

Between Mr. Ride's and Mr. Adams' tenancy Mr. McKee had worked the mill on his own account, employing a miller named Howe to run it. This did not, however, prove a profitable venture. During Mr. Adams' occupation

MILL BASES.

1. SHEERNESS, Great Mill (G. E. Ride).   2. PLUMSTEAD COMMON (W. Manwaring).
3. DOWNE (A. H. Nicholls).   4. SHEERNESS, Marine Town (G. E. Ride).

See pages 197, 257, 275, 276

Facing page 276

W. H. Evernden

Facing page 277

EVENTIDE

By Smarden Smock Mill.

See page 280

two of the mill sweeps were thrown off in the wind and were not replaced.
Except for the missing sweeps the mill was in splendid order when it was pulled
down in 1878. It is thought that, being so small a mill, it was unable to take
full advantage of the wind and, as the town grew, she became too hemmed in
by house property.

When the Catholic Church was built near the mill, Mr. McKee claimed
recompense for loss of wind power, maintaining that when the wind was due
east the Church hindered effectual working. The case was not taken up
seriously, however, and the mill was at work for about twelve years after the
completion of the Church.

The brick base alone remains and is now used as a store for beer, wine,
and spirits of the Sea View Hotel.

Mr. Geo. E. Ride, nephew of the late Henry Ride, writes :

> There was also a dressing machine in this mill. My uncle did a fair amount of flour
> trade among the bakers in the town, there being no railway into the town in those
> days. You could sell flour as fast as you could make it.

SHELDWICH
(NEAR FAVERSHAM)

5 furlongs W. of Church. 1769.

For this mill I can only give the 1769 map reference.

SHEPHERDSWELL (Sibertswold)
(NEAR DOVER)

3 furlongs NE. of Church. * 1903-10.

When I visited this mill in 1910 I found it without fantail or sweeps. I
understood it last worked in 1908 and that a pair of stones then went to
a mill at Nonington. I have no record of its disappearance. It was a smock
and stage mill on a brick base. It worked three pairs of stones.

A miller friend tells me that an uncle of his worked the mill about 1857
and it was by no means a new mill then. Josiah Baldwin had it a great
number of years and did a large trade.

SHORNE
(NEAR GRAVESEND)

Shorne Hill Mill. * ¼ *mile NW. of Church. Standing to-day, disused.* 1596,
1610, 1736, 1769, 1819-43, 1903-10.

I cannot say definitely whether the mill of which some remains stand to-
day is the same as that which stood here in 1596. It is, however, of great age.
Its condition to-day is little changed from when I photographed it in 1905.

Its sweeps blew down in 1870 and its milling career was thus brought to a
close. About 1890 the structure was used for a short time as an observatory

for astronomical purposes by its owner, the late Mr. G. M. Arnold, of Gravesend.

Some notes of Mr. Arnold's, dated August 8th, 1895, state :

> At Shorne Mill I met Mr. Hancock, who said he used to occupy the mill under Mr. Whatman. It drove two pairs of stones and would often work all night when lower mills were still for want of a breeze. The pole with the wheel at the end, by which the mill was turned to the wind, was bought by him at Chatham and placed by him. It was an old mast of a ship. He could see the fireworks at the Crystal Palace nightly.

The present appearance of the mill is due to the fact that in order to make the structure rigid and secure, for the purposes of an observatory, it was underpinned with brickwork and altered somewhat to the new requirements.

The trees that now surround the mill were planted about 1902, evidently to protect the structure from the wind.

SISSINGHURST
(NEAR CRANBROOK)

Crampton's Mill.* ½ mile W. of Church. Standing to-day, derelict. 1819-43, 1903-10.

This smock mill which stands to-day disused and without sweeps and fantail, is believed to have been moved from Hartley, near Cranbrook, and is probably the one shown on the 1769 large-scale map at a quarter of a mile west-north-west of Cranbrook Church. The transfer must have been made about 140 years ago, for the mill is clearly shown at Sissinghurst on the first Ordnance Map of 1801. Strangely enough, however, it is believed locally that the mill was re-erected in 1839, the year after Sissinghurst Church was built. If this is correct, it would seem that the mill shown on the 1801 map was an earlier mill on the same site.

The mill cost £800 to rebuild in Mill Lane, Sissinghurst and, two years after its erection, was bought by George Crampton, whose brother once had the Cranbrook Common Mill. It was held by the Crampton family for the whole of the remainder of its milling career.

It was a small mill, working two pairs of stones, one set of Peak and one of French burr, but a good business was done years ago. On one occasion it ran without a stop for a whole week, making flour.

The miller for about twenty-one years, up till his death in 1897, was a Mr. Marsh, who had previously worked at the Cranbrook Common Mill.

Mr. F. R. Crampton, son of the original owner, recalls the unpleasant sensation he once experienced when, during a gale, he happened to be looking out of a window in the mill and suddenly one of the sweeps was blown off in the wind. Its fellow sweep later had to be removed and the mill worked for a while with two sweeps until its other two could be replaced.

As at Guston and Headcorn mills, a chronicle was kept on a spout in the mill of all interesting incidents in its history.

The site, viewed at the present time, hardly seems suitable for a mill, the district being full of trees. It must be remembered, however, that at the time

the mill was in its prime, it stood out in the open where the wind was unchecked. When trees were being planted so freely in the locality, Mr. Crampton
protested that their growth would eventually ruin his business. The complaint
was unheeded and the trees grew and took the wind, less money was spent on
repairs, and gradually the mill fell into disuse. It was last worked in 1926.

The sweeps were removed in May 1928 and sold for £5 (!) to Mr. A. W.
Tomlinson of Leigh. They are now to be seen on his mill at Stocks Green,
near Hildenborough. The two sets of stones were also sold to him for £2 !

The body of the mill is now used as a store. It is in a bad state of repair
and may soon be pulled down.

SITTINGBOURNE

½ mile W. of Church. 1819-43.

This mill is shown on the 1819-43 map as standing on the north side of
Watling Street at its junction with the road to Milton, quite close to the
railway.

It was a tarred smock and stage mill, with two floors under the stage, and
working two 'patent' sweeps and two cloth sails.

Mr. G. Ride, who later held the Great Mill at Sheerness, was born at
Sittingbourne and his father held the mill there ; in fact, the whole family
of seven, most of whom later on had some connection or other with our
Kentish windmills, were born at the Mill House.

Steam was installed as auxiliary power in 1880, during the time when a
Mr. Harris was the miller, but was used only for a few years. The mill became
derelict and was finally burnt down.

One miller's wife once had a wonderful escape. She was working in the
kitchen of the Mill House and had occasion to leave the room a moment or two.
In her absence one of the sweeps of the mill broke off and pierced the roof of
the house, finally embedding itself in the floor of the kitchen, at precisely the
spot where the miller's wife had been standing a moment or two previously!

SMARDEN
(NEAR ASHFORD)

*West Mill, Town Mill or Cornes' Mill.** 1 furlong S. of Church. Standing to-day,
    derelict.* 1769, 1819-43, 1903-10.

This is undoubtedly a very old mill. Miss M. I. Batten writes :

This mill claims to be the oldest windmill in Kent, for previous to 1680 there was a
dispute as to who should repair the round-house. But whether it was the round-
house of the present mill or a previous one is not definite. The local inhabitants also
say that there has been a windmill on this site since the twelfth century. It is a post
mill with a brick round-house painted white. The four sweeps, which are still in
position, were canvas covered. It has three pairs of stones. The tailpole has been
broken off, and the whole mill is in bad condition.[1]

[1] *English Windmills*, Vol. I, 1930.

The mill was worked for many years by the Cornes family, in whose possession it still remains. Mr. H. N. Cornes says the mill was working in 1912. Mr. Frank Pain remembers it as a working windmill in 1884. Repairs were carried out by T. R. Holman as late as 1899.

Mr. George Jarvis of Bethersden was once asked to buy the mill for demolition but he was not prepared to pay the sum required.

East Mill, or Black Mill. ½ *mile NNE. of Church. Standing to-day, derelict.* 1903-10.

The deeds of this smock mill date back to 1804. It was evidently built just after the earliest Ordnance Survey was made, for it is not shown on the 1819-43 map.

There were three pairs of stones—wheat, oats and hog corn. The mill has now been cleared of machinery and stones. One pair of stones went to a watermill at Wye and the others with various appliances have been distributed among other mills.

The mill was last worked in 1923, for grinding food for poultry and pigs. It had then been working for some time with two cloth and two spring-shuttered sails.

Charles Buss, the father of Richard Buss who worked Pluckley Mill for nearly half a century, once rented this mill at £50 a year and was later able to buy it outright for £500. On the death of Charles Buss, it was sold to T. Cornes, who owned the other Smarden mill. On his decease in 1920 the mill came into the possession of the late Walter Hicks at whose demise the mill passed to his executors, who still hold it.

A few years ago an American, touring through Kent, was struck by the appearance of the mill and thought he would like to purchase it for transfer to his home across the water. He was prepared to pay a high price for it but, on making enquiries, he found that the cost of dismantling, transport and re-erection would make the proposition prohibitive.

The mill is covered with tarred sheeting. It has lost its fan but the four sweeps are still on the mill, although the shutters have been removed.

SNARGATE

(NEAR ASHFORD)

S. of Church. 1610.

J. Speed's map of 1610 shows this mill but it cannot be traced on later maps.

SNODLAND

As the notes on Gillingham state, Stedman's Mill used to stand at Snodland, near the present Clock Tower. It was purchased about 1839 by one of the Stedman family, transferred to Gillingham and re-erected there.

SOUTHBOROUGH
(NEAR TUNBRIDGE WELLS)

¼ mile SW. of Church. 1819-43.

This mill stood on Southborough Common and must have disappeared over a century ago. Its site to-day is enclosed by a high hedge, used as a garden and called Mill Platt.

SOUTHFLEET
(NEAR GRAVESEND)

Betsham. 3 furlongs NW. of Church. 1829.

Although not shown on the 1819-43 Ordnance Survey Map, this mill is clearly drawn on the 1829 Greenwood map, as standing just south of the road leading to Westwood, to the east of the cross roads intersecting at Betsham.

It stood on Joyce Hall Farm and Mr. E. Snelling Colyer, who owns the property, has been to much trouble to trace some information regarding the mill.

It was of post type, painted white, and exceptionally small ; in fact it must have been a quaint little structure. It only used one pair of mill-stones. The brick round-house, which still remains and is used as a store, is only 6 ft. 10 in. high and 12 ft. in diameter. It has a thatched roof and is a picturesque little building, the only mill base with a thatched roof I know of in the county. I am sorry it has not been possible to obtain a photograph of it in time for inclusion in this volume.

The Mill House stood until 1928. Situated about a hundred yards from the mill, it was a substantial brick building with a reed thatched roof that had never been touched from the day it was built. Mr. Snelling Colyer writes :

> I had to pull it down five years ago as it was unfit for habitation, being built on a bank with no damp course. It contained the old baking oven which, of course, kept the whole house dry when in use. A brick was found when the house was demolished with the initials and date S. & J. 1816 cut in the face (I have this brick). I take it that it is the date the house was built.

The mill was probably built at about the same date, which would explain why no earlier map than 1829 indicates the mill.

It was last used about 1868 by a miller named Webb. He had been preceded by Randell, who worked it for many years. Mr. Snelling Colyer's late gardener, who had been in his service for forty years, recalls that the mill, about sixty-five years ago, was in rather a shaky condition. The body was turned into the right position for the wind by a tailpole which rested on a large wheel. In its last working days the mill was used for grinding the local farmers' corn into food for pigs and poultry and for grinding the gleanings from the surrounding cornfields. The sweeps and body were taken down about 1873 and the base roofed over as above described. (See also Addenda, p. 315.)

STANFORD
(NEAR ASHFORD)

¼ mile SW. of Church.* Standing to-day, active. 1903-10.

Stanford Mill was erected in 1857 by John Hill, the Ashford millwright. It is a solidly built specimen of a 'tower' mill. It is working and is in a good state of repair. The five-storied brick tower is kept well-tarred and the woodwork painted regularly every year.

Two new sweeps were fitted in 1930, a thirty-two feet length of pitch pine having been purchased from Sandwich for the midling, and Mr. Frank Pain was employed to make and fit the sweeps. The other pair of sweeps were fitted about seven years ago.

There are four pairs of stones, also two steel mills and rollers, which are all in constant use. An oil engine has been installed to work the mill when there is no wind.

There is very little grinding done for the neighbouring farmers, who seem to prefer to sell their corn and buy concentrated feeding cakes for their stock.

In 1878 the miller at Stanford was Thomas Rolfe. To-day the mill is owned by Mr. H. Taylor, of Broad Oak House, Mersham, who has held it for twenty years. His son-in-law, Mr. G. R. Holt, who works it, finds that competition is very keen but that motor transport, buying corn wholesale, collecting it direct from the docks and delivering the ground corn (sometimes as far as forty miles) by road, has relieved this to some extent by lessening carriage costs.

STANSTED
(NEAR SEVENOAKS)

½ mile SSE. of Church. 1736, 1769.

The 1736 Bowen map refers to this mill as "Stansted Mill." It is also shown on the 1769 map.

STAPLE
(NEAR CANTERBURY)

Barnsole.* 3 furlongs ESE. of Church. 1903-10.

John Holman built this mill and also executed repairs from time to time. Messrs. Holman Bros., in 1910, had work to do here to the value of £22 after the mill was damaged by lightning.

It was worked by the Franks family for some years and George Franks was there in the 1870's. It was in good working order when burnt down one Whit Sunday night about 1914. It is said that a quantity of lime had been stacked in bags close to the mill and that the lime, having got wet, heated to such an extent that it set light to the tarred weather-boarding of the mill.

A spectator, who left his bed to go to the fire, says it was a wonderful display to see the sweeps burn right to the top and then topple over.

STAPLEHURST

1 furlong W. of Church. 1769.

According to the 1769 map, this mill stood some little way down the lane that turns off from the main road opposite the Church. No trace remains to-day and the site is often used for village fairs.

Near E. side of Church.* Base alone remains. 1819-43, 1903-10.

The base alone remains of this old smock mill situated behind the church, and is used as a garage by the owner Frederick Hardes, a shopkeeper in the village.

The mill was burnt down 'for devilment' on Coronation Day, June 22nd, 1911—an unofficial part of the celebrations. It had stood a hopeless derelict for many years and was falling to pieces and, some arrangements for a general 'flare up' having fallen through, it is thought that a few of the villagers decided, come what may, to have a bonfire, and the old mill became the victim.

The lower part of the mill was at that time used as a fowl-house and, as the conflagration began after ten o'clock at night when the birds had gone to roost, the conspirators must have removed them one by one, for they had certainly all been let out.

The wooden structure was soon ablaze and there was great excitement in the village. The local photographer took a picture—which, by the courtesy of Miss Thomas, I am able to reproduce.

The mill had been in the Reeves family throughout the whole period of its history, Edward Reeves, who was born there, being the chief owner.

Local people say that the mill has not been worked for quite fifty years (1882). The generally accepted story is that a miller named Orpen (who also ran Maplehurst watermill, Frittenden) hired it from Mr. Reeves and purposely let it go derelict in order to bring trade to his watermill.

A Mr. Corke is known to have worked it at one time. Latterly it was occupied by G. D. Sycamore for about ten years up to 1911, then by a Mr. Searle—during whose tenancy it was set alight.

The mill is known to have worked with two spring sweeps, two cloth sails and a fantail.

STELLING MINNIS
(NEAR CANTERBURY)

Brambleton Mill. 1 mile S. of Stelling Church. 1 *mill*—1736 ; 2 *mills*—1769 ; 1 *mill*—1903-10.

Although only one mill appears at this position on the 1736 map, there were two very near to each other in 1769, according to the map of that date.

Both mills must have disappeared early in the nineteenth century, for Brambleton Mill (shown there on the 1903-10 Ordnance Map) was a successor of one of them and did not come on the scene until about 1850, when it was moved from Petham (see Petham, Mill Downs Mill) and re-erected in a meadow behind the Rose and Crown Inn at Stelling Minnis. A mill-stone in the turf can still be seen.

As noted under Petham, the mill continued to be worked at Stelling Minnis for some years by the Bartlett family. One of this family was injured severely by the sweeps of the mill and it is believed that this hastened his death for he died a few weeks later. In 1871 T. R. Holman put in a new pair of 3 ft. 10 in. Peak stones for John Bartlett.

For three years from 1878 to 1881 the mill was used by the Davison family who have held the other mill at Stelling Minnis for over half a century.

Brambleton Mill was an open trestle post mill, with four cloth sails or 'commons.' It worked two pairs of stones. Mr. T. H. Gambrill, of Petham, remembers dressing these stones for John Bartlett about 1876, having made a special journey to Stelling Minnis to do his old friend and late neighbour a good turn.

Davison's Mill.* 1¼ *miles SSE. of Stelling Church. Standing to-day, worked by engine.* 1736, 1769, 1903-10.

A post mill occupied this site until 1866, at which date it was pulled down and a smock mill (the one that stands to-day, known as Davison's Mill) erected by T. R. Holman in its stead.

The old post mill had been owned and worked by a Mr. Colver for many years. It was of the old type of open trestle post mill, working two pairs of stones, with four 'common' sails.

The new smock mill was built for George Goble, on whose death, in 1878, the property was acquired by Henry Davison who came from old Hawkinge Mill. It has been held by the Davison family for fifty-four years.

Its career as a windmill ceased in 1925 but milling operations are carried on by the aid of a Hornsby oil engine. There are two pairs of stones—one French, one Peak. Flour has not been made there since about 1907.

STOCKBURY
(NEAR SITTINGBOURNE)

¼ *mile SW. of Church.* 1736, 1769.

I have no other references to this mill save the 1736 and 1769 maps.

STODMARSH
(NEAR CANTERBURY)

1 *mile N. of Church.* 1819-43.

This mill is shown as standing near the banks of the Great Stour and one wonders if it was used as a pumping mill.

Rex Wailes

A. W. Tiffin

SISSINGHURST (CRAMPTON'S MILL)

See page 278

W.C.F.

SMARDEN (SMOCK MILL)

See page 280

W.C.F.

SMARDEN (POST MILL)

See page 279

Facing page 284

A. W. Tiffin

A. W. Tiffin

STANFORD

STAPLE (Barnsole)

See page 282

See page 282

W.C.F.

Jack Holman

SARRE

See page 272

Facing page 285

LOWER STOKE
(NEAR ROCHESTER)

*7 furlongs NE. of Stoke Church.** 1819-43, 1903-10.

Two mills are plainly marked at Lower Stoke on the 1819-43 map. I can only trace points of interest in connection with *one* of these mills. It was a fine old ruin when I visited it in 1905, with its derelict sails and fan. A tall brick base carried the structure. There were four 'patent' sweeps latterly.

Some twenty-seven years ago it was in occasional work—"cracking a few beans and doing a bit of work for local farmers." Since then it fell into disuse and absolute decay. It was taken down a few years ago and the old miller who owned and dismantled it died recently, being nearly a century old, which speaks well for a miller's life in the Hundred of Hoo.

A Mr. Cooper was the miller in 1878. He was a carrier as well as a miller and used to drive a two-horse 'bus from Stoke to Rochester daily, his son working the mill in his absence.

STROOD
(NEAR ROCHESTER)

Strood Hill Mill. 1 furlong WNW. of Church. 1819-43.

This smock mill stood at the bottom of Strood Hill, in the grounds of The Cedars, the present house being part of the old Mill House. It was demolished about 1860. My miller friend, Rose, knew this mill and told me of its vagaries and of the winds that should have driven it but refused to do so, its position in the valley being quite unsuitable for a windmill.

For a short time, about 1842, the mill was hired by Thomas Manwaring, from Preston Mill, near Wingham. He was only about twenty-one years of age then, and it was the first mill he worked on his own account. His son, William Manwaring, who now owns Willesborough Mill, says he well remembers his father saying that one night the cap was nearly torn off in a high wind and had to be tied down with ropes until the millwrights arrived.

Broom Hill. Field's Mill. ½ mile NW. of Church. 1819-43.

This, with Killick's Mill, formed a pair of mills that stood on the eminence, overlooking Strood. It was burnt down about 1875. Alfred Clark was the miller and he lived at the old Mill House. His employer, Edward Field, the owner of the mill, was a bachelor and occupied rooms in the Mill House, Mr. and Mrs. Clark acting as his housekeepers. It is said that Mr. Field was a very good amateur musician and that his large sitting-room in the Mill House contained three instruments—an organ, a piano and a harp.

Mr. Edwin Harris, the well-known Dickensian scholar and antiquarian of Rochester, tells me of a very interesting incident in connection with this mill, related to him by an old schoolfellow, Sidney Field, who was a nephew of the owner of the mill. It appears that when the old barrel organs that once accompanied the hymns in our churches began to be replaced by more modern instruments, the one with sixteen tunes from Loose Church, near Maidstone, was purchased by Edward Field and installed in his mill on Broom Hill. He fixed it in such a way that the mill when at work also turned the handle of the organ. Charles Dickens would often, in the course of his walks, stroll into the mill, smoke his pipe and listen to the music of the organ. Mr. Field's nephew also stated that his uncle was the original of the 'Mad Organist of the Mountains' in one of Dickens' works.

Broom Hill.* Killick's Mill. ½ mile NW. of Church. 1819-43.

This was the other of the pair of mills on Broom Hill. The tower was standing until recently, although falling to pieces, but was pulled down as being unsafe. I give a print of this picturesque derelict.

I learn that the cap and four sweeps of the mill were blown right off on two occasions. The last time was in 1880 when on a certain Sunday the mill was caught in a sudden shift in the wind. Henry Payne & Sons, millwrights, reconditioned the mill, which stood for about a year with a tarpaulin over the top of it while the new cap and sweeps were being made.

In 1890 the mill was taken for about a year, more or less as an experiment, by a Mr. Simmons, but he found it did not pay him to employ a miller to work it. It was, therefore, shut down and I cannot say whether it ever worked again.

It was one of the few mills that had only six sides to it instead of the customary eight.

SUTTON VALENCE
(NEAR MAIDSTONE)

½ mile E. of Church.* Standing to-day, worked by engine. 1819-43, 1903-10.

Sir Charles Igglesden, writing in 1923, said :

> Along the road to East Sutton, and close upon its boundary, is a tall windmill. It is the second highest mill in Kent, Cranbrook's mill being higher by a few feet, as it has two lower chambers instead of one. The old wooden structure can be seen for miles around though devastated of its sweeps, and remains an imposing reminder of what well-constructed buildings the old windmills of Kent used to be. Five years ago (1918) it was strained and considered sufficiently unsafe to make its owner, Mr. Ward, cry halt ; so to-day it stands idle and still.[1]

In 1930 my archæological friend, Halford L. Mills, wrote to me :

> Town-Sutton windmill stands bold on the rag ridge, but looking pitiful in meekness with four sweep-frames like armless sleeves hanging in empty and maimed impotence beside its shaggy body.

I have had several chats with Mr. W. R. Ward, the veteran miller of this mill, who has been there since 1875 and is now eighty-seven years of age. I found him a veritable mine of information concerning the decline and fall of windmills. The milling industry of days gone by is a subject very dear to his heart, coming next only to East Sutton Church, which owes much to him for

[1] *Saunters Through Kent With Pen and Pencil*, Vol. XVI, p. 79.

its restoration—about £3,000 subscribed personally and considerable sums collected from friends.

The mill was rebuilt in 1798 after the top had been blown off in a strong wind, and the staging raised about ten feet, to give another floor under. This was done during the time the Boucher family had the mill. The original structure is thought to date from about 1720, for there used to be a post in the mill commemorating a terrific gale in 1730 or 1740. Strangely enough, the 1769 large-scale map does not credit Sutton Valence with a windmill.

A few years ago an American wanted to buy the mill and take it over to the States for re-erection, but it was considered by experts to be too old and weather-beaten.

'Kia-ora' tells us in the *Kent Messenger* :

> The mill at Sutton Valence, a landmark seen all over the Weald, has a tragic event connected with it. A lady artist, seated on the gallery surrounding it, sketching what is perhaps the finest scenic panorama in Kent, the Weald below, someone without knowing started the mill, and the enormous sweep killed her instantly.

From another source I learn that the lady's name was Miss Pooley and that the accident occurred about sixty years ago during the occupation of a Mr. Robinson.

Mr. Jack Holman tells me that in 1872 R. Summerfield was the miller at Sutton Valence ; he hired it from the owner, Sir Edmund Filmer. In this year T. R. Holman fitted a new iron windshaft, brakewheel and new sweeps.

The picture here given of the mill in its active state I obtained from the block of the design printed on the flour bags which are still in use to-day, for though the sweeps revolve no longer the stones are worked by a gas engine. I may also add that a well-kept garden, tastefully laid out with a wealth of flowers, separates the Mill House from the mill. In addition, there are wide and entrancing views across the Weald of Kent.

In the years to come, when the old mill has vanished, the beautiful church will stand as a memorial to Mr. Ward's long years of devotion, while the fine peal of bells which he had re-cast and re-hung will echo a reminder across the Weald of the splendid activities of this miller churchman.

7 furlongs N. of Church. No map reference.

I first heard of this mill from Mr. W. R. Ward. Had he not mentioned it I might easily have missed it altogether, for it does not appear to have been noted on any map. It had disappeared, Mr. Ward told me, before he came to Sutton Valence in 1875.

On searching out the spot, on the left of the main road to Langley, between the cross roads at Wormlake and the Plough Inn at Five Wents, I found a row of six cottages known as Windmill Row, and along a little track to the rear of them, passing on the right the site of the mill (now a garden), stands Mill House—a one-storied, tarred brick dwelling.

One of the tenants at Windmill Row, a woman of over eighty, who had lived in the district all her life, had no recollection of the mill as having stood in her time.

Mr. A. Sandford, who lives at Mill House, could give me no information, but referred me to Mr. Sloman, living at Homewell near by, who owned the property until a few years ago. Mr. Sloman regretted he could not help me. He had never heard anything of the history of the mill or of its disappearance. He thought it must have been cleared away quite a hundred years ago.

Truly a lost mill !

SWINGFIELD
(NEAR FOLKESTONE)

Old Mill.* 1 mile W. of Church. 1858-72.

This smock mill, a successor of a post mill on or about the same site, was blown down during a severe gale in 1884. I understand that the miller had gone to a missionary meeting at Uphill when the gale sprang up. Upon arriving home he found the remnants of his mill scattered broadcast !

James Smith, who owned the mill and carried it on until his death in May, 1883, had taken it over from a Mr. Gardiner who, it is thought, originally had the mill built. It was, therefore, not an old mill although it was known as such to distinguish it from the New Mill that succeeded it. Mr. Smith's executors held the mill for a short time until it passed into the possession of William Prebble.

The picture reproduced shows the wreckage of the mill after its collapse. Of the two figures one is Mr. Pain, the miller (a brother of Frank Pain mentioned in the notes on Selstead Mill), and the other Mr. Prebble, the owner, for whom a new mill was built, as noted next.

New Mill.* Same site as Old Mill. 1903-10.

William Holman built this mill for William Prebble in 1885. It was a fine smock and stage mill, with all the latest improvements, and was the last corn mill to be built in Kent. There were two pairs of stones to begin with. In 1886 the mill was purchased by Frederick Gammon, who worked up a large business and had a third set of stones laid in.

In 1897 the mill was sold to a Mr. Finn. Two years later G. W. Barwick bought it and carried on until August, 1911, when, owing to the explosion of paraffin vapour in the engine house attached, in which was installed an 11 h.p. Blackstone oil engine as auxiliary power, the mill caught fire and was soon reduced to ashes. Thus disappeared Kent's latest corn mill.

Selstead Mill.* 1 mile NW. of Church. No map reference.[1]

This smock mill on Denton Hill, standing east of the main road to Denton, was struck by lightning and burnt down in the Spring of 1885. A mound marks the site to-day. It had three pairs of stones and was complete and working up to the time it was destroyed.

It was held on a twenty-one years lease by James Smith, who worked it in conjunction with the Old Mill until his death in 1883. Singularly enough, the next tenant was another James Smith, who was not related in any way to

H. W. Davison   N. Coles Finch

STELLING MINNIS (Davison's Mill)

See page 284

W.C.F.   W.C.F.

STROOD (Killick's Mill, Broom Hill)   LOWER STOKE

See page 286   See page 285   Facing page 288

SUTTON VALENCE

See page 286

SWINGFIELD. Erected in 1885.
The last corn windmill built in Kent.

ST. MARGARET'S BAY. Built in 1929.
Kent's latest windmill, for generating
electricity.

See page 238

See page 268

Facing page 289

his predecessor ; he had been a baker at Denton but, in his earlier years, a journeyman-miller. The mill was held by him until the time of its collapse.

The picture given was taken in 1880. The lad standing in the doorway is Frank Pain, aged then about fifteen years, who later had the Star Mill, Chatham, and became so well-known in connection with the mills of East Kent. He was born at the Mill House at Selstead, a one-storied building that preceded the house known to-day as Mill House. His father worked at the mill for twenty-one years.

Mr. Pain tells me that Selstead Mill was built as a successor to a post mill that previously stood on Denton Downs (see Denton), and that he has understood that the brake wheel in Selstead Mill came from that mill.

[1] Later I learned that although the greater part of the hamlet of Selstead is in the parish of Swingfield, the mill itself stood in the parish of Wootton, as does the present Mill House. The earlier bungalow residence, which stood immediately to the south of the present Mill House, was said to be partly or wholly in Swingfield ; in fact, the holding, consisting of the mill, miller's house and about 3½ acres of land, had the distinction of being in three parishes—Swingfield, Wootton and Denton ; the mill and most of the land being in Wootton.

SYDENHAM [1]

2½ furlongs NNW. of Church. 1819-43.

Except that this mill is noted on the above map, at one furlong west of the road to East Dulwich, I have no record.

TENTERDEN

Mill Mound. 1 mile 3 furlongs N. of Church.

There is a mound at a very exposed spot (local people think it is the highest in Kent) in Shoreham Lane, Tenterden, a little to the rear of St. Michael's Church, which elderly residents call 'Mill Mound' or 'Mill Bank.' By its size, and its position near the gate of a field, it looks very much as though a mill once stood there—probably centuries ago, for five *old* fir trees crown the mound to-day.

There are a few references to windmills in old Tenterden records, which Mr. A. H. Taylor has kindly looked up. The oldest entry in the Tenterden registers concerning a miller is that of 1599 : "Robert Glover, windmiller, was buried ye 28th day of June."

On June 11th, 1628, according to a volume of the *Archdeacon's Visitations*, 1627-1637 (Canterbury Cathedral Library), William Standley, late miller of the Town Mill of Appledore and then miller of Tenterden Mill, was summoned for "gryndinge upon the Sabbath Day, being contrarie unto the lawes of the churche." The breach of church law apparently occurred at the Appledore Mill.

In 1674 John Wybourne was fined for exacting excessive tolls at his mill at Tenterden. In 1686 Elizabeth Cumber, a spinster of Tenterden, was struck on the head by a sweep of the windmill in John Wybourne's occupation, it being stated at the inquest that she was unconscious for four days

[1] See note on page 151.

T

½ *furlong NW. of Church.* 1858-72.

My only authority for this mill is the 1858-72 map. Strangely enough, the many elderly residents of Tenterden with whom I have been in touch have never heard of a mill here. According to the map it was situated in a field not far from the rear of the church. The Vicar of Tenterden, Rev. D. W. Carmichael, M.A., regrets his inability to throw light on the matter, either from old records or elderly parishioners.

5 *furlongs NE. of Church.* 1736, 1769, 1819-43.

A mill once stood along the right-hand side of the road from Tenterden to St. Michaels, near the Fat Ox Inn. Bowen's map of 1736 is the earliest reference to it and the 1769 map names it Tenterden Mill. To-day the name of Mill Farm is reminiscent of it and the farm house, though now enlarged, was doubtless originally the miller's dwelling.

Mr. Aaron Pinyon, who knows Tenterden well and has given much useful information regarding the old mills of the district, says that the mill must have been pulled down before 1851, for it was not standing when he first knew the locality at that date. He remembers seeing the building in which flour was dressed with a horse-driven boulter, when there was no wind. The last tenant of the mill was a Mr. Santer.

Goods Hill Mill. 1½ *miles NW. of Church.* 1819-43, 1858-72.

This was an open-trestle post mill without a round-house, and was of similar construction to its neighbour, Ashbourne Mill. It was probably built at about the same time—1807. It was situated on very high ground to the south of the main road from Biddenden. A fine view can be obtained from this prominence.

The mill was last worked by a Mr. Sayers in 1890 and was demolished by being thrown in 1896. It had a chestnut main post and carried two pairs of stones. It worked in conjunction with a watermill about half a mile down the road, nearer Tenterden.

The site of the mill is now in the garden of "Livorno," the home of the late Capt. A. A. Black.

*Ashbourne Mill.** 1 *mile* 1 *furlong WSW. of Church.* 1819-43, 1858-72, 1903-10.

Ashbourne Mill was a well-built structure of the open-tripod type, very similar in appearance to Goods Hill Mill. It was built in 1807 by the millwright, Ralph, of Sissinghurst, for a Mr. Boorman of Tenterden. It is said that Ralph had a reputation for good work and people did not mind paying for it ! All the timbers and quarterings in the mill were planed. The main post was of unusual construction, built up from four baulks of timbers, which were clamped together by long bolts and iron bands. The rounded portion of this post appeared to have been turned in a lathe of some kind and Mr. A. Pinyon, who owned the mill, had often heard millwrights debating how this was done. It was believed to have been the second post in the mill, replacing the original some time prior to 1851, when Mr. Pinyon's father took over.

There were originally two pairs of stones, each 4 ft. 2 in. in diameter. Mr. A. Pinyon had one of these pairs removed and two pairs 3 ft. 10 in. in diameter were substituted, making three pairs of stones in all.

One pair of sweeps was removed about 1908 and for a short time the mill was run with two sweeps only, until last worked about 1910. It was demolished in December, 1912, being pulled over by a wire rope and a traction engine.

(See also page 91.)

Leigh Green Mill. * 1¼ *miles ESE. of Church.* 1819-43, 1858-72, 1903-10.

The date of this mill's erection was cut in a beam on the ground floor—1818. It was a fine smock and stage mill, with two floors under the stage. It was the last of Tenterden's windmills to remain standing. It had a drastic end, being demolished by fire on the night of November 26th, 1913. It is said that the mill was working at 10 p.m. and was well alight at 11 p.m.

A well-equipped mill, it had many useful machines, and latterly there were no less than five pairs of stones—three pairs of Peak and one pair of French burr on the stone floor and an additional pair of Peak stones on the second floor. A suction gas plant was the auxiliary power. Much of the machinery was installed by Mr. J. Pilbeam, who bought the mill in 1887 and ran it for many years until Messrs. Forster and Ward took it over and worked it last.

Mr. George Jarvis of Bethersden did many repairs in this mill from time to time, including the fitting of a new windshaft in 1890 and replacing rotted timbers in the cap.

Mr. Stephen Judge, a former owner of this mill, once walked from Tenterden to Canterbury and back in a day, to attend the Corn Market—twenty-six miles each way! There were no 'buses then. He evidently had to start very early in the day. This was about 1850, during the Crimean War. He foresaw that the price of corn would increase and he was anxious to buy.

TEYNHAM
(NEAR SITTINGBOURNE)

Conyer Quay. ¾ *mile N. of Church. No map reference.*

Although not marked on any of the many maps I have searched, a large smock mill stood on Conyer Quay, worked at one time by two brothers named Sidders.

It was a source of wonder to many people how it was that the sweeps of this particular mill were always running, wind or no wind ! Steam power had been installed and the sweeps were coupled up to the engine and, as millers said, acted as a fly-wheel.

Unfortunately the Sidders brothers were ruined owing to a heavy fall in price of wheat at the close of the Crimean war.

THROWLEY
(NEAR FAVERSHAM)

Parsonage Mill. 7 *furlongs NE. of Church.* 1736, 1858-72.

This mill was a white smock, with a brick base, working two pairs of stones—a Peak and a barley stone ; also a flour machine. It was known to be working in 1884 and was probably last worked by William Foster who took over the mill from Gabriel Lee Hougham in 1881. William Carr and Daniel Southee were also millers here in days gone by. Lord Sondes was the owner. Extensive repairs were carried out by T. R. Holman in 1871, at a cost of £237.

The 1736 map calls it Throwley Mill. I cannot say if it was the same mill that stood latterly or an older mill, perhaps of post type, that preceded it.

Clare's Forstal. * 7 *furlongs SSW. of Church.* 1858-72, 1903-10.

By the courtesy of Mr. W. J. Page of the village post office, I am able to give a picture of this mill as it appeared in 1914, with the fan missing. It was pulled down in 1915 ; why, I could not ascertain, for apparently it was in good condition although it had not been worked for many years. Probably, as with the majority of the recently vanished mills, the reason was a financial one—the business could not pay its way.

The mill served a useful purpose to the end, for it was pointed out to me that the garden fences of the village cottages had been substantially repaired with the timbers of the old grinder.

As to the site upon which it stood, I found in a meadow but a slight depression covered with grass.

There were two cloth and two spring sweeps, three pairs of stones were used, and latterly there was an 8 h.p. portable steam engine installed to work the mill in calm weather. For some years the mill was in the occupation of William Foster and he was the last to work it. A previous owner, who held it for many years, in the 1870's, was Nathaniel Coast.

There is a Windmill Inn at Throwley Forstal to-day, reminiscent of the mill.

TONBRIDGE

Uridge's Mill. ½ *mile N. of Tonbridge Castle.* 1819-43.

Uridge's Mill was so named after an early owner. Later owners include the names of Cox, Holloway, Ridgeway and Knell (who worked it last.) Bobby Woodman, a dwarf, a well-known local character, worked there for many years. After giving up milling he, accompanied by a white dog, used to go round the town with fruit and vegetables. The local paper published a picture of him a few years ago.

Mr. Geo. E. Skinner, of Tonbridge, tells me the mill was pulled down about 1872. The land was required for building. But it was standing in 1868, although it was then no longer in use, for, as a lad, Mr. Skinner often played in it.

W. H. Evernden

F. Pain

SELLING

(SHOTTENDEN OR PERRY WOOD MILL)

SWINGFIELD (SELSTEAD MILL)

See page 272

See page 288

W.C.F.

W. T. Page

TENTERDEN (LEIGH GREEN MILL)

THROWLEY (CLARE'S FORSTAL)

See page 291

See page 292

Facing page 292

See page 290

1905

W.C.F.

TENTERDEN (Ashbourne Mill)

In process of demolition, 1912

Ridley's Studios, Tenterden

Facing page 293

It stood on a brick base foundation, on which the body of the mill rotated, being pulled round into the wind by a horse. There was a beam attached to the body of the mill, the end coming within a few feet of the ground, to which there was a spread-bat to take the traces from the horse. The mill had a circular hedge round it of a diameter to allow the pole to turn the upper part of the mill on its stump. One of the arms of the mill was blown off on a stormy night some little time before it was demolished.

Conversation with another elderly resident, Mr. J. Barton, whose recollections of the mill go back seventy-six years, confirmed its disappearance about 1872, and he gave me the following further information :

No. 64 Shipbourne Road, a three-storied house at the corner of Uridge Road, now a greengrocer's shop bearing the name of I. M. Evans (proprietor Herbert Brooker), was originally the miller's home. Close by used to stand some outbuildings used as bakeries, for the miller was also a baker.

The site of the mill is to-day occupied by Clifton Villa, a house at the end of Uridge Road, which is a *cul-de-sac*, ending in a brick wall bounding the grounds of the Tonbridge Nursing Home.

There used to be a back lane leading to the mill from Shipbourne Road. This lane to-day is known locally as Back Hill. Actually, part of it is thrown into cottage gardens now but its course can easily be traced.

* * * *

Since writing the above I have received a letter from Mr. John C. Knocker, of the firm of Messrs. Stenning, Knocker & Co., solicitors, of Tonbridge, who writes :

I have now in front of me an old conveyance dated in 1870 (when George Lambert purchased some property adjoining Uridge Road) which shows the site of the wind-mill on property then belonging to Mrs. Cox, and the site would seem to be Lot 6 of the sale in 1892 after the death of my late partner, Mr. Stenning. The house was then in the occupation of Dann (I believe he was his gardener) and it was sold to W. A. Perkins. I will make some enquiries as to who might have removed the mill, but believe the house was erected a good many years previously to the date when we sold the property.

TONGE
(NEAR SITTINGBOURNE)

¼ *mile SSW. of Church.* 1819-43.

Tonge Mill probably disappeared about a century ago. It is known that John Scott had the mill between 1815 and 1820. His name and the date 1816 are cut in the plaster on the third floor of a disused old watermill, near the site of the windmill, with which it at one time ran in conjunction.

The windmill stood on a mound near where Tonge Castle once stood and, after the mill was removed, about three feet of earth was taken off the top of the mound to make a garden in the mill-pond of the watermill. The garden is still existing as an island. No trace remains of the windmill, the site of which is now an orchard.

* * * * *

Since writing the above I learn from Mr. E. T. Clark that in volume 44 of *Archæologia Cantiana* there is reference to the first Land Valuation of Tonge Parish made about 1834 and that mention was then made of "Tonge Mills," and in more detail as "Windmill and Orchard" and a "New Water Mill Head and Island."

The windmill was therefore standing as late as 1834.

TUNBRIDGE WELLS

Calverley Mill. Near site of St. Peter's Church. 1769, 1819-43.

The public library at Tunbridge Wells has a splendid collection of local guide books dating back to early in the nineteenth century but in none of them is reference made to the two old windmills that once stood in the district.

On street plans accompanying guide books of 1832 (Britton) and 1847 (Colbran), and also on Colbran's Visitors' Map of 1854 (scale $\frac{3}{4}$ in. to a furlong), the Calverley Mill is plainly drawn, shown as standing a little to the south of Bayhall Road, near its junction with Calverley Road, and a little to the east of the Royal Oak (an hotel of this name stands to this day). What is now a populated district was then open country, the only apparent sign of habitation being Lark's Nest Farm, a little to the east of the windmill. An old brick house, The Lark's Nest, stands to-day, alongside Bayhall Road, with steps to it up a bank formed when the road was lowered many years ago.

The 1847 plan shows that the ground near the windmill was "Mr. Ward's Land," and the 1854 plan notes a brickyard adjoining the mill. It is named Calverley Mill on the plans mentioned, evidently by reason of its proximity to Calverley Park.

The actual site of the mill is to-day occupied by houses in Windmill Street, near the junction with St. Peter's Street, about 200 yards to the rear of St. Peter's Church. The parish of St. Peter, Windmill Fields, was formed in 1876, the church having been built the previous year.

Early in January, 1933, following a report in a local paper on the celebration of the diamond wedding of Mr. and Mrs. F. L. Smith, of 53 Napier Road, Tunbridge Wells, the writer called on these dear old people and found them bearing their respective ages of eighty-three and eighty-five remarkably well. They had lived all their lives in the neighbourhood, having in fact played together as children beneath the shadow of the old windmill. Mr. Smith recalls that he had many times hung on the sweeps of the old grinder !

Mr. Smith remembered the mill as a very old, weather-boarded structure on a brick base, worked by fantail-operated gear ; its sweeps swept very close to the ground. It was last used for corn-grinding about 1860 and then *moved* a little distance away, and re-erected near the present golf links. The old structure was not used as a windmill at its new home—Mr. Smith does not remember seeing its sweeps at work after its removal. It was used by the purchaser, a Mr. Joslin, as a super shed, and pulled down, soon after its massive windshaft, wallower wheel and tackle remaining scattered about.

The Calverley Mill appears on the 1769 map but I am informed by Mr. Arthur W. Brackett, an authority on the past history of Tunbridge Wells, that it is not shown on an older map published by John Bowra in 1730, although such things as brick kilns are marked. It would, therefore, seem that the mill was built between 1730 and 1769.

Culverden Mill. 1½ *furlongs W. of St. John's Church.* 1819-43.

In addition to being shown on the early Ordnance Survey Map, Culverden Mill is noted on a plan of Tunbridge Wells accompanying an 1832 Guide by Britton. It is also clearly drawn on the 1854 Visitors' Map by Colbran but it does not appear on later maps.

It was situated just off Down Lane, at the corner of what is now Culverden Park Road but which, according to the old maps, was open land near Coney Burrow Wood.

It has been thought by some local residents that the site of the mill was in what is now a copse adjoining the premises of Messrs. J. Crates & Sons, and that it stood on the steep bank that slopes down to Culverden Park Road. Also, buried beneath the undergrowth of the copse, are, it is said, some stone steps that were used by the miller as a back way to his mill. From a close study of the old maps, however, in comparison with an up-to-date street plan, the position of the mill was evidently at the junction of Culverden Park Road and Down Lane, as stated.

Mr. A. R. Kelsey, of Tunbridge Wells, was very kind in seeking information about the mill. He discovered an elderly native of the district, Mr. Saunders, upon whose knowledge he bases the following particulars :

1. Mr. Saunders describes it as a weather-boarded mill, similar to Argos Hill Mill in Sussex, so that I suppose it is an old post mill.

2. The owner of the property at the time the mill existed appears to have been the Hon. James Master Owen Byng.

3. The name of the miller I do not know,[1] but at the time of the demolition of the mill the surrounding land was a market garden, and the mill was merely used as a store. It had ceased to function as a mill possibly some twenty years before it was pulled down.

4. It was demolished over sixty years ago, probably about the year 1870.

5. The reason for demolition was that the structure was so old and rotten as to be dangerous.

6. My informant does not remember that it was ever called Culverden Mill (though I should think it very probably was) but always remembers it as Mill Plat Mill, which seems to be putting the cart before the horse, as the plat would be so called because of the mill.

7. I know of no book in which the mill is referred to.

8. I have never seen a photograph or picture of the mill and do not know if any such exists.

[1] From the list of millers in the addenda to these notes it will be seen that Henry Ashby was the miller at Culverden Mill in 1839. (W. C. F.)

ULCOMBE
(NEAR MAIDSTONE)

Ulcombe Hill. ¼ mile SSE. of Church. 1819-43.

There have been two windmill sites at Ulcombe, according to the Ordnance Survey Maps. The 1819-43 map shows a mill at the above position, which is about half a mile east of the mill on Windmill Hill next described.

There is not the slightest trace of a mill on the site to-day. A local resident pointed out the spot where the mill is supposed to have stood, in a field next to a house called The Gables.

A little distance away, at the foot of the hillock on which the windmill stood, is Mill Cottage, whither I went to enquire, and soon realised that a *watermill* had given the cottage its name. There was still a little trickle of water in a stream near by but of the watermill there was little or no trace. The old wheel, I learned, was cleared away two or three years ago. In its place there is a repository for rubbish. The mill pond has dried up and is overgrown with weeds. Heaps of stones were lying about and I gathered that very soon there would not be even a bit of masonry left to show that once a watermill was busy at work. It will soon be as lost as the windmill that once stood a hundred yards or so away.

One wonders whether, in days gone by, the watermill and windmill ran in conjunction with each other. The cart track leading from the main road was doubtless the Mill Lane for both mills, for the site of the windmill is passed on the way down to the derelict watermill.

The windmill must have disappeared nearly a century ago. As I came through the village I had a chat with an old man of eighty, a native of Ulcombe, and to him it was a fresh item of local intelligence that there was ever another windmill in Ulcombe besides the one on Windmill Hill.   "It must have been long before my time," he said, "or I would have heard of it." Another man, who had been familiar with the immediate vicinity fifty years ago, said there was certainly not the slightest trace of the mill existent then.

Windmill Hill. 5 *furlongs ESE. of Church.* 1903-10.

I had at first listed this mill as standing on Knowle Hill, and this was helpful in tracing it on an Ordnance Map but, on visiting Ulcombe, I learned that it was Windmill Hill that claims the privilege of once having been crowned with a windmill, Knowle Hill being a little farther on.

The mill stood on a bank, on the right-hand side of the road up the hill, a little higher up than the house named Homesby Court. The miller's dwelling still stands and bears the name Mill House. Part of the house was once a bakehouse.

In the garden, in front of the cottage, there are the foundations of the mill, a bare patch of concrete and an inch or two of masonry being all that is visible above ground. The occupier of the cottage, who has been here seven years, has frequently debated with himself whether he should 'grub up' the old foundations and take in the mill site for a little more garden, or leave the concrete patch as it is and erect a fowl-house on it.

It was a small, tarred, smock mill, working two pairs of stones—one wheat, one barley. There was no stage, and the sweeps came close to the ground. Tassell, Gilbert, Henry Hooker (1878) and G. Mackelden (who last worked the mill in 1892) are names of some of the millers and owners here. It had been worked by wind only.

Since 1892 it had been used as a store but became very old and shaky and was pulled over by a wire rope attached to a traction engine, on July 16th, 1911.

UPCHURCH
(NEAR SITTINGBOURNE)

*Wakeley's Mill.** ¾ *mile WSW. of Church. Base alone remains.* 1819-43, 1858-72, 1903-10.

This was one of the most picturesque of our mills. It stood on a woody eminence near Otterham Creek, overlooking the Medway, from which it appeared as a familiar landmark for about a century.

The late William Wakeley some years ago raised the whole structure upon a brick base to get better wind-power.

The mill was in full work at the time of its destruction by fire in September, 1910. I am able to give a picture of its smoking ruins. Only three or four years prior to its destruction a new iron upright shaft was installed to replace the old wooden shaft, and new spur wheel and wallower wheel fitted by Mr. Littlewood, the millwright of Milton.

The mill was once struck by lightning, many years ago, splintering one of the sweeps.

An unusual feature of the mill was the way in which the weather-boards were affixed to the cap, being placed vertically instead of horizontally.

UPHILL
(NEAR FOLKESTONE)

¾ *mile WNW. of Hawkinge Church.** 1903-10.

Nothing remains of this smock mill which was last worked in 1914 and pulled down in May, 1931. It worked with only two sweeps during its last year and these remained until it was demolished, except that the shutters had been removed. At one time it worked with two cloth sails and two spring-shuttered sweeps.

Towards the last it was in a bad state of repair and its owner, Mr. Lewis Kettle, thought it better to remove it than allow it to fall to pieces gradually.

The mill had no brick base and its sweeps almost swept the ground.

It had always been in the Kettle family, having been built for Stephen Kettle in 1790. Henry Kettle was the miller-owner in 1878.

The 1769 large-scale map of Kent shows Hawkinge Mill Green near the site of Uphill Mill and one wonders whether, centuries ago, one of the old post mills stood there.

Uphill Mill has often been known as Hawkinge Mill and the windmill at Hawkinge as The Old Mill, to distinguish them.

WALMER
(NEAR DEAL)

SW. of Church. 1736.

Bowen's map of 1736 shows a mill south-west of Walmer Church but I cannot trace a mill there on any later map. It is evidently one of the long lost post mills.

WALTHAM
(NEAR CANTERBURY)

Cloke's Mill. * ¼ *mile NW. of Church.* 1858-72, 1903-10.

This mill stood behind the post office. It had been idle for some thirty years and much of the timber had rotted away. It was blown over during a high wind on the night of February 11th, 1931. It had been unsteady in its old age and doubtless would soon have been taken down, as it was getting dangerous. For some time prior to its collapse it had been used merely as a garage and shed, for which purpose the base is now used.

The *Kentish Express*, dated February 27th, 1931, gave the following account of the fate of the old mill :

OLD WINDMILL FALLS IN GALE
WALTHAM LANDMARK GONE

That well-known landmark, Waltham Mill, has fallen, and lies now like a gigantic pepperbox—its interior of beams and metal workings thrown far out into the meadow.

Mr. Cloke, whose father built, owned and worked the mill, suffers from loss of memory, and can remember but little of its history. Mr. Rogers, an old worker in the mill, and who lives close by, informed our representative that the mill has not worked now "this thirty year," and before that time it used to shake sometimes so that they were afraid to go up it Our representative suggested that the mill might have stood there a hundred years. "No, no, not a hundred." "Seventy, then?" "Aye, that be about it, tho' I don't justly know how long."

The present owner (Mrs. Monger) states that certain beams in the mill fell last summer, and the whole weight seemed to be left in the top portion (the wind shaft alone weighed 32 cwt.). She gave a graphic description of her awakening when the old structure fell during the last week's gale. Her first impression was that her wardrobe had collapsed. She had a look round, but discovered nothing amiss. Subsequently she realised that what she had anticipated had happened—the mill had fallen!

I am surprised to find that the mill is not noted on any earlier map than 1858-72.

Dilnot's Old Mill. * 5 *furlongs W. of Church.* 1858-72, 1903-10.

I learn from an old miller that this mill was a tarred smock, built about 1850. During the Great War, in common with Cloke's Mill, it was used by soldiers for purposes of observation and signalling.

After having braved many severe gales, it collapsed one calm day, the May 20th, 1910, the day of the funeral of King Edward VII. Fortunately, no one happened to be in the mill at the time. It had not been worked for about two years. There were two pairs of stones.

By the courtesy of Mr. M. Dilnot, I am able to give a picture of the old mill in its days of activity, also a group of the miller family (on the left) with Mr. Gambrill, of Chequer's Mill, Petham, and Mr. Scott, the baker and miller, who, despite the fact that the three middle fingers of his left hand are missing, continued the task of dressing the mill-stones at the old mill.

It is interesting to note that William Hooker, the founder of the large steam-milling business of W. Hooker & Son, Canterbury and Chatham, began business here. He hired the mill from Mr. W. H. P. Dilnot and had it at least as late as 1878. Later, a son of Mr. Dilnot took it over.

Mr. Prior Dilnot, of Chilham, writes :

My grandfather used to live under the stage of the mill until he built the present house ; the stage was exceptionally well built, with brick wall surroundings, double boarded and felt and tarred.

WAREHORNE

(NEAR ASHFORD)

E. of Church. 1596.

One of the very earliest of post mills must have stood in this position, for it is marked only on the 1596 map.

3 furlongs NW. of Church. 1769, 1819-43.

This old post mill is noted on the 1769 and 1819-43 maps. I learn from a milling friend, who was present at its demolition about 1900, that the sweeps were first removed, then the body was levered over until it crashed to the ground. There was excitement at the slaughter when rats and mice, in a swarm, attempted to escape.

A Mr. Collins had this mill at one time, having taken it over from a Mr. Pearson. In 1878 the miller was Lester Barling.

WESTERHAM

5 furlongs W. of Church. 1819-43.

Beyond the map reference given above, there is nothing available regarding this mill.

Hosey Common. 1 mile SSE. of Church. 1596, 1610, 1858-72.

This mill stood upon the high ground on the Westerham-Edenbridge road, on Hosey Common, near Horn's Hill.

Tradition has it that here Henry VIII's courtiers blew a blast with the horn, to advise Anne Boleyn, at Hever Castle, of his coming.

An elderly miller friend recalled the site as distinct from its surroundings, being a small enclosure of land, unused and desolate. The mill was burnt down about 1860. The last miller's name was Dicker.

I cannot say if it was the mill that stood in 1596; probably it was a successor, for the 1769 map does not show a mill at this position, although it gives Windmill Common. One wonders if this was the previous title for Hosey Common.

WESTWELL

(NEAR ASHFORD)

Tutt Hill Mill.* 1¼ miles SW. of Church. No map reference.

Although in the Westwell Parish, this mill stood on the edge of Hothfield Common and has sometimes been known as Hothfield Mill.

The Mill House, of timber and plaster, is still standing, situated not far from the main road.

Thomas Taylor is known to have been the miller here in 1878. He was probably the last to use the mill, for it was burnt down in 1880 as a result of being tail-winded.

WHITFIELD

(NEAR DOVER)

½ mile W. of Church.* 1819-43, 1903-10.

Whitfield Mill was pulled down about 1916. Nothing remains to mark the site except that the Mill House still stands. The mill stood near the Royal Oak Inn. It was a large structure, particularly as to breadth and size of cap.

For many years, indeed for three generations, it was in the Cadman family, who did a considerable business of baking and milling. Henry Cadman was the miller in 1878. Later Frank Mummery held the mill for seven or eight years.

I am glad to be able to give two pictures of the mill. One shows it in its active days, with the miller's van and baker's cart alongside; the other, taken in 1905, shows it without sweeps and fan—as it probably stood until finally destroyed.

(See also page 57)

G. Wells

JUST BEFORE THE COLLAPSE

G. Wells

THE MILL FALLING

G. Wells

THE ENGINE ABOUT TO HAUL DOWN THE MILL

ULCOMBE (WINDMILL HILL)

See page 296

Facing page 300

Lewis Kettle   M. Rowland Packer

UPHILL, Near Folkestone

See page 297

W.C.F.   W.C.F.

UPCHURCH (Wakeley's Mill)   WORTH

See page 297   See page 308   Facing page 301

WHITSTABLE

Borstal Hill. Black Mill.* 1 mile SW. of Church. Standing to-day. 1736, 1819-43, 1903-10.

This mill is believed to have been built about 1815. If it was, the one shown on the 1736 map was an earlier mill on the same site.

In about 1860 Henry Somerford was the owner of the mill. It was last worked about 1905 by James Callingham, who had taken over from Mr. Somerford in October, 1866. It was a powerful mill in its day and a large trade was done.

In 1885 several new cant posts were put in and the mill covered with new weather-boarding. It was then tarred ; previously it had been a white mill. When the change took place the Trinity House had to be notified, as the mill was a landmark for seamen.

Captain Laurence Irving, the famous artist (grandson of the late Sir Henry Irving), who owns the mill, has written to say that the present house was added to the mill in 1928 and that the mill appears in a Turner engraving of Whitstable, which is dated 1830. The mill and the addition referred to form a picturesque residence.

In a previous note concerning the first abandonment of this mill, I find :

This mill is now turned into a studio, and printing presses have replaced the mill-stones, while the cap is used as a sanctuary by wild birds.

Borstal Hill. 1 mile SW. of Church. 1819-43.

This mill stood nearly opposite the one previously described. It is said to have been a pumping mill in connection with the Whitstable waterworks close by.

Feakins' Mill.* ½ mile W. of Church. 1819-43.

This was a wooden smock mill, very similar in appearance to the Black Mill on Borstal Hill. It was an estate mill, at one time the property of Mr. Wyn Ellis, of Tankerton Towers. It was run for many years by Robert Feakins, after whom it was named, and was later worked for a number of years by his executors. Mr. Feakins-Johnson, a nephew of the late owner, lives in the Mill House to-day.

It is known that in 1849 the mill was worked with four canvas sails ; in 1868 two of these were replaced by 'patent' sweeps ; and when the mill ceased working by wind power in 1891, all were 'patents.'

Two of the sweeps removed from the mill, which continued to work by steam power, were re-erected on one of the Drapers' Mill at Margate. Feakins' Mill was pulled down in 1905, the wood and iron sold for firewood and scrap iron, and the brickwork used in the foundations of the houses in Millfield.

* * * * *

Since writing the above I learn from Mr. Geo. E. Ride that there used to be another mill, of post type, and that the two stood side by side, to the rear of the old railway station. I have no information to give regarding the post mill or its disappearance.

WILLESBOROUGH
(NEAR ASHFORD)

½ mile NNE. of Church. Standing to-day, active. Old Mill—1819-43. New Mill—1903-10. *

There was an old type of smock mill at Willesborough up to about 1868. I understand from Mr. W. Hawkins, who worked in it that its sweeps came very close to the ground ; that it had a fantail, was painted white and worked two cloth and two spring sweeps. There were four pairs of stones— three French burr and one Peak, also a flour dressing machine. Latterly it was owned by Messrs. Cornes & Sons. It became very dilapidated and had to be pulled down.

To replace it, the present smock mill was built for Messrs. Cornes by John Hill of Ashford in 1869. Mr. William Manwaring purchased it from Messrs. Cornes in 1920, when it had been closed for over two years.

It is now one of the few remaining active windmills in Kent, and was in excellent condition in 1931 when I last visited it. An electric motor is the driving power in calm weather. It is fitted throughout with electric light. There are four pairs of stones and an extra pair for the motor to drive at the same time as the mill is working by wind.

WINGHAM
(NEAR CANTERBURY)

Wingham Well. * 5 furlongs SW. of Church. Standing to-day, derelict. 1903-10.*

This is one of the few remaining tower mills in the county. From enquiries at the Mill House I learned it had been idle since about 1912. The last miller to use it was a Mr. Maplesden. "Mrs. Elizabeth Maplesden and Son" is the entry for millers in an 1878 Directory. There were three pairs of stones—two barley, one wheat.

To-day the mill is fanless, with sweeps falling to pieces.

¾ mile NE. of Church. 1769.

Mr. J. Brockman, of the neighbouring village of Ash, when asked about this old mill, wrote :

> The mill you mention north-east of Wingham, two miles from Ash (1769 map), I presume was a post mill. In fact many mills of this type dotted about here and there have long since disappeared and forgotten. I'm afraid when I disappear another old landmark will follow.

The mill was situated, according to the 1769 map, at "Sand pitts," just west of Shatterling.

WITTERSHAM

Old Post Mill. * 3 *furlongs NE. of Church.* 1736, 1769, 1819-43, 1858-72, 1903-10.

This old mill stood in a meadow nearly opposite the village inn. I fortunately possess a negative I made in 1905 of this unusually quaint structure, complete with round-house. It was at that time in splendid condition but it was a great disappointment to me recently to find that it had been completely removed. The mill mound alone remains.

Sir Charles Igglesden, writing in 1923, says :

Another change in the aspect of the village has been caused by the destruction of the old windmill that stood in the meadow just across the roadway. It was a distinctive mark for miles around.[1]

It was indeed a fine old mill and in its prosperous days was kept busily occupied, literally night and day. The following list shows the succession of miller-owners since 1816 :

Peter and Robert Parton	..	1816-1854
Thos. W. Collard	.. ..	1854-1882
J. Pilbeam	.. .. ..	1882-1908
C. J. Banister	.. ..	1908-1922

In about 1817, to take greater advantage of the wind, Mr. Parton had the mill raised up on brick columns ; previously the main timbers were on the ground.

In 1870 the fantail was fitted and was a great improvement.

In 1882, the cills of the main timbers having rotted, the mill was lifted bodily and new ends spliced on and clamped together with stout iron bands, which proved a success.

The mill was worked right through the Great War. Mr. T. Hinkley, who had worked in it since 1886, was hard put to it to keep it going through that difficult time. His two sons had to serve in the war and he was left alone to do the baking, milling and rounds. Fortunately, he had a daughter aged twenty-two at home, who was able to take the vanman's place until one of her brothers came home from the war in 1919.

By this time the mill was getting rather worn out. The breast timbers were beginning to get very weak, the brass bearing was very worn, and the large brake wheel used to rub on the brake and get very hot. Mr. Banister thought it would hardly pay for doing up, although the four sweeps were in good repair, two of them as new. When the fantail was blown off in a gale, and boards began to be torn off in the wind, the mill was thought to be unsafe. She was, therefore, sold for demolition in 1922.

[1] *Saunters Through Kent with Pen and Pencil*, Vol. XVI, p. 38.

The Stocks Mill.* 1 *mile ENE. of Church. Standing to-day.* 1819-43, 1903-10.

This mill is situated near where the village stocks once stood, although in these enlightened days there are no stocks there for the punishment of petty offenders.

In the main post of the mill the initials R.V. are carved, and the date 1781. If this is the date of erection, it would explain why the mill is not shown on the 1769 large-scale map.

Mr. Norman Forbes-Robertson, the famous actor, who owns the mill and the delightful old-world house and grounds, believes the mill to be older than 1781 and suggests that it may originally have stood elsewhere and that 1781 is the date of its re-erection at Wittersham. As can be gathered from the history of other Kent mills, it was by no means an uncommon occurrence for a mill, particularly of the old post type, to be transferred, maybe, to a better site for prevailing winds.

When Mr. Forbes-Robertson came to Wittersham about 1900 he was anxious to discover the age of the mill and in the course of his enquiries he conversed with an old man of ninety-two who was able to remember his great-grandfather's recollection of the mill ! This may not fix the date but it is certainly an unusual example of both memory and longevity.

When I visited the mill in 1908 I found it in perfect preservation—complete with round-house, shuttered sweeps and tailpole. I was agreeably surprised on a recent visit to find it looked even better cared for than it did on my previous visit. The whole structure was painted white and formed the principle feature of the exquisitely laid-out gardens and lawns, surrounding the Mill House, a splendidly restored Tudor residence, the possibilities of which were foreseen by Mr. Forbes-Robertson. He has been anxious for the mill to be put to its original use and has been prepared to let it at a nominal rent, or even rent free, but there has been no response.

The centre post of the mill, on which the body of the structure revolves, is of great size. It is thought to be one of the strongest oak centres in an English mill.

The ground floor of the mill is used to-day as a garden shed. The first floor is now a store for fruit, etc., but about twenty years ago it was made into a comfortable room for a son of Mr. Forbes-Robertson, who, quite a lad, wished to make the mill his castle. In making this 'room' snug, and to keep out draughts, laths and plaster were used to fill up recesses between the beams. One point was overlooked—the rocking of the old post mill was not taken into consideration, and laths and plaster did not stand the strain !

On the second floor the two pairs of stones still remain, and on the top floor, of course, are to be seen the huge brake wheel, massive iron windshaft, etc.

About 1870 the mill was owned and worked by Thomas W. Collard, who also ran the Old Post Mill at Wittersham.

(See also page 94)

*   *   *   *   *

M. Dilnot

WALTHAM (Dilnot's Old Mill)

See page 299

Prior Dilnot

WALTHAM (Dilnot's Old Mill)

See page 299

N. Coles Finch

WALTHAM (Cloke's Mill)

See page 298

Facing page 304

RUCKINGE

A. W. Pearce

Facing page 305

See page 267

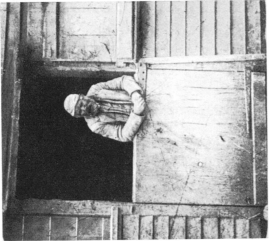

A KENTISH MILLER OF THE
OLD SCHOOL

DIED IN 1914

Aged 86 years

(T. Taylor)

WESTWELL (TUTT HILL MILL)

G. W. Taylor

See page 300

Since writing the above it is with very much regret that I learn from a newspaper account that Mr. Norman Forbes-Robertson died as a result of being knocked down by a car when he was walking near his country house outside Exeter on the September 26th, 1932. He was within two days of his seventy-fourth birthday. Very vividly I now call to mind his kind welcome when I last visited the Stocks Mill, how we climbed the old mill together, wandered round his delightful garden, and afterwards looked through my collection of windmill photographs. He showed unusual interest in the making of this Windmill Book.

WOODCHURCH
(NEAR ASHFORD)

Upper Mill.* ¼ mile NNE. of Church. Standing to-day, derelict. 1769, 1819-43, 1903-10.

The Upper Mill is the older of the pair of smock mills at Woodchurch known as The Twins. They do not look like twins to-day, but the similarity can be seen from a photograph taken about 1890, at which date both mills were painted white and in good working order. The picture also shows the Mill House and the Mill Cottages.

This older mill is said to be two hundred years old. It is believed to have originally stood at Place Lane, about a quarter of a mile away, where a mill mound is still to be seen. The transfer, it is said, took place about 1750, which would be confirmed by the 1769 map, on which the mill is shown in its present position nearer the church. This theory is upset, however, by the fact that the late Mr. Ditton (whose son, aged seventy-seven, still lives in Woodchurch) well remembered a mill at work at Place Lane. He died in 1916 at the age of ninety and if his statement is correct, the mill was standing at Place Lane as late as about 1840. It is, of course, possible that the Place Lane Mill was transferred in order to replace an older mill at the site nearer the church. Here, however, I must leave the matter.

The mill has no stage and was built on a mound of earth dug out from the ground near by, causing the pond that is there to-day.

Originally the mill cap was operated by a wooden 'Y' wheel to which a chain was attached for pulling the cap round into the wind. There were two pairs of stones—one pair a 4 ft. 2 in. Peak and the other 4 ft. 6 in. French burr.

The mill is known to have been in the Parton family for quite half a century—1800-50. In about 1848 John Parton was beheaded by one of the revolving sweeps. His son, John, continued the business until his death three years later, at the early age of forty.

During the next eight or nine years the Lower Mill was erected close by. In 1860 both mills were taken over by the Tanton family from West Hougham, near Dover, in whose possession they have been ever since. The Upper Mill was used mainly for the rougher trade, grinding cattle and pig corn for the neighbouring farmers, and the Lower Mill was kept for the better-class flour trade.

U

The Upper Mill was last worked about 1910. Its sweeps were removed a little later and the cap followed soon after, the body of the mill then being roofed over.

During the Great War eight men were stationed at the mill, which was used as an observation post. A model aeroplane is still to be seen affixed to the top of the mill and is a reminder of the occupation.

(See also page 55)

*Lower or Great Mill.** ¼ mile NNE. of Church. Standing to-day, derelict.*
1903-10.

This mill, like its companion, had a previous home, being removed to its present site from Susan's Hill Farm, about half a mile distant, in about 1852. Its age is not known, as it does not appear on any earlier map than 1903, but on the lid of the flour dresser is inscribed : "Peter Davis, Woodchurch, 1820." This seems to prove the mill's existence at that date.

There is, in the possession of Mr. A. Tanton, the present owner of the mills, an interesting little book once kept by Peter Davis at Susan's Hill. In it, besides a detailed inventory of the apparatus used in the mill and bake-house there, are recorded the transactions between 1842 and 1849. The remains of the bake-house still stand at Susan's Hill to-day. No baking business was transferred to the mill's later site.

The prices paid for corn are interesting. In 1843, for instance, four quarters of foreign wheat were purchased at 46s. 6d. per quarter. Other prices paid are as follows :

Wheat, varying from 47s. to 60s. per quarter.
Barley, 28s. and, later (1845), 32s. per quarter.
Beans, 26s. per quarter.
Peas, 28s. per quarter.

An entry in the book states : "April 20th, 1848—Sold to Mrs. Holyer, 1 pair of mill sails, £1 5s." This must mean that the mill at that time had the old cloth sails, the patent sweeps being substituted after the mill's removal to its present site. It would be interesting to know what the said Mrs. Holyer did with the old cloth sails !

The history of the mill after its transfer is, of course, linked with that of the Upper Mill. It was kept very busy at one time. Mr. Tanton has known as many as a hundred quarters of wheat waiting for grinding.

The mill has four stories above the stage. The ground floor beneath the stage was the store room for the flour ; the first floor the weighing room; the second floor for the three sets of stones (two pairs of French burr and one pair of Peak) ; the third floor the sack receiving room and for wheat bins ; and the top floor, of course, is the cap with its massive windshaft and brake gearing.

From time to time, as the mill-stones became too far worn for further 'dressing' and new stones being so costly, stones were bought from other windmills that were being demolished. In this way a pair of French stones was transferred from an old post mill at Kennington and a pair of Peak stones from the smock mill at Dymchurch.

A grandfather of Mr. A. Tanton, an engineer of Dover, installed various gear in the mill, and among the different engines used to supplement wind power from time to time was a 7 h.p. portable steam engine, which proved a very useful auxiliary power.

The sweeps have had a varied career, having graced two other Kent windmills. They were transferred from Aldington, when that mill was demolished, to High Halden post mill and, when that in turn came to grief, found their third home at this mill at Woodchurch.

Although to a casual observer it appears still to be a complete mill, with its four sweeps and fan, it is idle, having last been worked in 1926, and needs much repair. It has been a favourite with artists. I have before me a print from a painting by Mr. A. C. Leighton, A.R.B.A., of Hastings, who has painted more than fifty windmills in different parts of the country.

(See also page 55)

WOODNESBOROUGH

(NEAR SANDWICH)

S. of Church. 1695, 1736.

Robert Morden's map of 1695 and E. Bowen's map of 1736 both show this mill as south of Woodnesborough Church. I have no later reference to it.

WSW. of Church. 1736, 1769.

As noted under Ash (Mount Ephraim Mill) this Woodnesborough Mill was moved there. Its original home was at Ringleton, just in the Woodnesborough Parish, and it was moved to Mount Ephraim, a distance of about half a mile, in 1818.

WOOLWICH[1]

*The Co-operative Mill.** 5 *furlongs SSE. of Church.* 1769, 1819-43.

Vincent's *Records of the Woolwich District* gives an interesting illustration of this mill as it looked in 1845, and the following reference :

The Co-operative Mill. The mill built by the shipwrights appears to be the first co-operative effort of which this country has any trace. In Holyoak's *Self-Help a Hundred Years Ago* it is stated that the Bishop of Durham was the inventor of the principle, and that he applied it to a village shop at Mongewell in Oxfordshire in 1794, for the benefit of the poor, his example being followed in 1800 by Rev. Dr. Glasse, of Greenford, near Harrow, Middlesex. Mr. Holyoake also says that the oldest co-operative corn mill was established at Hull in 1795, another being commenced a year later on Barham Downs. But the co-operative mill of the Woolwich shipwrights was certainly in existence as early as 1760. The property was sold about sixty years since and the proceeds divided among the descendants of the dockyard people who founded it.[2]

[1] See Note on page 151.
[2] *Records of the Woolwich District*, by W. T. Vincent, 1890, p. 806.

Mr. Vincent traced an old document relating to the mill being burnt down :

March 24th, 1760.—Whereas the mill built by the shipwrights belonging to His Majesty's Dockyard at Woolwich was on Sunday, the 16th of this instant, consumed by fire ; and it having been scandalously and maliciously reported that the bakers belonging to the said town were concerned in setting the same on fire ; therefore, we, Thomas Fleet, John Hodgkinson, Thomas Asslott, George Sargent, George Moore, and Robert Shewring, all of Woolwich, in the County of Kent, Bakers, do severally make oath and say that they neither knew nor heard of the same in flames, and that they nor any of them did not set the same on fire, or were in any manner whatever accessory to the said accident. Signed, &c. All six sworn before me, Thomas Chitty, Mayor. (Lord Mayor of London.)[1]

The mill must have been rebuilt after the fire thus recorded, for one is noted on the 1819-43 Ordnance Map.

The following reference will help readers who know the district to trace the site of the mill :

Rose Mount was a picturesque row of cottages on the bank where the Engineer Office stands, the mill being on the one side of it and the grimy old Barrack Court on the other.[2]

I understand that Mill Lane, although still known locally as such, is to-day part of New Road, Woolwich.

Mr. Rex Wailes, after seeing a photograph of this mill, described it as follows :

An octagonal smock mill, with brickwork up to the second floor level. The octagonal cap is unusual ; it appears to have been turned by a hand chain and wheel.

WORMSHILL
(NEAR SITTINGBOURNE)

½ mile NW. of Church. 1819-43.

A pair of mills stood at this position, close together, due north and south of each other, near Beddington. I have no details.

WORTH
(NEAR SANDWICH)

*½ mile WSW. of Church.** 1769, 1819-43, 1903-10.

This was a smock mill without a stage. From external appearance I suspect it was built by the millwrights who built Northbourne Old Mill. There were three pairs of stones.

It was one of the first windmills in Kent to use steam power as an auxiliary. Later the steam engine was discarded for a suction gas plant.

Edward Terry was the miller in 1878, but for many years the mill was

---

[1] *Records of the Woolwich District*, by W. T. Vincent, 1890 p. 806.   [2] ibid. p. 97.

F. A. Johnson

WHITSTABLE (Feakins' Mill)

See page 301

Jack Holman

WHITSTABLE (Borstal Hill)

See page 301

A. W. Tiffin

WHITSTABLE (Borstal Hill)

See page 301

Facing page 308

E. A. Mummery

WHITFIELD

See page 300

Walter Mills

A. W. Tiffin

WHITFIELD

WILLESBOROUGH

See page 300

See page 302

Facing page 309

worked by F. G. Billing. It was pulled down about 1903, when a brick addition to the base formed a new mill in which the present business of F. G. Billing & Son is carried on with an oil engine.

WROTHAM
(NEAR SEVENOAKS)

Fry's Mill. 1½ *miles SE. of Church.* 1819-43.

This mill stood on high ground between Borough Green and Wrotham Heath, near Platt, where the railway crosses the Maidstone-Godstone road. It disappeared many years ago and no trace remains. It was known as Fry's Mill after Thomas Fry, the miller in the 1870's.

An old miller friend can remember the mill standing when he was a boy, fifty years ago, although he cannot remember its condition.

Mr. E. T. Clark, of Maidstone, has sent me the following extract from the Rev. T. S. Frampton's book, *A Glance at the Hundred of Wrotham at the time of the Early Edwards* :

> In the case of the gallows . . . the precise locality can be ascertained almost without a doubt. Persons who are acquainted with the main road leading from Sevenoaks to Maidstone will have noticed in front of them, after passing Borough Green, a windmill occupying a very elevated position on a spur of the high ground which here overlooks the Sevenoaks and Maidstone branch of the L.C. & D. Railway. The view from the top of the hill is particularly striking : it extends from beyond the Knockholt Beeches on the west to far down the valley towards Ashford on the east, and in another direction almost includes Rochester. This hill, in the map of the Hundred of Wrotham, which is given in Hasted's History, published about a hundred years ago, is called Galley Hill, and it is stated by a very old inhabitant of St. Mary's, Platt, in which district it stands, that in his young days it always went by the name of *Gallows* Hill. This by itself would be sufficient to indicate the purpose it once served—but the same authority also says that when he was a boy he often heard his father remarks that at the time the windmill was built, about the end of the last century (the book is dated 1881—W.C.F.) the workmen who were digging the foundations came across several human remains which were then believed to be those of felons who had been hung there. If publicity were aimed at, it is hardly possible to conceive any position better calculated to ensure it than this conspicuous hill on which the windmill stands.

WYE
(NEAR ASHFORD)

¼ *mile WSW. of Church. Base remains to-day.** 1819-43, 1858-72, 1903-10.

I find no note of this mill on early maps and when reading Sir Charles Igglesden's volume, was reminded that as yet I had not taken a picture of it. I therefore made my way to the spot only to find it had gone, having been pulled down about 1920. There remains but the base, which has been converted into a store.

Of this mill Sir Charles wrote :

> The windmill, standing sentinel-like just off the street, and the white watermill overlooking the Stour, as it winds along the fields, splashes over the sluices, sparkles

in countless eddies under the bridge and hides itself from view while streaming along the valley past Olantigh, towards Chilham.[1]

Walter Jerrold also had a word to say in connection with the mill :

> Wye, lying at the foot of the Chalk Downs, which rise to the east of the Stour, with its dismantled windmill and its old timbered houses. . . .[2]

It was a white smock and stage mill on a brick base, working two pairs of stones and had four spring sails. It was for some time worked by George Harris, who held it in 1878.

YALDING
(NEAR MAIDSTONE)

Rugmore Hill.　1¼ miles SE. of Church.　1819-43.

At first I thought that *Hunton* had the right to claim this old mill (it is 1¼ miles south-west of Hunton Church) but all the people with whom I discussed the matter on the spot assured me that Rugmore Hill was in the parish of Yalding, so Yalding it must be.

A directory of 1839 gives William Mercer as the miller at Hunton.

When hunting up this old mill, I first called on elderly Mrs. Tame, who lives in one of the houses on Rugmore Farm. She thought the mill was at work when she was a girl sixty or more years ago (1870) when local people, who baked their own bread, used to take their corn to be ground into flour. She believed it was of the old post type and was able to point out the Mill Platt, a small strip of land enclosed by hedges, on which the mill stood.

I next found Mill House, which is near the site of the mill and stands just off the main road from Collier Street to Yalding, nearly opposite the little Benover Gospel Meeting Room. It is a large old house, now divided into two. In one I found Mr. Martin, aged over seventy, who is a native of the district but not able to give me any information beyond that the mill *may* have stood sixty years ago. He directed me to Mr. John Weston, who was born in the Mill House, eighty odd years ago, but lives now in a lovely old thatched cottage near the Woolpack Inn.

I found Mr. Weston in his garden, hoeing some strawberry plants. A more hale and hearty a man for his eighty odd years one could not wish to meet. He was glad to pause from his work and enjoy a chat. He told me that though born in the Mill House, his parents moved a little distance away when he was only a few months old, after they had been living in Mill House a short time. Their predecessor was Mr. James Harris and, before him, a Mr. Clark, who had worked the mill. He had no recollection of ever seeing the mill at work but he remembered seeing "some old tackle lying about that belonged to the mill"— after its demolition.

Thus evidence of the history of the mill on Rugmore Hill is very indefinite.

Mr. Weston told me that he *believed* there used to be a windmill somewhere at Claygate, Yalding, many years ago, "or so I've heard tell." Here

---

[1] *Saunters Through Kent with Pen and Pencil*, Vol. I, p. 16.
[2] *Highways and Byways in Kent*, Walter Jerrold, 1907, p. 229.

again there was nothing definite ; and I hinted at such ; whereupon **Mr.**
Weston said : "Well, I *do* know of one other mill in the Yalding Parish and
that stood on Downs Farm, through the village, past the church. It was an
old stump mill." I gleaned all the information possible from Mr. Weston
concerning this mill before proceeding to the spot he described—when I
realised that I had definitely made a discovery of yet another old Kentish
windmill. The maps, lists and summary for this book having now been
complete, a description of this other mill, therefore, will be found in the
Addenda, page 316.

* * * * *

The above account of a search for the site and information of one of our
old mills of Kent is typical of what has happened in scores of instances ; but,
of course, space would forbid entering into a similar description in regard to
every windmill that is given in these Historical Notes.

ADDENDA TO HISTORICAL NOTES

A FEW further Kentish windmills were traced since the completion of the
Maps and Lists and are, therefore, not shown thereon, but particulars of
these are given in the following notes, as also some additional information
of mills previously described.

ADISHAM
(NEAR CANTERBURY)

Bekesbourne Mill (*see page* 152.)

Sad to relate, another of our Kentish windmills has vanished. At 10.30
a.m. on August 29th, 1933, a grass fire that had started about a quarter of a
mile away spread to the old Bekesbourne Mill, and the heat-dried, tarred
timbers of the old structure were soon in flames. For about ten minutes
the building was a blazing beacon, then it collapsed, and by midday nothing
but a heap of burning wreckage remained. About ten acres of grass dried by
the sun was burned also. The *Kentish Express* reported that desperate
attempts had been made by the owner and others to beat out the flames but,
fanned by the breeze, the fire rapidly spread towards the mill, and it was
hopeless to attempt to save the old relic. As there was no water available
in the vicinity, the fire brigade was not called.

BOXLEY
(NEAR MAIDSTONE)

½ *mile W. of Church. No map reference.*

Information came to light regarding this old mill during enquiries in
connection with another windmill at Boxley (see page 171). The following is
an interesting letter from Miss Marian Foster, of The Yews, Boxley :

The mill was owned for several generations by the Fowle family, who came from Fowle Hall, near Yalding, until Mr. William Fowle died in February, 1865 (two of his ancestors were placed after their death in a part of the mill, but afterwards were properly buried in Boxley Churchyard). The windmill was working as late as 1867. It was taken down between 1876 and 1880, and the upper part brought down to the village and used as a granary and pigeon cote at Street Farm.

My brother says that the top part of the mill was dismantled of sweeps, etc., and then put on what he calls a 'Bavin Tug' ; and the sweeps may have stood *beside* the re-erected part for some years (but I do not remember them) and the top part had to be pulled down for safety somewhere about 1917-18. There are several of the old grinding stones about the village.

The original site of the mill, about half a mile south of the Pilgrim's Way, is reached by taking Forge Lane, opposite Boxley Church. The Mill stood some distance from the road through the village, and one would now have to cross two fields to get to the spot. In days gone by there was undoubtedly a stone cart track that led up to the mill, for Mr. J. Clifford, who owns the property to-day, says he has found difficulty in ploughing the land in the vicinity of the mill site, owing to the quantity of stones. It is probable that a farm road once linked up from Boarley Farm to the mill.

In connection with the burial of two members of the Fowle family in a cellar beneath the mill, there is a local rhyme, the truth of which I cannot vouch for :

> Beneath this mill
> Lies the body
> Of Poor Will.
> Odd he lived,
> And odd he died ;
> At his funeral
> No one cried.

An elderly man living on Detling Hill tells me that about seventy years ago (1863), as a lad of about eight years of age, he was taken down into the cellar of Boxley Mill to see the millers' grave, and he has some recollection of seeing the above lines inscribed on a stone in the cellar, but of this he cannot be sure. Miss Foster says that the old folk used to repeat the lines, but where they were inscribed she did not hear.

I had hoped to learn that the millers had such a love for their old mill that even in death they could not be parted from it ; but the truth of the matter is that one of these gentlemen had had a quarrel with the then vicar on account of the village school being built opposite his home (now The Yews, adjoining Street Farm, and occupied by Miss Foster). Perhaps he feared unruly disturbance from the village lads who were to be schooled so close to his house.

At its later site the mill must have stood on a large number of stone 'mushrooms.' Some of these stones lie about to-day and are put to various uses—one does duty as part of a stile into a meadow a little way down the road and some are supporting a chicken-house.

*   *   *   *   *

Having found the site of this old windmill at Boxley, I was tempted to look for the remains of the Boxley watermills noted in *Abbey Possessions*

(26 Henry VIII)—"the Fulling Mill called Poll Mill ; two Corne Mills called Sandlyng Mill and the Ovlott Mill."

By the help of Miss Foster, I found the site of one near Stream Cottage. Every vestige of the mill was gone, only the wrecked mill-race remained, over which the now diminutive stream cascaded. The local water authorities had taken the bulk of the water.

Another, quite near the banks of the Medway, was standing. The mill-wheel, or what little remained of it, lay buried in the debris of the neglected building. The stream there had been diverted and the mill-pond was dried up.

An old veteran of eighty years said that the Stream Mill was once a 'blanket mill' but was idle in his boyhood days, the making of blankets having then ceased. No doubt, in the early days, these mills ministered to the wants of the Cistercian monks of the Abbey near.[1]

BRIDGE
(NEAR CANTERBURY)

Further to my notes on Bridge Mill (page 174) Mr. J. Holman informs me that this mill has recently (June, 1933) been repaired to some extent. He writes :

> The midling has been cut off at the end of the cheek pieces, the cap re-boarded and creosoted. The back of the cap has been cut off short and boarded up, while the tower has also been repaired. Although the cap looks a bit strange, I am glad that repairs have been carried out since the mill was getting into a bad state. I believe it is now used as a store.

CHALLOCK LEES
(NEAR ASHFORD)

1 *mile NNW. of Challock Church. Additional mill for* 1819-43 *period.*

Since the completion of the main body of the Historical Notes, I have carefully examined the 1819-43 Ordnance Survey Map, and find that a *pair* of mills are shown at the above position.

In confirmation of this, an elderly miller friend tells me there definitely *were* two windmills at Challock, about two hundred yards apart from each other, and that they were both burnt down.

(See page 178.)

DETLING
(NEAR MAIDSTONE)

¾ *mile NE. of Church. No map reference.*

Detling Mill is not shown on any of the many maps I have searched. It had an ideal position for a windmill, on the top of Detling Hill, open to the winds from all quarters. It stood on the left of the main road from Maidstone

---

[1] In *In Kentish Pilgrim Land* there is a description of this abbey. It was one of the premier houses of the Cistercian order in England.

to Sittingbourne. To-day a cart track, doubtless the Mill Lane at one time, leads to three Mill Cottages and Mill House.

In the mill's time there was only the Mill House with its outbuildings. Mill House has been enlarged to make two dwellings and the outbuildings have been converted into two cottages.

The mill was of the usual weather-boarded smock type, on a brick base. I learn from Mr. G. Brown, who lives on Detling Hill and well remembers, as a boy, having taken corn to be ground at the mill, that it was used for both hog corn and wheat grinding. At some earlier time in its history it was used for crushing seed, for an old mill-stone that lies near is grooved on its *edges* like a silver coin, and must have worked vertically.

When the property was purchased in 1866 from Stephen Kelcey by Robert Green (who kept the Cock Inn at Detling), the mill had been idle for two or three years. Mr. Brown says that trade had gone, and he remembers having to take corn to Newington Mill when Detling Mill was closed. Mr. Kelcey had owned and worked the mill for many years and was the last to use it.

Mr. Green did not allow the mill to become a tottering derelict but pulled it down almost immediately, and carried out the alterations to Mill House and the outbuildings. There was nothing remaining of Detling Mill in February 1868.

GOUDHURST

Further to my notes on Goudhurst Mill (page 211), Mr. W. P. Haskett Smith sends the following extract, dated about 1803, from the notebook or diary of John Rofe, who was a working mason and regularly entered in it the instructions which he received for inscribing tombstones, and added a good deal of interesting gossip, between 1790 and 1810 :

> A young man apprentice to Humphrey, millwright, was killed by a fall as they were rising Mr. Birch's mill, Goudhurst. Broke both his legs or thighs and both arms ; nay, six broken bones. He came from Pevensey, Sussex, aged twenty-two to twenty-three.

HAWKHURST

From a conversation with Miss Warren, aged 86, a survivor of the millwright family, I learn that it was her grandfather, George Warren, who originated the millwrighting business at Hawkhurst of that name. His son William, George and Richard succeeded him and, later, William and Frank, two sons of William Warren, carried on the business. Local people recall that it was once a familiar sight to see the late Mr. William Warren and his two sons going through the village, carrying their tool bags, trudging on foot to one or other of the surrounding villages on windmill repair work. It is said that they walked many and many a mile in the course of their labours. (See also page 50.)

KESTON
(NEAR FARNBOROUGH)

1¼ miles NNW. of Church. Additional mill for 1819-43 period.

Further close examination of the Ordnance Survey Map of 1819-43 reveals a mill faintly drawn at the above position, on the south-east verge of Hayes Common, about a quarter of a mile north of the old post mill described on page 229. Maybe this is Olive's Mill, mentioned on page 229.

OARE
(NEAR FAVERSHAM)

When recently in the marsh-lands of the Swale, in the vicinity of Oare, at about a quarter of a mile to the north-west of the prominent derelict tower mill, I found, by the side of the canal, a small derelict windmill-pump (facing p. 245). Woodmen had been cutting the willows which there abound, and in so doing had exposed the old mill.

It is an interesting derelict, and although it has no connection with corn mills, it claims notice here in our survey of lost windmills, for doubtless many other windmills, traced on Kentish maps, were used for a similar purpose. There was such a mill at Brookland years ago, for draining part of Romney Marsh, and another at Newenden, just within the Sussex border, on the southern bank of the River Rother. A windmill shown on the 1819 map at Stodmarsh was probably used for pumping water from the River Stour.

I sent Mr. J. Holman a print of the Oare specimen and he wrote to say that a very similar mill stands on the marshes at East Tilbury, Essex, a description of which is given in Volume 2 of *English Windmills.*

The Oare mill, though but a skeleton of its former self, is in fairly good preservation, particularly the framing and the sweeps, also the cupola and the ironwork of the pump gear ; the fantail, however, has completely collapsed. It appears to have been idle over forty years, during the greater portion of which period it has been hidden in the dense growth of willows.

SOUTHFLEET
(NEAR GRAVESEND)

7 furlongs W. of Church. No map reference.

In seeking information about the mill at Southfleet previously described (p. 281) I discovered, through correspondence with the Rector of Southfleet, that there was also once a windmill "on the Pack Way, near Troy's Island." I was recommended to get in touch with Mr. J. J. Chambers, J.P., who in turn wrote :

> I enclose a letter from Sir Thomas Colyer Ferguson in reply to mine asking for information about the windmill that once stood on land bordering on Longfield and Southfleet parishes. That one stood there at one time is without question, but it has been gone for so many years that authentic data is not forthcoming.

The said letter from Sir Thomas conveyed his regrets that he had no information about the windmill on Troy's Island, much as he would have wished to help in the matter.

This particular mill must, therefore, be counted among the lost mills of the County. I may add that a close search of numerous old maps fails to reveal the slightest trace of a windmill at the position mentioned.

YALDING

(NEAR MAIDSTONE)

Downs Farm Mill.* ½ *mile NE. of Church. No map reference.*

The discovery of this old mill was the outcome of enquiries made in connection with the other windmill at Yalding (see page 310). Certainly it is true in connection with the search for old windmills that "one thing leads to another."

The mill on Downs Farm which, by the way, I cannot trace on any map, was an early type of post mill, with a round-house. Miss E. Turner-Smith, who owns the property and lives in the beautiful old thatched house on the farm, tells me that the farm has been in her family for over two centuries, and that her great-grandfather, Mr. Town, used to own and work the mill. Miss Turner-Smith showed me a fine water colour picture of the mill, and later very kindly allowed me to copy the painting for reproduction here (facing page 321).[1]

The site of the mill to-day is an orchard. To reach the spot one would follow the cart track (evidently at one time the lane to the mill) across the little green by the War Memorial. The mill stood to the left of the track, at the highest point of rising ground. It is believed to have been pulled down about 1870.

CONCLUDING NOTE

I would like to say, in closing these Notes, that, for simplicity's sake, the account of my friend Mr. A. W. Tiffin's peregrinations in windmill land has been woven into my own to form one complete identity. I would assure the reader that his contribution especially to these Historical Notes has added materially to the exhaustive and interesting manner in which it has been possible to deal with so difficult a task. For this and other valuable assistance my indebtedness to him is considerable.

From first to last we both met with nothing but kindness and cordial co-operation from all with whom it has been our pleasure to get into touch, in the writing up of such a wealth of interesting matter in connection with the corn windmills of our beloved County. This will ever be recalled as the one great charm surrounding the production of this volume.

[1] It is distressing to relate that while this picture was in my possession, Miss Turner-Smith's house, seven centuries old, was completely destroyed by fire.

SWINGFIELD (Old Mill)

Jack Holman

See page 288

WALTHAM (Cloke's Mill)

Mrs. Monger

See page 298

UPHILL, Near Folkestone

Jack Holman

See page 297

WALTHAM (Dilnot's Old Mill)

Jack Holman

Facing page 316

See page 299

WRECKAGES

W.C.F.   A. W. Tiffin

WINGHAM (WINGHAM WELL)

See page 302

W.C.F.   A. W. Tiffin

WITTERSHAM (OLD POST MILL)   WITTERSHAM (THE STOCKS MILL)

See page 303   *See page 304*   *Facing page 317*

LISTS OF MILLERS

COMPILED FROM OLD DIRECTORIES

In February 1933, since the compilation of the Historical Notes had been completed, my co-worker, Mr. A. W. Tiffin, had an opportunity, by the courtesy of Kelly's Directories, Ltd., of studying a number of nineteenth century directories. From these he has compiled lists of millers at various dates.

In these old directories the names of windmillers were not distinguished from watermillers but in the lists here given millers *known* to be watermillers have been omitted.

From the 1839 Directory, extracts had to be made from the various village headings ; the 1845 list is the fullest list of all—these names were taken from a complete list of millers. To avoid repetition, many names have been omitted from the 1852 and 1862 lists, new names and different windmills having been sought for.

These lists should serve as a useful supplement to the names of millers given throughout the Historical Notes.

PIGOT & CO.'S

Royal National and Commercial Directory, 1839

pp. 239-386

ALDINGTON
William and Thomas Williams

APPLEDORE
Henry Crux

ASH
George West

BAPCHILD
James Kelcey

BEARSTED
Thomas Tuddenham

BEXLEY HEATH
John Dann

BIDBOROUGH
Nicholas Arnold

BIDDENDEN
John Dungey
Henry Heath
Stephen Sharp

BOBBING
John Goord

BOUGHTON-UNDER-BLEAN
William Beull

BOXLEY
William Fowle

BRENCHLEY
James Clemetson

BRIDGE
Thomas Johnson

CANTERBURY
Samuel Beard, St. Martin's
Thomas Marsh, St. Martin's
Henry Somerford, Old Dover Road
John Parker, Dane John Mill
John Gobell, St. Thomas's Hill
Henry George Thornton, St. Stephen's Road

CHARING
Richard Chapman Jennings

CHARTHAM
John Snoulton Rutter

CHATHAM
John Gilbert, Chatham Hill
William Gilbert, Star Mill, Chatham Hill
Henry Huggins
John Field, Chalk-pit Hill
Samuel Gates, New Road
Thomas Simmons, Ordnance Place
George Stoddard, Ordnance Place

CHISLEHURST
Joseph and Rowland Snelling

CRANBROOK
Samuel Jenner, Camden Hill
John and George Russell, Stone Street

CUDHAM
Joseph Paddy

DEAL
George Matson, Upper Deal
Richard Chitty, Middle Deal
Thomas Bushell, Alfred Square
James Gardner, Sandown Mill
John Lawrence, Walmer Road

DEPTFORD
John Sewell, Blackhorse Fields
Richard Taylor, Mill Lane, and Tanner's Hill

DOWNE
Henry Bannister

DYMCHURCH
George Singleton

EASTRY
Thomas Clark
John Gayen

EDENBRIDGE
Frederick Stanford

FAVERSHAM
William Weldish, Market Street
Thomas Carr (and Water Mill, Ospringe)

FOLKESTONE
James Gardner, Shellon's Lane

FRINDSBURY
John Fisher
Thomas Josiah Jarvis
George Town

FRITTENDEN
Job Sanders

GILLINGHAM
James Stedman
Isaac Friday, Grange

GOUDHURST
Henry Allen
John Slaughter
    (One of these was a watermiller)

GRAVESEND
Michael Slaughter Woollett, Windmill Hill
John Keddell, Milton

GREENWICH
William Carpenter, Greenwich Road

GUILTON, NEAR ASH
Stephen Wootton, Guilton Mills

HAWKHURST
Edmund Tobit

HEADCORN
William Boorman
George Mercer

HERNE
John Lawrence, Herne Street Mill

HERNE BAY
Henry Thorpe, Parade

HIGH HALDEN
Richard Reader

HUNTON
William Mercer

HYTHE
Joseph Norton, Stade
William Marshall, High Street
William Pay, Hythe Mill

KENNINGTON LEES
Stephen Sharpe

KENNINGTON
Daniel Young

KESTON
John Ellis
George Wilmott

LENHAM
Job Spicer
Edward Tanton
Daniel White

LYDD
Thomas Finn

MARGATE
Daniel Gouger, Margate Mills

MILTON, NEXT SITTINGBOURNE
Richard Snoard

MINSTER, SHEPPEY
Baldwin Howe

NEWINGTON, RAMSGATE
Robert Foster

NEWNHAM
John Barnett

OARE
Robert Shrubsole, Luddenham

OSPRINGE
Thomas Amos
William Elliott

PRESTON, NEXT FAVERSHAM
John Rickwood

QUEENBOROUGH, SHEPPEY
Thomas Spain

RAMSGATE
William Holman, Nr. Victoria Crescent
Thornton & Co., Sandwich Road

ROCHESTER
William Stedman
Isaac Belsey
Robert Horsnaill, St. Margaret's

NEW ROMNEY
John Parton

RUCKINGE
John Russell

SANDHURST
James Collins

SANDWICH
James Baker, St. Clement's
Wm. Nethersole, Delph Street

SEVENOAKS
William Knott

SHEERNESS
Thomas Webb
Francis Venables

SMARDEN
James Homewood
Job Sanders

SOUTHBOROUGH
Henry Peerless

STAPLEHURST
John Reeves

STROOD
William Killick

TENTERDEN
Henry Santer, Boars Isle
(Known as St. Michael's to-day)
George Bridge, Ashbourne
Stephen Judge, Leigh Green

TONBRIDGE
Edgar Uridge, Cage Green

TUNBRIDGE WELLS
George Cronk, Calverley Mill
Henry Ashby, Culverden Mill

WAREHORN
James Barling

WESTERHAM
Thomas Green
John Howard

WHITSTABLE
Lawes & Carr
Robert Feakins

WILLESBOROUGH
Thomas Perkin

WINGHAM
John Chapman
William Inge, Wingham Green

WITTERSHAM
Robert Parton

WOODCHURCH
John Parton

WOODNESBOROUGH
Hodgson & Co.
Stephen Martin

WYE
Thomas Kennett

W. KELLY & CO.'S
DIRECTORY OF 1845

ADISHAM
Stephen Burton

ALDINGTON
T. Williams

APPLEDORE
Henry Crux

ASH
George West

ASHFORD
Stephen Sharp, High Street

BARHAM
Edward Lawrence

BENENDEN
John Reeves

BETHERSDEN
Mrs. P. Adams

BEXLEY
Stephen Cannon

BEXLEY HEATH
Geo. Strickland & Son

BIDBOROUGH
N. Arnold

BIDDENDEN
Carey Witherden
John Dungey

BIRCHINGTON
James Hudson

BLEAN
Thomas Glover

BOBBING
John Goord

BOUGHTON-UNDER-BLEAN
Stephen Jackson
John Goble
George H. Coulter

BOXLEY
John Simmons

BRABOURNE
John Mate
Rd. West

BREDHURST
John Wyles

BRENZETT
Mrs. Holyer

BRIDGE
Thos. Johnson

BROADSTAIRS
T. Hodgman, St. Peter's Road

BROOK
Stephen Andrews
Richard Punyer

CANTERBURY
Wm. Cannon
Richard Fuller, Old Dover Road
Thomas Marsh, St. Martin's

CHALLOCK
John Chapman

CHARING
R. C. Jennings
Wm. Missing

CHARTHAM
Josiah Woodhams

CHATHAM
Matthew Bacon, Ordnance Place
John Field, 230 High Street
Wm. Willis, Ordnance Place

CHEVENING
Wm. Barton

DARTFORD
Charles Payne

DEAL
Thomas Bushell, Alfred Square
George Chitty, Middle Deal
Mrs. Mary Watson, Upper Deal

DEPTLING
Stephen Kelcey

DOVER
John and Edward Pilcher, Buckland

DOWN
Henry Bannister

DYMCHURCH
James Pryor
John Smith

EASTLING
John Matcham

EASTRY
Thomas Clark

EDENBRIDGE
John Bassett
Jas. Mellish
Fredk. Stanford

ELHAM
George Lord

ELMSTED
J. Newport

FAVERSHAM
John and Thos. G. Gillett
Wm. Weldish, East Street

FOLKESTONE
Stephen Court, Eltham
Jos. Gardner, Sandgate Road
Geo. Pain, Horn Street, Cheriton
James Smith, Cheriton

FRINDSBURY
Wm. Kimmins

GILLINGHAM
J. Friday, Junr.
John Gilbert

GOUDHURST
John Pope

GRAVESEND
Jas. Broadbridge, Milton

GREENWICH
Wm. Carpenter

HARBLEDOWN
Richard Goble
Z. Hudson

HARTLIP
Wm. Friday

HEADCORN
Chas. Boorman
Geo. Mercer

HERNE
Edward Lawrence

HERNE BAY
Thos. Winder

HIGH HALDEN
Stephen Judge

A. Tanton

WOODCHURCH (about 1890)

See page 55

W.C.F.

W.C.F.

UPPER MILL

LOWER OR GREAT MILL

WOODCHURCH (1930)

See pages 305-6

Facing page 320

See page 316

YALDING (DOWNS FARM MILL)

Miss E. Turner-Smith
Facing page 321

HIGHAM
Henry Everist

HOATH
James Collard

HOO
Richard Ballard

HOUGHAM
Jas. Tanton

HYTHE
Joseph Horton
Wm. Pay, East End

KENNINGTON
Daniel and Thos. Young
Stephen Sharp

KESTON
Thos. Ellis
Martin J. Hoath

KINGSNORTH
J. Cooper

KINGSTON
Henry Smithson

KNOCKHOLT
Wm. Ashby

LANGDON
John Stanger, Martin

LEEDS
John Goddard

LENHAM
John Palmer
Job Spicer
Edward Tanton

LENHAM HEATH
John Tanton

LUDDESDOWN
John Waterman

LYDD
Thos. Finn

LYMINGE
Stephen Gibbs

LYNSTED
Wm. Stone

MARGATE
Daniel Gouger

MEOPHAM
James Killick

MILTON, Next Sittingbourne
Francis Hartridge
Wm. Jay, Mill Quay
John Prentis
John Scott
Richard Snoard, Borden

v

MINSTER, Thanet
Geo. Rigden

NEWINGTON, Sittingbourne
R. Foster

NEWNHAM
Henry Filmer

NONINGTON
Thos. Clark

NORTHBOURNE
Thos. Harvey

NORTHFLEET
Thomas Allen
Walter Westrop & Co.

OARE
John Kennett, Luddenham

OSPRINGE
Thomas Carr
Henry Elliott

PETHAM
Henry Gambrill

PRESTON, Next Faversham
Wm. Filmer

PRESTON, Next Wingham
Geo. Robinson

RAMSGATE
Wm. Holman, 20 High Street
Wm. Hudson, St. Lawrence

RIPPLE
Henry Mummery
John Mummery

ROCHESTER
I. Belsey, Star Hill
E. Horsnaill, Borstall Road
Wm. Stedman, Star Hill

RODMERSHAM
G. Baker

ROLVENDEN
George Bridge
L. Foster

ROMNEY
John Parton

SANDWICH
James Baker, Gaol Street

SARRE
Thomas Holman

SELLING
John Sutton

SEVENOAKS
John Fleet
Charles Knott
John C. Thorpe

SHEERNESS
Thomas Webb, High Street, Mile Town

SHORNE
Wm. Woollett

SIBERTSWOLD
Stephen Andrews

SITTINGBOURNE
Wm. Jay

SNODLAND
Edward Martin

SOUTHBOROUGH
Milton & Co.
Edgar Uridge

SOUTHFLEET
Martha Carter

STAPLE
Wm. Gardner

STAPLEHURST
John Bailey
John Reeves

STELLING
John Bartlett
Mrs. Mary Goble

STOKE, LOWER
Frederick Baldock

STROOD
Maria Horsnaill
Geo. Jacques, Strood Hill
Wm. Killick

SUNDRIDGE
Wm. Barton

SWINGFIELD
Jas. Nixon
Thos. Nixon

SYDENHAM
Francis Brigden

TENTERDEN
Geo. Bridge
Stephen Judge
Richard Parton

TEYNHAM
H. Divers

THROWLEY
Coast & Rayner
Thos. and Jas. Raines
James Souther
Daniel Souther

TONGE
Thomas Denne

WALTHAM
Wm. Dilnot

WAREHORNE
Jas. Barling

WESTERHAM
Geo. George
John Howard

WESTWELL
Wm. Head
Peter Davies

WHITFIELD
Robt. Cadman

WHITSTABLE
Wm. Carr

WILLESBOROUGH
J. Cornes
T. Perkins

WINGHAM
John Chapman
Richard Maplesden
John Stoddard, Chittenden

WITTERSHAM
G. Burch

WOODCHURCH
John Parton

WOODNESBOROUGH
W. Brown
Stephen Martin

WORMSHILL
J. Shornden

WORTH
John Nethersole

KELLY'S DIRECTORY OF 1852

ADISHAM
F. Longhurst, Bekesbourne

ALDINGTON
B. Hobbs

ASH
T. S. Thorp

BARHAM
G. File, Derringstone
F. Longhurst

BEARSTED
J. Bunyard

BENENDEN
J. Barton

BEXLEY
M. J. Hoath, Hall Place Mill

BIDDENDEN
G. Stapley

BOUGHTON
G. H. Coulson
I. K. Richards

BOUGHTON MONCHELSEA
D. Day

BRABOURNE
J. Mate

BREDGAR
J. Wyles

BRENCHLEY
J. Homewood
J. Clemetson

BRENZETT
Mrs. E. Grist

BRIDGE
T. Johnson

CHARTHAM
J. Dives

CHATHAM
J. Pelling, Luton
W. Willis, Upper Mill, Ordnance Place

CHEVENING
H. Barton

COBHAM
D. Dallen
Mrs. J. E. Batchelor

CRANBROOK
H. Harmer, Cranbrook Common
G. Harris, Cranbrook Common
S. Jenner, Cranbrook Common
J. and G. Russell, Union Mill

DARTFORD
R. Sears, East Hill

DEAL
F. Matson, Upper Deal

DODDINGTON
W. Rowland

DOWNE
H. Bannister

EASTLING
R. Kelcey

EDENBRIDGE
J. Bassett

ELHAM
G. Gilbert

ELMSTED
J. Newport

FRINDSBURY
H. Everest
T. Manwaring

GOUDHURST
J. Hope

GRAVESEND
Young & Todd, Milton

HEADCORN
T. Burden
G. Mercer

HERNE BAY
T. Winder

HILDENBOROUGH
J. Everest

HOATH
R. Nash

HUNTON
W. Mercer

HYTHE
Tickner & Allen, Stade Mill

IDE HILL
W. W. Barton

KENNINGTON
T. Young

KINGSDOWN, Sevenoaks
W. Longley

KINGSNORTH
G. Meers

KINGSTON
J. Southee

KNOCKHOLT
R. Burfoot

LYDD
S. Birch
T. Goble

LYMINGE
L. Francis

LYNSTED
E. Champion
E. Strouts

MARGATE
J. Banks, Drapers' Mill

MILTON, Next Sittingbourne
F. Hartridge
G. Ride
J. Scott, Senr.

NEWCHURCH
J. Rye

NEWINGTON, Next Sittingbourne
R. Foster

NEWNHAM
T. K. Hope

NORTHBOURNE
R. Fuller
T. Harvey

NORTHFLEET
H. Laxton

OARE
T. Juge, Luddenham

OSPRINGE
W. Elliott

PLUCKLEY
R. Ashbee

PRESTON, Wingham
G. Robinson

RIPPLE
H. Mummery

RODMERSHAM
J. Austin

ROLVENDEN
L. Foster

ROMNEY, NEW
W. Hammond

RUCKINGE
J. Russell

SELLINGE
W. Moore

SITTINGBOURNE
W. H. Filmer, Chalkwell

SMARDEN
C. Buss

SOUTHBOROUGH
T. Knowles
W. Milton

TENTERDEN
G. Bridge

THROWLEY
J. Southee

TONBRIDGE
E. Uridge

TONGE
T. Denne, Tonge Mill

TUNBRIDGE WELLS
J. Dadson, Calverley Fields

ULCOMBE
G. Cradduck

UPHILL
J. Kettle

WALMER
J. Bushell, Walmer Mill

WALTHAM
W. Dilnot

WESTERHAM
J. Brand

WESTWELL
W. Head
J. Large

WHITSTABLE
R. Feakins, High Street, Seasalter

WILLESBOROUGH
J. Perkins

WINGHAM
R. Lawson
R. Maplesden

WORTH
J. Nethersole

WROTHAM
Carter & Jull
T. Fry
J. Saxby

KELLY'S DIRECTORY OF 1862

ADISHAM
R. Bax, Bekesbourne

ALDINGTON
T. Cheesman

APPLEDORE
D. Turner

ASHFORD
S. Sharp, Windmill Street

BARHAM
J. Sackett, Breach

BENENDEN
F. Richardson
C. Collins

BIDBOROUGH
R. Durrant

BIDDENDEN
J. B. Allen

BOUGHTON
G. H. Coulson

BRABOURNE
H. Gibbons

BREDGAR
J. Wyles

BRIDGE
G. Fryer

BROADSTAIRS
W. Hills

BROOK
W. Cook

CANTERBURY
J. Chantler, St. Lawrence
J. Durrant, St. Martin's Hill
M. Gooderson, St. Martin's Hill

CHALLOCK
J. Chapman

CHARING
R. C. Jennings
R. Millgate

CHATHAM
M. Bacon, Front Row

CHIPSTEAD
R. Burfoot

CHISLEHURST
W. Brigden

CHISLET
J. Packer

CLIFFE
A. Mummery

CUDHAM
J. Alwen

DEAL
C. Brown, Great Mill
G. W. Chitty, Wellington House
Henry Gambrill, Sandown Mill

DODDINGTON
H. Jarvis

DOWNE
C. Sawyer

DYMCHURCH
T. Prior

EASTLING
R. Clackett

ELMSTED
T. Marshall

FAVERSHAM
J. Ralph, Gravel Pit Mill

GOUDHURST
J. Norrington

GRAVESEND
J. King, Denton

GUSTON
J. Mummery

HARBLEDOWN
T. Hancock

HEADCORN
N. Cornes
D. Goodwin

HERNE BAY
Wm. Minter, Nr. Clock Tower

HIGHAM
E. Chittenden

HILDENBOROUGH
J. Hollands, Watts Cross

HOATH
W. Bigglestone

HYTHE
H. Marbrook, Stade Street

IDE HILL
J. Rose

KESTON
B. Hoadley

KINGSNORTH
J. Fukes

KIPPINGS CROSS
G. Clarke

KNOCKHOLT
A. Nichols

LANGDON
J. Stanger, Martin

LYDD
S. Birch

LYMPNE
J. Brenchley

LYNSTED
J. Ferrell

MARGATE
D. Gouger, East Cliff

MILTON, Next Sittingbourne
J. Ride, Vicarage Road
F. Hartridge

MINSTER, Sheppey
W. Hook

NEWCHURCH
J. Callingham

NEWINGTON, Next Sittingbourne
G. W. Franks
NONINGTON
T. Dilnot
NORTHBOURNE
T. Harvey
OARE
H. W. Elliott
OSPRINGE
T. Grinstead
PLUCKLEY
G. B. Chambers
PRESTON
S. Croucher, The Mall
RIPPLE
W. Davison
ROCHESTER
I. Belsey, Star Hill
RODMERSHAM
T. Witham
ROLVENDEN
R. Clemetson
ROMNEY, NEW
R. Ashbee
SANDHURST
E. Collins
SANDWICH
T. Bates, Mill Walls
SARRE
T. Holman
SELLING
J. Sutton
SELLINGE
T. Laslett
W. Noble
SEVENOAKS WEALD
R. Elses Burfoot

SHEERNESS
H. Ride, Marine Town
J. Clark, 109 High Street, Mile Town
SIBERTSWOLD
S. Andrews
SISSINGHURST
G. Crampton
Marsh & Crampton
STANFORD
J. Fox
STAPLEHURST
J. Reeves
STELLING
G. Culver
STOKE
R. Allen
SUTTON VALENCE
T. Burden
TENTERDEN
Thomas Pearson
And at Leigh Green
THROWLEY
W. Coast, Clare's Forstal
TONBRIDGE
A. Knell, Cage Green
TONGE
J. Austen
UPCHURCH
Wakeley Bros.
WALTHAM
T. Cloke
WESTWELL
H. Carey
WITTERSHAM
S. Birch
T. W. Collard
WYE
J. Hayward

INDEX TO WINDMILLS

The total of 410 windmills known to have stood in Kent between 1596 and 1930, does not include mills known to have replaced older mills on the same sites. Mills that have been moved from one village to another are only counted once—at their later positions, not at their original sites. In two cases, Lamberhurst and Newchurch, there are only names reminiscent of windmills— Windmill Farm and Mill Bank. Having no assurance of an actual windmill at these places, they have not been included in the total.

370

SUBJECT INDEX

(For General Chapters I–X)